IVOR M

FIELD
TO THE BL
OF
SOUTHERN AFRICA

STRUIK

CONTENTS

Struik Publishers
(a member of The Struik Publishing
Group (Pty) Ltd)
Cornelis Struik House
80 McKenzie Street
Cape Town 8001

Reg. No.: 54/00965/07

First published 1987
Second impression 1992
Second edition 1994

Copyright © text, maps and photographs:
Ivor Migdoll 1987, 1994

Designed by Joan Sutton
Edited by John Comrie-Greig
Photoset by McManus Bros (Pty) Ltd, Cape Town
Reproduction by Unifoto (Pty) Ltd, Cape Town
Printed and bound by Kyodo Printing Co.
(Pte) Ltd, Singapore

ISBN 1 86825 624 3

FOREWORD

It is more than 30 years since the publication of my book *Butterflies of South Africa, Where, When and How They Fly* (1953), and it is now long out of print. I am therefore delighted to see Ivor Migdoll's new field guide and particularly pleased to note how much more information he has managed to include about the habits of southern African butterflies than my own book did. There may be a book or two on the life-histories of our butterflies from which one might glean more information than from this one, but there is nothing with this book's unique combination of detailed information, compact format and magnificent photographs.

The *Field Guide to the Butterflies of Southern Africa* does not claim to be a complete record of all 830-odd southern African butterflies: The writer aimed rather at providing a pocket-sized book – something which can be carried around by the naturalist and collector. With this in mind, he felt that the best solution would rather be to deal in some detail with the most readily encountered species, introduced in his text with vivid and informative descriptions which are a delight to peruse.

Above all, however, Migdoll's book demonstrates his skill as an insect photographer. He has combined his artistic flair with some of the most modern techniques to produce photographs which will enthrall and fascinate the reader in no small measure.

He is also entitled to boast that he furnishes the butterfly-collector with the most detailed descriptions so far published in this country of how to collect, breed and mount butterflies. He also explains in detail how to construct setting-boards, storage cabinets, hand-nets and butterfly-traps – a subject rather sketchily dealt with in other works. I do not, however, wish to touch upon all the practical features this book offers, but leave it to the reader to judge for himself.

Ian Sinclair's *Field Guide to the Birds of Southern Africa* was the first of the new series of Struik field guides to be published and it has met with remarkable success. I have no hesitation in predicting that Migdoll's field guide will soon be found side by side with Sinclair's, and that its popularity will grow as more people begin to realise that butterflies are just as interesting as birds, and arguably more beautiful.

I heartily congratulate Ivor Migdoll on producing this truly fine piece of work which will enrich the knowledge of our growing community of amateur naturalists and stimulate a deeper interest in those small things in nature which are too often overlooked as being of little or no significance.

DAVID A. SWANEPOEL
DURBAN 1987

ACKNOWLEDGEMENTS

I would like to acknowledge with thanks the advice and help I received from the following individuals, without whom the information for this book would have taken many months longer to acquire.

My wife Margaret is particularly thanked for the endless hours of typing, for her help in checking through the initial manuscripts, and for willingly giving up other activities in order to assist.

For Deryck Whiteley words of thanks are not enough. He has, over the last ten years, been an indefatigable companion in countless collecting trips, covering perhaps over 100 000 kilometres. I thank him for his unstinting help which he has so generously given in all aspects of the compilation of this book. This is particularly true of the photography – many of the photographs which appear here would have been virtually impossible without Deryck's invaluable help and patience.

I am also indebted to Philip Zwart for his advice and comments on the first chapters and for his constructive criticism of the transparencies from which the selection in this book was made; his companionship and friendship on many collecting trips were greatly valued.

Alvin Patterson of Photocraft Professional Lab. in Durban rendered first-class service in the developing of film and production of transparencies.

Johan Marais (author of *Snake versus Man*) is thanked for his encouragement and for willingly imparting his photographic knowledge particularly in the field of macrophotography.

My friends at the Bluff Camera Club also freely gave advice and assistance when required.

David Swanepoel, author of *Butterflies of South Africa, Where, When and How They Fly* (1953), stayed with me in Durban and gave me valuable information on 'when and where they fly'; he also lent me a few of his specimens to photograph and provided invaluable information in the compilation of the distribution maps.

Wendy Freer very kindly took the photographs illustrating collecting techniques which appear on pages 143 and 144.

Clive Quickelberge was extremely helpful with the selection of some of the specimens which appear in the book and also provided several specimens for photographic purposes.

Like butterfly names, plant names have a habit of changing every now and again as taxonomists continue to unravel the complex relationships of the different species. I am therefore grateful to Gerrit Germishuizen of the Botanical Research Institute in Pretoria for providing up-to-date names for the many larval host-plants which have undergone such name changes in recent years.

IVOR MIGDOLL
AUGUST 1987

FOR DERYCK, MY FRIEND AND GURU;
MY WIFE MARGARET AND DAUGHTER KIM;
MUM AND DAD.

INTRODUCTION

Butterflies with their beautiful and vibrant colours have fascinated mankind through the ages. Ask almost any schoolboy, and he will assure you that during at least one of his school holidays he has spent endless fun-filled hours collecting butterflies in the fields close to home. Perhaps such a schoolboy will be fired with enthusiasm and decide to take his butterfly studies more seriously. At the outset he will damage many specimens from lack of experience. His initial catches will consist mainly of the larger and more common local species which he will pop excitedly into a box or glass jar and proudly take home. Once home, the questions begin. 'What do I do now?' Off he goes to his mother's sewing-box and takes a handful of her best pins with which to pin his newly found butterflies. The next question is – 'What do I pin them on to, and how?' Then, once they are pinned – 'What do I do with them, and how do I stop them from becoming broken and damaged?' And so the stream of questions continues, to the dismay of parents and teachers who know they can never quite satisfy the inquisitive youngster's curiosity.

Collecting-fever may strike at any age, however, and this book is written with both collectors and naturalists in mind. I have attempted to provide answers to the questions most likely to be asked, together with general guidelines for the collection, setting and storage of butterflies. There are of course different ways of going about each of these tasks. What may suit one collector may not suit the next; for instance, how many of each species does he want to collect? What space has he available to him? Does he live in a small flat, or a large house? Even more important – how far can he travel? For in the collecting of butterflies, a great deal of travel may be required.

This book does not pretend to illustrate or describe all the butterflies occurring in South Africa; in fact, it deals with only 232 out of the approximately 830 southern African species. What it does attempt to do is to introduce the reader to many of the more commonly encountered species, with some rarer species also being illustrated to draw attention to the fact that specialised habitat requirements can be all-important to a butterfly's existence. I have attempted to select representatives of most groups which the reader may encounter, in hopes that he will be encouraged to undertake further research in definitive text-books when he finds himself unable to make a positive identification of a particular specimen. It is important to note that this book certainly has a measure of regional bias, perhaps understandably so as I am a Natalian; I do believe, however, that South African coverage is adequate for the purposes of this field guide and I would only caution the reader to note that in some instances where I comment on the rarity of a particular species in South Africa, it may in fact be the case that the same species is common in neighbouring territories such as Zimbabwe or Mozambique. The South African populations in some cases represent the extreme limits of a much broader African distribution pattern. Some indication of this situation may be apparent from the distribution maps which accompany each species description, where the ranges of certain butterflies stop abruptly at the political but not physical barriers of the Orange and Limpopo rivers. It must also be made clear that these maps are the first ever attempted for South African butterflies and that they only roughly indicate the region where a particular butterfly may be encountered in our country. It is obvious that the data on which these maps are based are totally inadequate to construct an absolutely accurate picture, of the type currently being compiled for butterflies in Great Britain by the Biological Records Centre, or for birds in South Africa by the Percy FitzPatrick Institute for African Ornithology. However, you as a collector can add to the information being accumulated and help to expand the bank of South African locality records. Such records are of course best backed up by properly collected and labelled specimens. And to the serious collector that can mean a major exercise in logistics.

There are over 800 different species of butterfly in southern Africa, to say nothing of subspecies, colour variants, and seasonal forms. If one had the good fortune to catch one male and one female of each, remembering that in most cases the male and female are different in appearance, that would mean providing facilities for the storage of a basic collection of at least 1 600 specimens! In many cases, for reasons to be explained later, more than one specimen of each sex is taken, possibly as many as 10 in my own case, which means we are now looking at the huge figure of 16 000 specimens. The adequate care of such a collection will certainly require an enormous investment in time and money.

This book focuses on many facets of the world of butterflies – their behaviour, their extraordinarily complex life-cycles and of course their exotic range of colours, shapes and patterns. It is difficult in a book of this size to do photographic justice to South Africa's wealth of butterfly species. Nevertheless, the approximately 620 photographs which appear here have been selected not only to illustrate key identification features, but also to attempt to convey something of their enormous aesthetic appeal to a new generation of potential lepidopterists. Many of the photographs of larvae and pupae in this book are 'firsts' and have not been published as colour photographs before.

I have often wondered how many butterfly-collectors there would be if all butterflies were drab or sombre in colour. Such butterflies do exist, but they are the exception rather than the rule. The majority are endowed with rich wing colours and have a delicate beauty which makes them desirable *objets d'art* as far as mankind is concerned. Yet this diverse and often startling range of colours does not exist to delight the human eye; it is entirely functional and forms an integral part of the survival strategy of each butterfly species, from reproduction and mate recognition, to camouflage and defence. Some of the brightest colours are in fact possessed by poisonous or unpalatable butterflies and are 'warning colours' which convey a 'hands-off' message to potential predators.

The collection of these exquisite creatures costs nothing – although travel and equipment can be expensive – and the rewards are many. One can use butterfly-collecting as an excuse to escape the smog and pollution of the city and to enjoy the fresh air and open spaces of veld and forest. But there is also immense satisfaction to be obtained from unravelling the finer details of the life-cycles and breeding habits of our butterfly fauna; for a surprising number of species, for example, we still do not know what the caterpillars' food-plants are.

For many collectors the ultimate ambition is to discover a previously undescribed species, subspecies or form of butterfly. This can still happen in South Africa and, who knows, you could be the lucky individual!

HOW TO USE THIS BOOK

Distribution maps. The distribution maps which accompany the individual butterfly accounts from page 145 represent the first-ever attempt to describe the ranges of South African butterflies in this way. They give a general indication of the presumed range of each butterfly species in South Africa (including the self-governing states), Lesotho and Swaziland, but by no means pretend to absolute accuracy. The author and publishers would welcome suggestions for improving the maps for subsequent editions of this work.

Nomenclature. The scientific names used in this book follow those listed in the taxonomic inventory of southern African moths and butterflies presented by Dr. L. Vári and Dr. D. Kroon in *Southern African Lepidoptera, a Series of Cross-referenced Indices* (1986). This list incorporates many name changes which will as yet be unfamiliar to most South African naturalists and lepidopterists. Family and subfamily name changes are listed on page 15. Changes at genus, species and subspecies level are referred to in the individual species accounts and, to assist further, the 'old' names have been included as cross-references in the index (page 253).

Wingspan. No indication of scale appears on the photographic plates, but minimum and maximum wingspans are provided for both male and female in the individual species accounts. This measurement is made from forewing apex to forewing apex when the butterfly is set in the usual manner with the 'inner margins' (see page 9) of both forewings forming one straight line. Ciliate fringes are included in the measurement where they occur. Although abnormally large or small butterflies do occur from time to time, their measurements have not been taken into account here.

Sex symbols. In the photographic captions from page 33, males are indicated by the symbol ♂, and females by the symbol ♀.

CHAPTER 1

Before embarking on your study or your collection, it is important to understand something of the origins, characteristics and behaviour of the butterfly – and of the mysteries of its world.

Although it is generally thought that the ancestors of our present-day butterflies and moths evolved concurrently with the flowering plants (angiosperms) whose origins are dated to about 200 million years ago, until relatively recently the most ancient butterfly and moth fossils on record dated back only about 50 million years. Such fossils are few and far between because of the fragility of these soft and delicate insects. Nevertheless new discoveries of well-preserved primitive moths in the Lebanon and Siberia, dated to between 100 and 130 million years ago, have shed more light on the evolutionary history of butterflies and moths. Since the new fossils are themselves clearly assignable to presently recognized families, *their* ancestors in turn must date to an even earlier period.

In view of the lack of fossil material, however, we can only speculate about the size, colour and form of butterflies of these earlier eras. It is interesting to note that of all the butterfly fossils found, none has been larger than any butterfly we have today.

WHAT IS A BUTTERFLY?

Together with moths, butterflies belong to one of the largest insect groups, the order Lepidoptera, with more than 150 000 species world-wide. Perhaps 12 000 of these occur in southern Africa, the majority being moths.

What is the difference between a butterfly and a moth? Although the distinguishing features are not in fact as conveniently clear-cut as we would like, four of the more helpful identification features are listed here.

1. The antennae of butterflies are usually clubbed at the tip (although those of the skippers are more tapered and frequently end in a little hook). In moths the antennae may be feathery in appearance, or slender and tapered or sometimes thickened towards the tip, but never end in a club. Because of these antennal differences, butterflies are occasionally referred to as Rhopalocera ('club horns') and moths as Heterocera ('other horns').

2. Most butterflies are diurnal, that is they are active by day, while most moths are nocturnal and fly at night. There are, however, many exceptions in both groups, with some moths flying by day and some butterflies flying at dusk and dawn. This activity peak during the twilight hours (known as 'crepuscular' activity) is found in some of the skippers and also in the satyrine butterfly, the twilight brown, *Melanitis leda* (page 146).

3. When at rest, most butterflies sit with their wings closed against each other over the backs of their bodies; moths on the other hand tend to sit either with their wings laid close along their bodies with the forewings completely covering the hindwings, or with both fore- and hindwings spread out flat. Again there are exceptions: in the case of some of the skippers the butterfly's wings are not held closed, but are held above the body in an almost half-open position, while other species sit with their wings in an almost flat, moth-like posture.

4. Butterflies do not possess a frenulum, which is a device on the wings of moths linking the fore- and hindwings together while in flight.

How do butterflies and moths differ from other insects? Firstly, both groups have their wings covered with a vast number of microscopic dust-like scales which are set into the wings and lie in rows very much like the tiles on the roof of a house. These scales give the colour and pattern to the wing, and in some instances also to the body of the insect.

Secondly, moths and butterflies both have a coiled proboscis or 'tongue'. This is situated below the head and in between a pair of small, scaly projections called labial palps. The proboscis can be straightened and inserted into flowers to suck nectar or on to damp patches of soil to sip moisture. Some of the skippers have a coiled proboscis which can be twice as long as the body – but they are out-reached by some hawk-moths with proboscis-lengths of up to 30 centimetres.

The covering of scales on the wings and body gave rise to the name of this order of insects – 'Lepidoptera', meaning 'scale-wing'. The colour patterns on the wings of moths and butterflies are commonly derived from colour pigments in these scales. In many groups, however, the insects derive their colour not from pigment in the scales, but from an elaborate microscopic sculpturing and grooving on the surface of each scale; the light falling on such scales is diffracted and diffused to produce for example the iridescent blue of some lycaenid butterflies such as the fig-tree blue *Myrina silenus* (page 78) and the sapphire *Iolaus silas* (page 82). Butterflies with 'structural' colours will not fade in collections while those deriving their colours from pigments present in the scales do tend to fade in time if exposed to light for lengthy periods, for example the blood-red acraea *Acraea petraea* (page 44) and the angled grass-yellow *Eurema desjardinsii* (page 110).

CHAPTER 2
THE STRUCTURE OF A BUTTERFLY

Butterflies are constructed along the same general lines as their other insect relatives. The body is protected by an armour of chitin which forms the exoskeleton. This is arranged in a series of rings or segments separated by flexible membranous zones which allow movement in similar fashion to the joints in the suits of armour used in mediaeval Europe. The body consists of three main regions, the head, thorax and abdomen, each of which will be discussed below.

THE HEAD

The head of the adult butterfly houses the eyes, antennae, labial palps and a coiled proboscis. As there are no functional jaws, food must be taken in liquid form through the extensible proboscis. This is coiled and tucked up under the head when not in use. It can be quickly uncoiled to probe deep into flowers and is extended by an increase in haemolymph ('blood') pressure. It is in fact a feeding-tube made up of two parts, like a tapered pipe that has been cut in half from one end to the other and then joined together again. The grooves on the inner surfaces of the two parts are joined along their length by special interlocking spines, forming a waterproof seal when in apposition. The liquid food is then sucked up the central channel by a special pumping mechanism formed by modified muscles and sclerites in the pharyngeal region of the head. The labial palps serve as special sensory organs that test the type of sustenance on hand.

Adults feed mainly on the nectar of flowers, but other foods include the liquid from decaying fruit, the sap that exudes from damaged tree-trunks and branches, and the moisture from the excrement of animals; (for some reason, lion and other carnivore droppings seem particularly favoured). Certain species of butterfly drink water that has collected on damp sandy soil, and after a shower of rain can be seen congregated together in large numbers to drink. Such an event is a great delight to watch as several different species often gather at the same place; the patient collector may take a useful series with minimal effort from these damp 'watering-holes'.

The antenna are normally club-shaped, a feature typical of butterflies, and each consists of a series of rings or segments. They are the sensory organs and are responsible for the senses of balance and smell. At the base of the antenna is a specialized organ which helps the insect's sense of orientation, particularly during flight. The smell sensors cover the entire surface of the antennae and, surprisingly, the senses of hearing and touch are also distributed in the antennae and the palps. Sensitive touch sensors are also located in the feet, and it is apparently with these that an ovipositing female can tell whether she has chosen the correct type of food-plant upon which to lay her eggs.

The vision of butterflies is much less acute than their sense of smell. Their compound eyes are large and conspicuous and are situated on the top and side of the head. They are composed of a large number of optical units, each unit equivalent to a simple eye with its own lens and photosensitive region. Each simple eye 'sees' a single image with the result that the butterfly perceives a picture very much like a mosaic, each simple eye within the compound eye being responsible for one small segment of the whole picture. Its vision can readily detect movement of objects, but is much less acute than that of vertebrate animals. It is, however, able to detect a limited number of different colours by discriminating between light sources of different wavelengths. Some species seem to be attracted to one colour more than another, and often a flower of one particular colour will attract swarms of butterflies, while a few metres away a flower of a different colour with an equally abundant supply of nectar is left untouched. Some years ago, while collecting at Balgowan in the Natal Midlands, I was amazed to see several bush kites or forest swallowtails (*Princeps euphranor*) flying low and dive-bombing my red car. Realizing it was the colour that was attracting them, I moved the car a few hundred metres up the hill and waited, and after a few minutes they spotted the car again and repeated this strange behaviour. A year or two later I was at Balgowan again, but this time I did not have a red car; I had instead a large red towel which

Figures 1 & 2: The structural features of a butterfly

1. Forewing
2. Wing-vein
3. Thorax
4. Antenna
5. Palp
6. Proboscis
7. Compound eye
8. Trochanter
9. Coxa
10. Femur
11. Tarsus
12. Tibia
13. Abdomen

14. Hindwing cell
15. Forewing costa
16. Forewing cell
17. Apex
18. Forewing outer margin
19. Forewing inner margin
20. Hindwing outer margin
21. (Hindwing) anal angle
22. Base of wing
23. (Forewing) inner angle
24. Hindwing costa
25. Hindwing inner margin

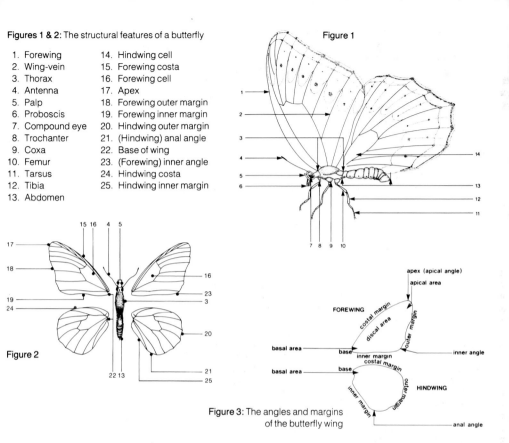

Figure 1

Figure 2

Figure 3: The angles and margins of the butterfly wing

I draped over low bushes beside the car. Within a short time the butterflies were again in attendance, clearly suggesting that they were attracted to the red cloth and not to the car.

Butterflies are capable of detecting ultraviolet light which is invisible to the human eye, and this suggests that they may well see colours in a different way from us.

THE THORAX

The thorax is that part of the butterfly to which the head is joined by a flexible 'neck'. The thorax is composed of three segments, each with a pair of legs which are adapted both for walking and clinging. Each leg consists of several parts: the basal joint (coxa), the thigh (femur), the shaft (tibia) and the 'foot' (tarsus). The coxa and femur are jointed by a small triangular segment, the trochanter. The 'foot' has five segments and ends in a pair of claws.

The two pairs of wings are attached to the second and third thoracic segments. The wings consist of an upper and lower membrane supported in between by a framework of hollow tubes, the veins. Each vein is given a name according to its position on the wing, and as wing venation follows fixed patterns depending on the family it has become an important tool in the classification of butterflies. At the base of the wings where they are attached to the thorax is a flexible articulated joint. These joints allow the beating of the wings in flight, and the folding of the wings when the insect is at rest.

Among the scales on the wings are specialized scent scales known as androconia; these are only found in the male butterfly. At the base of these scales are small glands which produce a chemical scent known as a pheromone, a sort of aphrodisiac used to excite the female during courtship. Molecules of this powerful scent pass up the hollow stalk of the scale and are dispersed into the air, often by fine hair-like plumes at the tip. During courtship the male often flutters around the female waving his wings in an attempt to stimulate her with scent.

THE ABDOMEN

The abdomen consists of ten rings or segments, of which seven or eight can be seen easily. The terminal portions are the segments that house the reproductive organs, known as the genitalia. In the female these segments are modified and narrowed to form an egg-laying tube called an ovipositor, which is slightly drawn into the body. Close to this is an opening which receives sperm from the male; the sperm are stored in sperm-sacs (spermathecae) within the abdomen of the female. It is worth noting here that the sperm are at first kept separate from the undeveloped eggs, and an egg will only start the process of cell division when a sperm has been introduced into it. This does not happen at the time of mating, but when the egg is passed out of the oviduct during egg-laying; at this stage minute amounts of sperm are released to accomplish fertilization. It may be said that after mating the female herself is fertile, but that the eggs are only fertilized at the time of laying.

At the end of the male's abdomen there is a pair of claspers, with which the female is held during copulation; the claspers enclose a centrally located ejaculatory organ.

Once a male and a female have been brought together by a combination of scent and sight, the courtship begins in earnest and the couple pair. The female settles and usually raises her abdomen, the end of which the male grasps with his claspers. Mating can take a few minutes or last several hours and, during this time sperm are passed from the male to the female in a package called a spermatophore; from this the sperm move to the spermathecae where they are stored until egg-laying takes place.

Often a male and female can be seen flying together while pairing, either the male doing the flying and the female hanging below or vice versa. It is often advantageous to catch them as they mate, as this is a sure means of identifying both sexes of the species. Such a pair of specimens would be labelled 'taken *in copula*'.

The external genitalia vary in shape and form between the different species and effective mating can only take place where the male and female genitalia 'fit' together. It is, in a manner of speaking, like having one key to one lock, and this is one of the factors that prevents species from hybridizing. This 'lock-and-key' part of the genitalia is situated at the end of the abdomen, and is a particularly useful tool in the identification of closely related species. The establishment of the identity of a species by its genitalia is accomplished by first removing the last few segments of the abdomen; this portion is then left in a solvent to dissolve fatty tissue, and after a few more chemical processes the genitalia can be examined under a microscope. A comparison is then made with published descriptions of the genitalia of the various related species and an accurate verdict can be obtained.

INTERNAL ORGANS

There are no veins, arteries or capillaries in the blood circulatory system of a butterfly. The blood or 'haemolymph' (there is no haemoglobin in insect blood) is restricted not by blood vessels but simply by the limits of the body cavity. There is, however, a long tubular 'heart' lying along the back of the butterfly which is supplied with contractile muscles; these push the blood towards the head, from where it seeps back through the tissues. The blood performs the same functions as in vertebrates, that is it carries and stores food, carries hormones to the tissues and delivers waste products to the excretory organs; it does not, however, transport oxygen.

The excretory system consists of a set of tubular glands, known as Malpighian tubules, which unite to form a duct which opens into the alimentary canal near the junction of the mid- and hindgut. The excreta are composed of uric acid and urates.

The butterfly's digestive system is characterized by extensive development of the pharynx, which functions as a pump to suck the insect's liquid food into the body. The digestive system is specially designed to cope with a liquid diet, and once the fluids have been drawn up through the proboscis, they enter the digestive tract and are stored inside a small reservoir (the crop) until required. The digestion of the food takes place in the 'stomach' and any material that is not required or is indigestible is passed into the hind intestine and is expelled from the body via the anus. Food that is digested is absorbed into the blood, or is stored as fat in a structure known as the 'fat body' where it remains until it is needed. This fat body takes the form of sheets of fatty tissue which underlie the integument of the insect, or surround the digestive system itself. The fat body is usually far better developed in the female than in the male because her developing eggs require nourishment over and above her own needs.

The respiratory system of the butterfly is similar to that of most insects. Oxygen enters the body through two pairs of thoracic spiracles and several pairs of abdominal spiracles. From the spiracles it is conveyed by fine internal tubes called tracheae (singular – 'trachea') directly to the tissues through smaller and smaller tubes called tracheoles. The exchange of oxygen and carbon dioxide is effected by simple diffusion at the end of the thin-walled tracheoles. The blood plays little part in respiration.

CHAPTER 3
THE LIFE-CYCLE OF A BUTTERFLY

The life-cycle of the butterfly is truly remarkable, and it is hard to credit some of the changes that occur from the time that the egg is laid until the newly emerged butterfly takes off on its maiden flight. There are in fact four phases, from the egg to the larva to the pupa and to the adult; the transformation from the larval to the adult condition is known as metamorphosis. The four phases are discussed below.

THE EGG

Butterfly eggs are deposited in different ways by different species. Sometimes 60 to 80 are laid in a batch, sometimes more, sometimes less. Members of the subfamily Acraeinae tend to lay their eggs in clusters (photograph **29a**, page 41) while pierids usually deposit them singly – a strategy which may give the larvae a greater chance of survival.

Although the eggs are laid in different places by each species, in general they are always laid on or near the food-plant the caterpillar will feed on. They may be laid in seed-pods or flower-buds, in the axils of leaves or on lichen on rocks. In some species of the subfamily Satyrinae the eggs are dropped during flight and merely scattered in the grass.

When eggs are laid on leaves the female usually attaches them to the undersides of the leaves to protect them from direct sun and rain, and perhaps also to hide them from parasites and predators.

The eggs may be pale cream, yellow or light green as they are laid, but after a day or two they darken and if viewed under a strong hand-lens the embryo can be seen forming. If the egg is scrutinized a few hours before hatching the tiny caterpillar can be seen curled up inside. From this protected position it will gnaw through the eggshell with its specially adapted mouthparts.

Eggs vary in surface structure from one species to the next and if examined under a microscope they can be seen to be either fluted, ribbed, pitted, sculptured or completely smooth. With practice, a lepidopterist can learn to recognize the unique distinguishing features of the various species' eggs, from size and shape to colouring and sculpturing.

Every egg has a depression at one pole in which there is a tiny hole, the micropyle. It is through this hole that the sperm enters to fertilize the egg when it is laid. Air and moisture also diffuse through the micropyle during the period the embryo is forming.

THE LARVA (CATERPILLAR)

Butterfly larvae, or caterpillars as they are commonly called, eat their way out of their eggs and their first meal is usually the eggshell itself (photograph **209b**, page 132). This contains valuable nutriments for their development, and in many cases the caterpillar will not survive unless it does this. It then starts to eat its food-plant which will either be under its feet or very close by.

Caterpillars vary in colour, shape and size from one species to the next, and with experience the differences are easily discernible. Their basic structure, however, is the same: a head followed by 13 trunk segments. The first three form the thorax, and the last ten are regarded as the abdomen. The larval skin, or cuticle, is soft and flexible and although it may be naked, in some species it may bear spines or bristles called setae (singular – 'seta'), which may or may not contain poisonous or irritating substances. Some bear bizarre branched processes and protuberances, warts, horns or other structures for camouflage or to frighten predators – see for example photographs **1c** (page 33), **36a** (page 44), **49a** (page 52), **52a** (page 54) and **53a** (page 55).

The head is a round hard structure and is totally different in shape and function from that of the adult butterfly. The mouthparts are specialized, and are designed to chew and nibble the food-plant. There is a prominent pair of toothed jaws or mandibles for biting off small pieces of food which are then shredded into fine pieces before being swallowed. Another highly specialized mouthpart, the labium, is modified to form the spinneret which is used in the spinning of silk. The silk is extruded, not from the mouth, but from two special spiracle-like tubes on either side of the mandibles. The silk is spun on to the leaf surface as the caterpillar walks along, where it hardens almost as fast as it is laid down. This forms a carpet that is stuck to the leaf surface, enabling the caterpillar to grip with its feet. This mat is used by the caterpillar when it pulls itself out of its old skin during its moults.

The caterpillar has no compound eyes, the main visual organs being the three pairs of lateral ocelli, which are simple eyes and which are arranged in two groups, one on each side of the head. Each ocellus resembles a single unit from the compound eye (see The Head, page 8) and can probably only detect the difference between light and dark, being of little use for the location of food. The caterpillar relies on its senses of touch and smell to ensure it is on the correct food-plant.

Three pairs of short stubby legs are attached to the first three segments (the thorax), each ending in a single claw. The third, fourth, fifth and sixth of the ten segments comprising the abdomen each have a pair of false legs called prolegs which are soft and have no joints. They are used to support the abdomen. The last segment of the abdomen has a pair of anal prolegs or claspers; these are very powerful in relation to the size of the caterpillar and grip with amazing strength. When picking larvae in the wild, you may find that the claspers grip so well that damage to the caterpillar can result; in fact the caterpillar may allow its body to be torn in half rather than relinquish its hold on the silken mat. It is advisable in these circumstances to cut the leaf of the plant instead, and allow the caterpillar to walk off in its own good time.

There is no skeleton within the body and the body shape is maintained by internal pressure beneath the skin. The skin does not grow with the caterpillar, it merely stretches to contain its contents. This cannot go on indefinitely, however, and in order to accommodate major size increases, the skin is shed from time to time, exposing a new and larger skin that has formed beneath the old.

The shedding process usually starts at the front end with the splitting of the now old head-shield, and continues down the back of the caterpillar until the old skin is shrugged off at the tail-end, in much the same way as a person takes off a wet clinging overcoat. This process is called moulting or, more technically, ecdysis. The larval stage between two moults is called an instar. Most caterpillars have four or five instars before the final moult and then change into the pupal stage of their metamorphosis cycle. The instars are controlled carefully and precisely by hormones. Although the number of instars is essentially fixed for each species there may be one more or one less than is usual, depending on environmental conditions, or perhaps because of a shortage of food. This is one reason why it is vitally important to keep fresh and adequate reserves of the appropriate host-plant when rearing larvae in captivity.

The caterpillar is the main feeding stage in the butterfly's life-cycle, and from its hatching to its pupation it will devour many hundreds of times its own original mass in food. Some species feed by day and others by night, but on the whole they feed continuously, stopping only to moult.

Caterpillar shapes and colour patterns are all part of their camouflage and they resort to some extraordinary subterfuges to conceal themselves from vertebrate predators. The caterpillar of Bowker's tailed blue, for example, nibbles a section out of a leaf, then settles into this cut-out, making the contours of its body the same shape as the leaf. Vast numbers of caterpillars, however, fail to reach the pupal stage, not because of predation by birds or other vertebrates, but because they are attacked by a variety of different insect parasites which are less susceptible to the finer points of caterpiller camouflage. Some of these parasites are wasps and others are flies; their larvae feed within the body of the living caterpillar and pupate either inside the host's skin or outside (see photograph **213b**, page 135). Larvae gathered in the wild for captive-breeding will often grow satisfactorily and appear healthy until the last instar, when they will suddenly die leaving small maggots to crawl out of their bodies to pupate and hatch nearby.

A particularly frustrating characteristic of some species is for the caterpillar to eat its fill, then to walk well away from the tell-tale leaf to rest; the collector will find leaves that have all the signs of fresh feeding upon them, and yet the caterpillar is nowhere to be found.

The caterpillars of the family Lycaenidae (blues and coppers) have a very characteristic slug-like shape, being tapered at both ends with a hump in the middle. They are often beautifully coloured, with markings that blend so well with their surroundings that they are rendered almost invisible on their food-plants. Sharp spines protect other caterpillars (for example, the acraeines – see photograph **20a**, page 38), while the larvae of the family Papilionidae (the swallowtails) typically possess a forked glandular process (behind the head) known as the osmeterium which is suddenly everted when the larva is threatened; the osmeterium is usually coloured red or orange ('warning colouration') and gives off a pungent citrus-like odour to deter potential attackers (see photograph **213a**, page 135).

The stomach is the largest region in the digestive tract of the caterpillar. Vast quantities of food pass through the alimentary canal, which is effectively a wide straight tube with muscular walls that maintain continual churning movements. The major part of the food eaten is indigestible cellulose. Consequently a large volume of droppings, or 'frass', is passed through the caterpillar and voided from the anus.

Like the adult butterfly, the larva has no lungs and breathes through the same branching system of tubes (tracheae and tracheoles) which conducts air to all parts of the body. The air is drawn into the body through nine pairs of small holes (spiracles), one pair on the first of the thoracic segments and the others on the sides of the first eight abdominal segments.

THE PUPA

When the caterpillar in its final instar has finished feeding, it is ready to pupate. Before it does so, however, its digestive system evacuates all material that is not required during the pupal stage. The caterpillar loses some of its colour and in some cases the skin becomes slightly transparent. It must now find a suitable place in which to shed its final skin and pupate. The choice of such a site varies with each species. Some pupate on their food-plants, under a leaf, or on a twig close by. Tree-feeding caterpillars may walk down to the lower part of the stem or trunk of the food-plant and pupate there, assuming the colour and rough appearance of the bark. Many will walk a considerable distance to pupate far from their original food-plants, on walls or on blades of grass. The caterpillars of still other species pupate underground within the nests of certain ants. These are butterflies whose life-cycles depend on their association with host ants. (See the section on the family Lycaenidae, at the top of page 19).

There are three main types of pupa. The first often hangs head down, attached only by the tail and with no other support (photographs **36b**, page 44; **61c**, page 60); this is the case with most of the family Nymphalidae (including its subfamilies Nymphalinae, Danainae, Charaxinae, Acraeinae and most of the Satyrinae). Others may be attached by the tail but supported head upwards or half-upwards by a silken girdle, as is nearly always the case in the families Lycaenidae, Papilionidae and Pieridae (photographs **207a**, page 130; **218c**, page 138). In the third type the pupa may be enclosed in a cocoon, as in the family Hesperiidae and a few members of the subfamily Satyrinae. The latter two groups usually make their cocoon from the leaves of their food-plant (photograph **231c**, page 142) and then shed their skin inside this protective covering; this would seem to be the simplest and easiest way to pupate.

In the second type of pupa mentioned above, where the pupa is supported by a silken girdle, the final-instar caterpillar starts by spinning a small pad of silk on a plant stem. It then moves forward until its claspers are directly over the pad which it then grips firmly. Lying head up, it bends its head and a few of the body segments back and to the side of the body almost one third of its length. It then attaches a silk thread to the stem on one side and, still bent, twists round, passing the thread over its back and attaching it to the stem on the opposite side. This side-to-side spinning goes on until a thread of sufficient strength has been spun. The larvae then straightens itself out and hangs within the girdle. After a period of time, usually a day or two, the larval skin splits, beginning with the head, and slowly by a series of alternate swellings and contractions the pupa pushes the larval skin backwards to the tail end, passing it under the girdle as it does so. For a split second the claspers are released from the silken pad, the pupa balances in the girdle, withdraws its tail and claspers from the encircling skin, which falls away, and a quick twist engages its cremaster into the silken pad. (The cremaster is a hook at the end of the pupa which is formed under the skin prior to pupation.)

This process is even more remarkable in the case of the pupa that hangs by its tail. Consider this question for a moment: if a caterpillar is hanging attached only by its tail, how does it manage to get out of its skin and disengage and discard it from the tail-end without falling from the silken pad? I can almost hear the ringmaster calling to the crowd – 'Ladies and gentlemen, we are about to witness an extraordinary feat – a caterpillar hanging upside-down will relinquish its support, discard its skin over its tail and re-attach itself to the same spot in complete defiance of the law of gravity!' The lights go down, the spotlight comes on, and one of Nature's tricks is performed. This is how it works. The larval skin splits behind the head and is pushed upwards to the tail end of the body. The skin is now pinched from the inside between the last two segments on the underside of the caterpillar (this holds like a small and powerful pair of tweezers); at the same time, the caterpillar twists upwards and grips the silken pad as well, now it relaxes its grip with the tail end, pierces through the skin above the last two segments and entangles the cremaster in the silken pad. What has just become the pupa, relaxes its grip on the skin and silken pad, and twitches and wriggles for some time until the old skin breaks away and falls off.

After the larval skin has been shed the pupa is still soft and wet and has not yet taken on its final appearance. However, after a short time the pupa hardens into the shape and colour characteristic of its species.

In most cases the pupa adopts the colour of its surroundings and most of them are extremely hard to find in the wild. I have often seen caterpillars of *Stugeta bowkeri* (Bowker's tailed blue) pupating on the lower trunk of their food-plant tree. If these larvae pupate on the bark where lichen is growing, they disguise themselves with the exact colour of the lichen. Others that pupate where moss is growing on the tree, have a moss-coloured pattern, and on one occasion I saw a pupa that was black to match the bark which had previously been charred in a grass-fire.

The pupa is immobile and therefore very vulnerable. It is for this reason that it must disguise itself so effectively against attack from predators. It must also be able to protect itself from harsh weather conditions, particularly in the case of those which have to remain in the pupal state for extended periods of time. The length of time a butterfly spends as a pupa varies from one species to the next. Those butterflies which only have one generation each year usually have a very extended pupal stage. Those having several generations each year may have only a 25- to 30-day period from egg to adult, which may mean only a few days as a pupa. This period in all cases may be interrupted by unfavourable climatic conditions, such as a prolonged spell of cold weather. The pupa will then enter a phase of arrested development, or diapause, that once started cannot be stopped until a pre-determined length of time has passed. It would be imprudent to say the least if the butterfly should emerge during unfavourable weather conditions. As an additional precaution, a female laying her eggs will not usually lay them all on a single plant in one egg-laying spree. Instead she will lay in a number of separate places over a period of several days to ensure that her entire brood will not all hatch on the same day only to be wiped out by an unexpected thunderstorm or other natural disaster. The duration of the life-cycle may therefore vary within one species, largely owing to the weather. If we were to take eggs from a mocker swallowtail (*Princeps dardanus cenea*) and keep half of them in a breeding-box in warm and favourable conditions, while subjecting the other half to cold conditions, there could be a difference of up to 30 days or more between the dates of pupation. If we were to take the pupae and subject them to the same warm and cold conditions we could expect a full year to pass between the hatching of the first and second batches; however, if the cold conditions were removed, the pupae could be expected to hatch within a few days.

EMERGENCE
At the time of emergence the pupal case first splits behind the head, then a small split runs down the front in the area of the feet. Slowly the butterfly pulls itself out completely (photograph **196b**, page 123). Now it is soft and flabby, its abdomen swollen with liquid. Free from the pupal case, the butterfly moves to a position where it can hang with its wings drooping downwards (**196c**). The wings at this stage are only a fraction of their normal size, being shrunken and limp. The butterfly can now commence pumping the haemolymph from its body into the wing-veins until they are fully expanded (**196d** and **196e**). When this operation is complete, the butterfly rests motionless with its wings held slightly apart until they are dry and hard. Depending on the size of the butterfly, the drying process can take from half an hour to several hours. Around this time the waste products accumulated during the pupal phase are ejected from the anus, often in the form of a thick red or dark-grey liquid. The butterfly is now ready for its maiden flight.

CHAPTER 4
BUTTERFLY SPECIES AND THEIR NAMES
The binominal system of naming and classifying animals and plants is credited to the Swedish naturalist Carolus Linnaeus (1707-1778). Under this system each different species of living organism is given a two-part (binominal) name derived from Latin or 'latinized' Greek, or from any other source as long as it is latinized.

We have grown up knowing animals by their common names. Most of the time it is sufficient to say, 'I have just seen an elephant', or 'I have seen a lion'; it is unnecessary to cite the full latinized scientific name when referring to such well-known animals. It is rather different in the case of butterflies, despite the fact that all of our species have common names; the reason for this will become clear later on in this section. It is true that most of the scientific names are long-winded and at first may be hard to pronounce – if not hard to remember. However, these names are universal, and in some countries butterflies do not even have a vernacular or common name. Newly discovered species are not automatically given a common name – only a scientific name following the regulations held down by the International Code of Zoological Nomenclature.

The description of a new species must be published in a recognized scientific journal; this description must not only show what the insect is like, but must explain how it differs from its known relatives. The genus will usually be evident from a careful comparison with other known forms, and the specific name will by chosen by the author of the new species. The name may be a descriptive one, such as '*punctatissima*' meaning 'most spotted', or it will make reference to the place where it was found, for example '*uitenhaga*' (from Uitenhage). Names are often given that refer to the collector, a practice frowned upon by many scientists.

The full scientific name normally has two parts and by convention is always written in italics. The genus name comes first and commences with a capital letter; the specific name follows and is always written in small letters even if it is derived from a proper name, for example *Dira swanepoeli*. A genus can contain several closely related species and the specific names distinguish the different members. When a species varies geographically and has distinct and recognizable local races, it may be separated formally into subspecies. These subspecies are given a third name, the subspecific name, also always in italic small letters, for example *Princeps ophidicephalus zluensis* and *P. o. transvaalensis* which, as their names suggest, are respectively the Zululand and Transvaal subspecies of the emperor swallow-tail. The full citation of a scientific name also includes the author's name and the date of publication of the species' name. By convention these are written in roman letters, not italic. Although many people believe the author's name and date should always be enclosed in brackets, this is not the case. Brackets are in fact only used if the genus name has been changed since the author first described it. For example, *Iolaus pallene* (page 185) was described by Wallengren in 1857 as *Myrina pallene*, so his name is placed in brackets; *Iolaus sidus* (page 186), however, was described under that name by Trimen in 1864 and his name and the date of publication remain unbracketed.

Butterflies, however, are subject to other types of variation within the species. Males may differ from females of the same species; or the wet-season form of a species may differ radically in appearance from the dry-season form; or as in the mocker swallowtail (page 233) there may be several genetically fixed forms within one population of a species which mimic other butterfly species or *their* forms. In such cases a latinized name may be applied to a particular colour variant and prefixed by the word 'form', often abbreviated to 'f.'. Form names, it should be noted, have no taxonomic standing and are merely convenient labels for recognizable colour variants. Two forms of the mocker swallowtail are illustrated on page 133 (f. *trophonius* and f. *cenea*).

From time to time still another type of variation occurs within a species when a specimen is found with, perhaps, an extra eye-spot on the wing, or a different coloured wing-stripe, or with one of its prominent features lacking. Such an unusual butterfly of rare occurrence is referred to as a sport, variety or aberration (photographs **185i** and **j**, page 117).

Lepidoptera are classified into families, genera and species according to tried and tested criteria based on such characteristics as wing shape, the arrangement of wing venation, the structure of the genitalia and colour pattern. As better series of butterflies are acquired and subjected to detailed scrutiny, however, it is sometimes found that a well-known species of long standing is actually a complex of two or more closely related species. This has happened, for example, in the genus *Poecilmitis* (family Lycaenidae) where *Poecilmitis nigricans* (page 210) has been separated from *P. thysbe* (page 209). The opposite situation can also occur, where two apparently valid species eventually prove to be one and the same, as has recently proved to be the case with *Aloeides penningtoni* and *A. natalensis* in Natal (page 206). In such cases the older of the two names is always accorded priority and the newer name is relegated to the obscurity of synonymy. Sometimes a reclassification of a whole group takes place when a taxonomist decides that a particular genus contains too diverse a grouping of species. Then a new genus may be established to accommodate one of the new groupings. Readers who are familiar with the older books on South African butterflies will notice several such generic name changes: some members of the genus *Papilio* have now been allocated to the genus *Princeps* and others to the genus *Graphium*; another example is the well-known pearl charaxes, formerly known as *Charaxes varanes* and now as *Stonehamia varanes*. These changes have been made to follow the taxonomic arrangement suggested by Vári and Kroon (1986).

CHAPTER 5

THE BUTTERFLY FAMILIES

In previous books on southern African butterflies, nine families have been recognized. A more recent proposal, adopted by Vári and Kroon (1986) and followed here, relegates the families Danaidae, Satyridae, Acraeidae and Nymphalidae to subfamily rank and separates out another subfamily, the Charaxinae. By the conventions of zoological taxonomy, the family name-ending '=idae' changes to the subfamily name-ending '=inae' as will be seen from the list which follows. All five subfamilies are considered to belong to the now-expanded family Nymphalidae.

1. Family **Nymphalidae**, subfamily **Danainae** – milkweed butterflies
2. Family **Nymphalidae**, subfamily **Satyrinae** – browns
3. Family **Nymphalidae**, subfamily **Acraeinae** – acraeas
4. Family **Nymphalidae**, subfamily **Nymphalinae** – nymphs, commodores
5. Family **Nymphalidae**, subfamily **Charaxinae** – charaxes
6. Family **Libytheidae** – snout butterflies
7. Family **Lycaenidae** – blues and coppers
8. Family **Pieridae** – whites
9. Family **Papilionidae** – swallowtails
10. Family **Hesperiidae** – skippers

1. SUBFAMILY DANAINAE

The Danainae or danaines are largely confined to the tropics and subtropics and include the monarch and milkweed butterflies as well as others with such curious names as the friar, the novice and the layman. They are tough insects and difficult to kill – they may recover even after the hard squeeze on the thorax normally used by collectors to dispatch their captured specimens.

All the members of this subfamily are distasteful to potential predators and some even contain substantial amounts of lethal toxins. These poisons are acquired at the larval stage from their host-plants, mostly in the family Asclepiadaceae (which includes the milkweeds). A bird which eats a danaine butterfly will immediately vomit, learning the hard way that danaines are best avoided. As the butterflies are conspicuously marked in 'warning colours' they make ideal 'models' for unrelated butterflies which mimic their colour patterns to a greater or lesser degree to capitalise on the learned avoidance reactions of sadder but wiser birds. (See page 247 and the discussion on mimicry).

The Danainae usually have orange and black, or white and black spotted wings, with their veins clearly outlined with dark scales. The sexes are sometimes easy to distinguish, the male having a scent-patch on the anal area of the hindwing. This can be seen particularly clearly in the southern milkweed butterfly, *Danaus chrysippus aegyptius*, where the female has three black spots on the hindwing above and below, while the male has four; the fourth and largest spot nearest to the inner margin is the scent-patch. In photograph **1a** (page 33) the forewings of the male conceal the hindwing spots with the exception of the scent-patch; photograph **1b**, however, shows the four spots very clearly on the male's hindwing underside, the largest black spot (with the white centre) being the scent-patch.

Danaines tend to fly along the sunny edges of forests and roadways; their flight is slow with a lazy flapping motion but if they are disturbed it becomes very rapid.

Danaine eggs have a flattened-dome shape and are prominently ribbed. The larvae are smooth-skinned and usually have brilliantly coloured body stripes and two to four pairs of filamentous tubercles (three pairs in *Danaus chrysippus* – see photograph **1c**, page 33), giving them a rather self-assertive look – perhaps justifiably in view of their poisonous qualities. The pupae are suspended head down from a silken pad and are squat and roundish, with a waxy feel. In colour some are bright green with gold or silver markings, while others seem to be covered with gold leaf as if they have just come out of the workshop of a master jeweller.

2. SUBFAMILY SATYRINAE

The satyrines are predominantly coloured in brown or shades of orange and brown, but a few are grey. Their wings are short and broad, typically with one or several eye-spots, especially on the underside. One of the features characterizing a satyrine is the thickening of the main forewing veins where they join the thorax. One genus, *Melanitis*, is crepuscular in habit and flies mostly in the early evening on the edge of thick bush or undergrowth (page 146). When settled, satyrines usually exhibit undersides which have a camouflage that is very much like dry leaves, helping them to blend into their backgrounds and escape notice (photograph **5a**, page 34). So confident are they in their camouflage that they only fly up at the last moment under the collector's feet.

The forelegs of both male and female are degenerate and bush-like.

The eggs are more or less rounded and melon-shaped, with grooves or fine ribs. In some species the female lays her eggs in flight, dropping them at random over grass, various species of which are the larval host-plants. This hit-or-miss method is clearly potentially wasteful and butterfly species which adopt this egg-laying system produce larger numbers of smaller eggs than those which carefully select the correct host-plant and attach their eggs to it.

The larvae are smooth-skinned and are distinguishable from other butterfly larvae by their forked tail segments (photograph **9b**, page 35). Some have a coat of fine short hairs and delicate stripes down the sides, which help to disguise them when they rest on the lower parts of grass stems during the day (mostly feeding at night). The pupae are generally suspended by the tail, but certain species in the subfamily pupate on or just under the ground.

The flight of satyrines is generally rather weak and has been likened to the slow bouncing of a ping-pong ball – 'boing, boing, boing'. They settle frequently and many species rest in the shade for long periods. Members of this subfamily are referred to affectionately by collectors as 'L.B.J.s' ('Little Brown Jobs').

3. SUBFAMILY ACRAEINAE

The wings of most members of this subfamily are long and narrow, and are often liberally spotted with black dots. The predominant colours are red or orange, the males of some species being blood-red when they first emerge. Some species have transparent, scale-less patches on the wings. Like the Danainae, butterflies of this subfamily are distasteful to predators, and again like the Danainae they have a tough integument and are hard to kill with the usual squeeze of the thorax; in fact they often 'come to life' long after they have been transported home.

When handled, acraeas can exude an unpleasant yellow fluid from the thorax; the acrid odour of this liquid gives them protection against their foes. Like other distasteful butterflies they are used as models by harmless species, the mimics thereby acquiring a degree of protection from predators. As an example, one can compare the photograph of the unpalatable female acraeine *Bematistes aganice aganice* (**19b**, page 38) with the photograph of the palatable female nymphaline *Pseudacraea eurytus imitator* (upper **54c**, page 56).

Their bright colours and slow flight are almost a form of advertising their unpleasant taste, and they are left well alone by birds. This slow flight pattern must not deceive the collector into thinking they are easy to catch, however, for if given the slightest hint of danger their turn of speed often leaves the collector with an empty net.

The abdomen is long and slender in proportion to the total body length, while the forelegs are reduced in size. The sexes are rather easy to distinguish, the lower part of the abdomen of the male being a slightly whitish or orange colour without distinct black areas spotted with white dots, whilst the female's abdomen is spotted along the entire length.

The eggs are typically laid in clusters of up to 100 or more (photograph **29a**, page 41). The larvae in the early stages are gregarious, eating only the surface of the leaves, but when they grow larger, the groups become smaller, and eventually they become solitary in the final stages. The larvae have spines along the surface, each of which branches several times along its length (photograph **20a**, page 38); when broken, these spines exude a yellow fluid containing cyanide. Pupation can be on the surface of the food-plant leaf, on a twig, a branch or a tree-trunk, or the larvae may simply wander off and pupate on anything that is convenient. The pupae are attached only by the tail, are dark brown and black with a row of spots down the sides. Acraeine pupae are the easiest to find on account of their disregard for disguise and concealment.

4. SUBFAMILY NYMPHALINAE and 5. SUBFAMILY CHARAXINAE

For the purposes of this account these two subfamilies will be treated together.

The Nymphalinae and Charaxinae contain some of the most beautiful and striking butterflies to be encountered in South Africa. Their sizes range from small and medium to some of the largest in the subcontinent. They are mostly brightly coloured and impressive and there is no limit to the range of colours as in other families, with all hues from blue, violet and green to yellow, orange and red.

Nymphs and charaxes are often referred to as the brush-footed butterflies, as their prothoracic legs (the forelegs) are degenerate in both sexes and are formed like tiny brushes. In the male they have only two segments and are liberally covered with setae (hairs); the female on the other hand has four segments to each foreleg, with a sparse covering of hairs, giving them a somewhat different appearance. With a little experience the sexes may be distinguished easily.

Nymphalines are palatable to vertebrate predators and certain species are Batesian mimics of various poisonous danaine butterflies (see page 247). An easy way to tell members of the two subfamilies apart is to look at the hindwing cell; in danaines it is 'closed' at the end (see for example photograph **2**, page 33), while in nymphalines it is 'open' to the outer margin (photograph **62b**, page 61).

Their flight is very quick and powerful, and they can be recognized easily from their habit of giving a few quick flaps of the wings followed by a long sustained glide. Some butterflies of both subfamilies will readily come to traps baited with rotting fruit, particularly the charaxes.

The eggs are round and are usually ribbed with a small flat area on the top. They vary in colour but are commonly lime green.

The larvae of the two subfamilies vary considerably, some having single spines, while others have spines that are branched over the entire body (photograph **52a**, page 54). The charaxes larvae are all very distinctive, having smooth green slug-like bodies and heads that are flat in front and which are decorated with one pair of large horns (photograph **39b**, page 46) and often two pairs (photograph **49a**, page 52).

The pupa is of angular shape, usually coloured green to blend with the surroundings, but always hanging head down and only supported by the tail hooks.

6. FAMILY LIBYTHEIDAE

There is only one member of this family in South Africa and in fact there are only two or three species in the whole of Africa. The forelegs of the male are degenerate, small and hairy, and of no use for settling or walking; the female's, however, are only slightly reduced in size and are functional. The name 'snout butterfly' is derived from the long and straight labial palps which project forward far beyond the eyes and proboscis, giving a snout-like appearance.

Their forewings are angled outwards on the outer margin near the apex and are mostly brown with orange bands and small white patches on the forewings.

The larvae are tubular with fine hairs, often with one or two spines behind the head.

The South African species is found rather locally in the wetter forests, seldom flying out into the open and preferring to remain in the shady parts; it may sit on the trunk of a tree for long periods. Large migrations have been reported from time to time.

7. FAMILY LYCAENIDAE

The Lycaenidae is the most complex of all our butterfly families. It contains some of our smallest species but at the same time some of the most exquisite, both in colour and shape. Although they are called 'blues' and 'coppers' these names, are, however, sometimes misleading. While blues can be a richly metallic blue, as for example the fig-tree blue *Myrina silenus ficedula* (photograph **99d**, page 78), others have no blue at all, as in the case of the Zulu blue *Lepidochrysops ignota* (photograph **163a**, page 106). Similarly with the coppers: Clark's sorrel copper *Lycaena clarki (photograph* **147a**, page 101) is truly copper in colour, while the male Barkly's copper *Aloeides barklyi* (photograph **152a**, page 102) is a metallic silver-grey in colour. On the whole, the colours of the butterflies of this family are bright and striking (the males more so than the females) and their undersides are typically very different from the uppersides.

Many lycaenids possess tails on the hindwing which are usually associated with prominent eye-spot markings; these features play a part in their survival strategy. The butterfly will settle very quickly on a twig or leaf and almost at the same instant spin around and position itself with its head pointing downwards and its tail pointing upwards (for example the lucerne blue, *Lampides boeticus*, photograph **138b**, page 96). In this position the tails and eye-spots bear a striking resemblance to the antennae and compound eyes of the true head. A hungry lizard or bird striking at what it thinks is the butterfly's head will only bite off a small portion of wing, leaving the now tail-less lycaenid to escape, slightly damaged it is true, but nevertheless alive. The deception may be reinforced by the butterfly's keeping its true antennae hidden while moving its hindwings gently back and forth, as is the case with the common blue *Cyclyrius pirithous* (page 178). Sometimes stripes or other markings on the underwings direct the attention of the predator to the false 'head' (for example the short-barred sapphire, *Iolaus aemulus*, photograph **112b**, page 85, or the Natal barred blue, *Spindasis natalensis*, photograph **114b**, page 86).

Lycaenids often have a quick and darting flight, which makes them difficult to net, but the flight duration is seldom long and sustained. They will fly off for short periods and return time and time again to the same resting-place.

Certain species are very localized in their distribution, a situation which bodes ill for the future of several of our rarer species (for example, *Poecilmitis aureus*, see page 249), and which makes the discovery of suitable colonies both a challenging treasure-hunt and moral dilemma for the collector. Naturally enough, colonies will only be established in areas where the larval food-plant is available close by. Once the collector has discovered his butterfly population, however, and established what and where its food-plant is, then the eggs and larvae can be found, and the whole life-cycle can be studied. Eggs and larvae can be taken home and allowed to develop through to the adult stage. This method of collecting will be discussed later (see page 29).

The antennae are clubbed, and the segments are often noticeably banded alternately in two colours, for example black and white.

A curious phenomenon in this family is that the females are usually more difficult to find than the males, which are often seen flying around the tops of trees and small hills. This behaviour still awaits a satisfactory explanation. One theory is that the males establish territories on prominent landmarks such as hilltops; there they engage in territorial clashes while awaiting the arrival of females, which are thought to go to the hilltops only to mate. To many lepidopterists, however, this theory is unacceptable and unproven and the true purpose of 'hilltopping' (as it is called in the United States) is still a controversial subject.

In many species the males have hair-tufts or -pencils on the middle of their hindwings from which a scent exudes to attract the females. There is an uncorroborated report of a collector who caught several males and put them into a cage which he hung in a tree. As a result of this strategy, it is said that he captured several females which had presumably been attracted by the scent given off by the males.

The larvae are grub-shaped and do not have the familiar caterpillar shape that we associate with other 'normal' butterflies (see photographs **85a**, page 71; **95a**, page 75; **97a**, page 77; **99a**, page 78).

The first instars are also unusually small. The lycaenid larva life-cycle is, however, no different from that of other butterflies, although in many species their survival is assured only if they cohabit with certain species of ant (photograph **100b**, page 79).

There are various degrees of association with ants and the details of most life-histories still have to be worked out. Essentially, however, those larvae which associate with ants either provide them with a honey-like secretion from specialized glands on their backs in exchange for protection, or produce a pheromone which mimics the scent of the ants' own brood; or they may produce both. In some cases the larva lives most of its life in the ants' nest underground and feeds on the ant brood. In other cases the larva spends the day in the nest and at night sallies forth to its food-plant following a scent-trail laid by the ants, protected all the while by a 'bodyguard' of ants. In still other cases the larvae are merely attended by ants on their food-plant, giving 'honeydew' in exchange for protection.

In the former two situations the larva will pupate inside the ants' nest. When it emerges as an adult it scrambles out of the nest, delaying pumping up the wings until a convenient place to hang upside-down has been found. The larvae which merely associate with ants, spend all their time on the food-plant, the ants only visiting them to feed from the honey-gland. They pupate on the bark of the trees or in cracks lower down on the root system.

8. FAMILY PIERIDAE

The family Pieridae consists mostly of medium-sized butterflies, some of which are fast and vigorous fliers. The lemon traveller *Colotis subfasciatus*, for instance, can show an astonishing turn of speed when disturbed, with an almost magical capacity for changing direction suddenly in flight. Others of this group, however, are slow and weak fliers, an example being the African wood white (*Leptosia alcesta inalcesta*) whose flight puts one in mind of a small piece of white paper floating and tumbling in the breeze.

Although the basic colour of a pierid in South Africa is 'white', this name can be misleading as some are yellow or pale blue in colour, like the (yellow) autumn leaf vagrant (photograph **176d**, page 111), and the (pale-blue) Cambridge vagrant (photograph **179a**, page 113). Many have black markings along the wing-veins to some degree, while others have the apical tip of the forewing coloured red, yellow, orange, gold, purple or black.

The forelegs are well developed in both sexes, unlike the families already discussed. In some species the males have a tuft of white hair, or hair-pencil, tucked under a flap on the inner margin of the hindwing; this gives off a scent which attracts the females.

The wings are usually evenly rounded, and no pierid has tails on the hindwings. They do, however, share with the subfamily Nymphalinae the possession of a distinct fold along the inner margin of the hindwing which is wrapped around the abdomen when the butterfly is settled.

The eggs are typically elongate, conical or spindle-shaped, and when viewed under a high-magnification lens show beautifully sculptured ribs. The colour of the eggs is pale yellow or white, sometimes orange, and they are laid singly in most species, the hatched larva eating its way through its various instars in solitary splendour. Others lay their eggs in clusters, the caterpillars being gregarious in the early stages and feeding in aggregations of up to 60 or more; this is the case, for example, with the twin-dotted border, *Mylothris rueppellii haemus* (photographs **208a**, **b**, and **c**, page 131). As they grow and pass through their instars, however, such gregarious larvae become less sociable and are found in groups of two and three. When they are ready to pupate, they often walk away from their food-plants for a considerable distance and pupate on walls, tree-trunks and blades of grass. Pierid pupae are attached by the tail and are supported by a silken girdle. Their shape is also characteristic, with most having a projection like a keel behind the head (photograph **207a**, page 130).

The larvae are usually green with small yellow, white or pink stripes down the sides and, although smooth-skinned, some do have a fine layer of short hairs (photograph **196a**, page 123).

Pierid butterflies provide a good example of the phenomenon of seasonal dimorphism, where wet-season (summer) broods differ markedly in colouration from dry-season (winter) broods. (These seasonal forms are designated 'd.s.f.' for 'dry-season form' and 'w.s.f.' for 'wet-season form' or, more rarely, 'w.f.' for 'winter form' and 's.f.' for 'summer form'. In this book we have chosen to use the former designation). The dimorphism is manifested mostly in the extent of the black pigmentation in the wings – extensive in summer and reduced in winter. Summer forms, however, are also usually larger. Unfortunately space limitations prevent the publication of more than one or two illustrations of this phenomenon but the reader is referred to photographs **196g** and **196h** (page 123) which show the female dry-season and wet-season forms of the false dotted-border (*Belenois thysa*), and to photographs **205a** and **205d** (on page 129) which show the female dry-season and wet-season forms of the diverse white (*Appias epaphia contracta*).

There is also considerable variation between the two extreme seasonal forms and it can be an interesting exercise to collect specimens in each month of the year to watch the gradual change in size, colour, and extent of black pigmentation.

9. FAMILY PAPILIONIDAE
Members of this family are among the largest and most spectacular butterflies to be found in South Africa and are usually the first butterflies to be sought by the beginner. Although the common names 'swallowtail' and 'swordtail' are descriptive of the elegant tails on the hindwings of many papilionid species, some lack tails altogether as in the white-banded swallowtail *Princeps echerioides* (photographs **210a** and **b**, page 134), while the mocker swallowtail *Princeps dardanus cenea* has tails only in the male and not in the female (photographs **209e** and **f**, page 132). The emperor swallowtail (*Princeps ophidicephalus*) is also the largest butterfly in South Africa with a wing-tip to wing-tip span of around 120 millimetres (photographs **215a** and **b**, page 136).

The head of the typical swallowtail is broad, hairy and has a large functional proboscis; the thorax is large and humped. The wings are large and broad, and generally tapered towards the apex. The hindwings do not possess a fold for the abdomen while the insect is at rest, thus distinguishing this group from the family Pieridae and subfamily Nymphalinae, for example. The tails may either be shortish and club-shaped as in some *Princeps* (photograph **215a**, page 136) or long, tapering and slender as is seen in some of the swordtails of the genus *Graphium* (photograph **219**, page 138) where they can be up to 30 millimetres long.

Their eggs are large, almost round (photograph **209a**, page 132), and are often yellow or pale green for the first 24 hours. After that they tend to darken, with a small band around the centre of the egg if the egg is fertile. In the first instar the larvae may be covered with small spines, but thereafter become smooth and may or may not have fleshy tubercles (photograph **209c**). Although many are greenish, some are banded with different colours (photograph **218a**, page 138) or have distinct coloured patterns on their bodies. In the later instars the larvae have a very humped or swollen appearance around the head and thorax which is typical of this family. The most characteristic feature of the papilionid larva, however, is the defence mechanism known as the osmeterium, situated just behind the head. This is a soft, brightly coloured glandular process which can be blown up and outwards into the shape of a small 'V' and which emits a pungent odour resembling that of rotten orange peel. When the caterpillar is threatened it will rear up on to the posterior body segments, supported by the prolegs, curl its body backwards and at the same time evert the osmeterium suddenly to discourage an attack from a would-be predator (photograph **213a**, page 135). When these larvae are handled, take care not to let the secretion of the osmeterium make contact with your skin; the smell can linger for many hours even after repeated washing.

The pupae are angular and usually have two points or 'horns' projecting forward from the head (photograph **213c**, page 135). They are attached by the tail often in an upright position, and are characteristically supported within a silken girdle (**213c**).

All southern African papilionids fall into two genera, *Princeps* and *Graphium*; the former group includes the broad-winged species such as *Princeps demodocus* and the latter includes the swordtails or kites. In some books, it should be noted, both are lumped together in the genus *Papilio*, but are separated at subgeneric level into the swallowtails (subgenus *Papilio*) and the swordtails (subgenus *Graphium*). The males of the genus (or subgenus) *Graphium* are distinguished by having a small tuft of long, scented hairs tucked under a flap on the inner margin of the hindwing; these hairs disperse a pheromone which attracts the females. The genus *Princeps* does not possess this feature.

10. FAMILY HESPERIIDAE
The members of this family derive their common name – 'skippers' – from their very erratic and darting flight, quite unlike that of all other butterflies. They fly and dart about their chosen areas, resting frequently for short periods, then take off again after a few moments' rest. They are regarded as being more 'primitive' than other butterflies, one of their 'primitive' features being the resting posture of some of the skippers in which the wings are held in a flat position. Nevertheless, several species also hold their wings in true butterfly fashion, that is closed together vertically over the back, while still others compromise and hold them half-open (photographs **226c**, page 140; **227**, page 141).

Their colours are mostly dull browns and greys, at least in South Africa, but some may also have orange, black or white markings. They are sturdily built, medium-sized butterflies for the most part, with the head wider than the thorax, and large, protruding, bulbous eyes. The eyes and antennae are more widely separated than in other butterflies (compare the hesperiid *Spialia spio* **225a** with the papilionid **216a**, for example). The antennae are of variable length but have a characteristically flat clubbed end which tends to turn outwards, assuming a hook-like shape (photograph **220a**, page 139). The legs are well developed and in some species quite long.

As a rule, they fly very actively in the bright sunny periods of the day, but some species are crepuscular, flying in the early morning and late evening (for example, *Moltena fiara*, page 243; *Artitropa erinnys*, page 244). Eggs are usually laid singly on their various food-plants, usually palms, grasses and shrubs. The eggs do not have a characteristic 'family' shape and although they are normally hemispherical, there is great variation in structure and sculpturing.

The larvae are long, thin, and cylindrical, tapering at both ends of the body, like old-fashioned hand-rolled cigars (photographs **230a**, page 141; **231b**, page 142). The head is large and bulbous and often a completely different colour from the virtually hairless body, which in some instances is banded with different colours. They live in the shelter of leaves, often cutting out and rolling a section of leaf, which is woven into a protective sleeve around the body with the aid of the silk-producing gland in the head. They emerge at night to feed, returning to the safety and camouflage of their refuge during the day. As they progress through their various instars and grow in size they build larger protective sleeves.

Hesperiid droppings are also of a characteristic shape, individual fragments being hexagonal, with a ribbed pattern along the sides. The frass is not just dropped from the anus of the caterpillar, but is 'fired' out and away from the caterpillar's position on the food-plant as a protective device to mislead predators. Frass that is merely dropped often collects on the leaves below and provides clear evidence to predators (and collectors!) that a caterpillar is somewhere above.

Pupation takes place within a protective sleeve of leaves, tied together with silk threads, and here the last phase of metamorphosis takes place.

Skippers are often overlooked by collectors for several reasons. Their colours, being rather dull, do not make a fine display, and they are not easy butterflies to catch. They are also very difficult to set because the muscles of the forewing are unusually strong and the wings tend to tear while they are being positioned on the setting-board. In addition, the hindwings have a habit of slipping out from, and over, the forewings. This frustrating tendency forces the collector to undo the forewing and restart the setting process.

CHAPTER 6

COLLECTING BUTTERFLIES

There are no hard-and-fast methods or rules on how to collect butterflies. Many and varied are the ways that they have been collected over the years, as is the equipment that has been used. However, there are some basic guidelines that ought to be adhered to and these will be outlined below.

NETS

Nets are to the collector what a racket is to a tennis-player or woods to a bowler – they have to 'feel right'. Many a net is made and discarded until a satisfactory one is procured. It is a good idea when making nets to make an extra one as a spare. There is nothing more frustrating than having a broken net when you are far from home.

Handles are usually made from bamboo, cane or aluminium tubing and are about 1,2 metres long. The hoops are made from the same materials and are usually 500 millimetres in diameter. The hoops can be bound on to the handles with string or tape, while aluminium hoops can be fixed in place with small bolts and wing-nuts. This latter type is very convenient when travelling, as the net can be dismantled and transported easily in the boot of a car. Another variation employs handles that can screw on and off.

The size of the hoop is important. Try not to make anything smaller than 500 millimetres in diameter. This will pay dividends, especially when collecting small, fast-flying butterflies. Another factor to consider is the weight of the net. Some constructed from solid-wood handles and thick wire hoops and wire binding can be very heavy and unwieldy.

Handles that can take extensions are also important because quite often while collecting in forests it is necessary to collect butterflies that fly or settle high in tree-tops. Extension sections about one metre long are commonly used and are easy to carry about. It is not unusual to see a collector in the field with what looks like a small golf-bag on his back, in which are several extension poles. To join the poles together quickly, the best method is to have one end of the tube tapered for about 10 centimetres so that it slips easily into the end of the next section. In this manner five metres of net handle can be extended in a

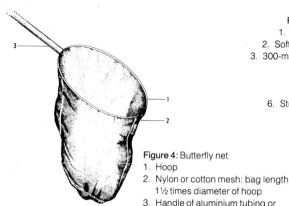

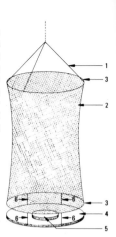

Figure 5: Butterfly trap
1. String to support trap
2. Soft nylon or cotton mesh
3. 300-mm diameter wire hoop
4. 300-mm diameter masonite disc
5. Bait container
6. String or wire to support masonite base

Figure 4: Butterfly net
1. Hoop
2. Nylon or cotton mesh: bag length 1½ times diameter of hoop
3. Handle of aluminium tubing or bamboo

matter of seconds. It is surprising how often extensions are required and you can imagine the frustration if they are not available to catch a specimen that is sitting just out of reach! (See photographs on page 143.)

The material of the bag of the net should be of a soft netting, with fine holes. A bag with heavy material and large holes will damage a specimen that is flapping in it, firstly by breaking any tails it may have, and secondly by rubbing off the wing scales to a degree which will make it look old and tattered. The depth of the bag should allow it to fold around the hoop one half turn. To test this, put a stone or heavy object into the bag, then turn the handle so that the bag wraps around the hoop and the stone comes to rest on the side of the hoop.

Nets can be purchased from dealers overseas who specialize in all types of collecting equipment. However, they are often very costly and there may be a delay of many weeks before they are received. Trout-fishing nets can be bought from leading sports shops and adapted for butterfly-collecting. These are generally of good quality and made from aluminium. The bags of course are useless for butterflies, and a new bag will have to be made as well as an extension to the handle which is often too short. With a little ingenuity, however, a lightweight net can be made from most materials found in any hardware store.

When a butterfly has been caught in the net the handle must immediately be given a half turn so that the netting folds around the hoop and falls flat on to it, thus trapping the butterfly between the folds, these are then pulled firmly and flattened to prevent the butterfly from flapping its wings to shreds.

TRAPS

People are often surprised to learn that butterflies can be attracted to traps, but in fact butterflies of several different groups are susceptible to this means of capture.

Making a trap is much easier than making a net, and the one shown here is not at all complicated. Each collector will of course have his own ideas as to the most suitable dimensions of a trap and those given here must be regarded merely as guidelines. The trap is essentially a hanging tube of netting, 30 centimetres in diameter and one metre long, kept open with wire hoops and with the top end closed with netting. Hanging five centimetres below the lower hoop is a disc of thin wood to hold the bait, suspended from the trap itself by three or four pieces of thin wire or string.

The trap is suspended by three short pieces of wire attached to the top hoop linked together at a central point, from which a long string can be attached. The end of the string can be thrown over a branch to pull the trap up into a tree. (See sketch above and photograph on page 144.)

The next step is to entice the butterflies to enter the trap by baiting it with a suitable mixture and suspending it from the branch of a tree in an area where butterflies are known to be flying.

(If traps are not used the bait can be smeared directly on to tree-trunks, but the chief drawback of this method is that the collector will have to patrol the area around the bait continuously to catch the butterflies as they feed on the bait.)

BAIT

There are several types of bait, the most common and effective being rotting bananas. A skinned banana is mashed to a fine pulp and placed in a container. After about three weeks of fermentation the bait is ready to use. Some collectors add the skins, chopped to a fine pulp, together with one or two spoon-fulls of brown sugar to help speed up the fermentation process, while others add raisins and a tot of rum or sherry. Some say that old bait will only attract males and fresh bait will attract females but I have never noticed any difference. Others believe that pineapple makes a more effective bait than banana. Charaxes, oddly enough, are attracted to fresh lion and other carnivore droppings, and these have been used in traps, uncommonly in South Africa, but more frequently in Central and East Africa.

A few words of caution about making bait: never fill your container to the top, because as soon as the bananas start to ferment they give off bubbles of gas which increase the volume and, after a week or so, an overflowing jar of rotting bananas is not a joy to clean up. More important, however, is never to close the lid tightly while the bait is brewing. Considerable pressure is generated by fermentation and containers can explode. The likely result can be left to the reader's imagination. After brewing for at least three weeks the lid can be tightened but it is probably best to leave it slightly loose.

Before transporting bait, tighten the lids of the containers, avoiding the use of those with snap-on lids. When transporting the latter in the boot of your car, the heat or a change of altitude can pop the lids off and result in a bootful of bait.

KILLING CAPTURED SPECIMENS

This is certainly a contentious question. How does one kill a butterfly humanely? The most common method is to squeeze the thorax between the forefinger and thumb (see photograph, page 144) – carefully and not too hard or you may damage a good specimen, rendering it useless for serious study at a later stage. The rule of thumb, so to speak, is to squeeze until the outer shell of the thorax is felt to crack, which appears to kill the insect instantly without causing unnecessary suffering. After a little practice this will prove to be the best and most efficient method. Acraeas and monarchs are not as easy to kill as other butterflies, often requiring a slightly harder pinch. Smaller butterflies are a little tricky on account of their size, but with practice the technique can be perfected.

Killing-bottles can also be used; these employ one of several poisons, potassium cyanide being perhaps the most popular. To make a cyanide killing-bottle, take a large jar and cover the bottom with potassium cyanide granules to a depth of about one centimetre. Cover this with a centimetre or two of clean, dry sawdust and then a layer or two of newspaper. Finally, add a layer of plaster of Paris about a centimetre thick. This will set in an hour or so but takes about two days to dry properly. Screw on the lid and the jar is ready for use. Do not forget to label it 'DEADLY POISON' and keep it away from children. Butterflies placed in this jar will be killed quickly and efficiently by the cyanide fumes. Do note, however, that danaines and acraeas, so difficult to kill by pinching, are also difficult to kill in a cyanide bottle, taking up to an hour to die.

There are many drawbacks to using cyanide: firstly poison control regulations make it very difficult to obtain; secondly, it is very noxious to human beings and chasing butterflies while you are carrying a glass cyanide bottle is fraught with dangers. Other safer killing-bottles can be made by simply pouring plaster of Paris to a depth of a centimetre or so into a glass jar, allowing it to dry until it has gone completely white, then pouring some ethyl acetate on to it and allowing this to soak in. Any excess is poured off and the jar is ready for use. It is better to turn the bottle upside down once the butterfly is inside so that it settles and dies on the dry lid without absorbing ethyl acetate into its wings and body. Ethyl acetate is extremely volatile and the bottle will have to be recharged at least daily if used constantly. Care must be taken when using ethyl acetate as it is highly inflammable. Other liquid killing agents such as chloroform, carbon tetrachloride and thinners should be avoided as they dehydrate the butterflies very quickly, making them very difficult to set.

Once the butterfly is in the net, unscrew the lid of the killing-bottle, reach into the folds of the net and catch the butterfly in the bottle. Replace the lid, and wait for the killing vapour to take effect.

PAPER ENVELOPES

To carry, store and transport butterflies, triangular paper envelopes are used, which are folded in a special way (see sketch, page 24). They are invaluable to the collector, and are inexpensively made from scrap paper or from tracing paper available from bookshops and stationers. Transparent tracing paper is best, because the specimens can be identified without having to search through and open the packets. They are easy to make and two or three sizes should be constructed to carry large, medium and small butterflies. If specimens are to be stored in them to be set at a later stage, all relevant details including the date, exact locality and collector's name must be written on the edge for future reference.

Specimens are placed in the envelopes with the wings closed and the feet towards the first fold. These envelopes can be carried safely in small flat tins or boxes which can be conveniently fitted into a jacket pocket.

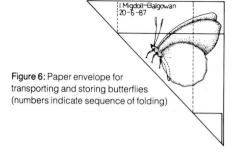
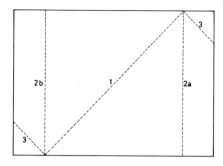

Figure 6: Paper envelope for transporting and storing butterflies (numbers indicate sequence of folding)

If butterflies are pinched lightly on the thorax, just sufficiently to stun them, they can be taken home and placed, envelope and all, into the killing-bottle. The fumes of ethyl acetate or potassium cyanide will penetrate the envelope and kill the already stunned butterflies without any fuss. In this manner excessive squeezing and potential damage to specimens is avoided.

Butterflies can be stored indefinitely in these envelopes. However, a few precautions must be taken first. As mentioned above, ensure that they are as fully labelled as possible, and then store them in an airtight box containing an adequate supply of naphthalene flakes to keep out museum beetles and cockroaches, otherwise considerable damage may be done and entire collections lost. Please remember, unprotected specimens **will** be attacked by pests. You have been warned! Fresh specimens in their envelopes can be placed in sealed plastic boxes, and placed in a deep-freeze. They can be removed after a few days, left to thaw for a few minutes and then set. If they are left too long they tend to dehydrate and are too stiff to set. If this should happen, there are methods to 'relax' them again prior to setting.

RELAXING

Dehydrated, unset specimens should be handled with great care because they are very brittle, and the antennae, legs and wings will break off easily. To relax these specimens, firstly obtain a large, flat, plastic container with a snap-on lid. This can be lined with a layer of plaster of Paris or a piece of polystyrene cut to size. A little water is then added to dampen the plaster or polystyrene. A fine plastic mesh should be laid on top, and the specimens laid carefully upon it. Do not lay them directly on the plaster otherwise they will become waterlogged. A few drops of vinegar or carbolic acid, or a couple of crystals of thymol or paradichlorbenzene, must be added to prevent mould. Snap on the lid and, depending on the temperature, the high humidity will soften the specimens and render them pliable enough to set, probably within 24 hours. Do not leave them too long as they tend to rot and when they are being set the wings will detach from the thorax.

Alternatively, hot water can be injected into the thorax of larger butterflies using a fine needle, or a mixture of alcohol, ethyl acetate and benzene can be used.

If space is not a problem, it is often much better to place pins into the butterflies and leave them unset, pinned to a sheet of cork inside a sealed storage box. Here again, provided naphthalene is kept in the box, and regularly replaced as it evaporates, the pinned specimens can be stored indefinitely. When ready for relaxing, the specimens are removed from the storage box and transferred to the relaxing box with the minimum of handling.

PINS

Some of the equipment required for setting butterflies can be purchased from the larger museums, but other items have to be constructed specially.

Entomological pins are standardized and are usually 37,5 millimetres long. They are manufactured from stainless steel or mild steel painted black. The former are best as they do not rust; the latter tend to rust after a year or two if used in our coastal areas, but if used inland they are as good as the stainless-steel variety. The best pins are manufactured in Vienna, Austria, but unfortunately these are becoming increasingly difficult to procure in South Africa. They come in different gauges denoted by numbers, *viz.* 000, 00, 0, 1, 2, 3, 4, 5, 6. Sizes 1, 2 and 3 are the most commonly used and are used for small, medium and large butterflies respectively.

Pinning the butterfly correctly through the thorax is crucial. This is the first step, and if not done properly, further difficulties will be encountered while setting.

PINNING

Pinning the butterfly prior to its placement on the setting-board is done in the following manner. Hold the thorax, wings up, between the forefinger and thumb, squeeze slightly until the wings open enough to allow you to see the top of the thorax – blowing softly through pursed lips also helps. Select the right gauge pin and place it precisely in the centre of the thorax, before pushing it completely through. Check that it is square to an imaginary line drawn from the tip of the head to the tip of the abdomen, and at the same time square to an imaginary line from wing-tip to wing-tip. Now push the pin through the thorax to about three-quarters the length of the pin, although this height does depend on the central height of your setting-board. Butterflies should not be set lower than half the length of the pin, and for this reason setting-boards must be constructed appropriately. (See sketch below).

Figure 7: Pinning a butterfly

SETTING-BOARDS

In recent years a new type of 'raised' setting-board has made its appearance, but although it is preferred by some, the majority of collectors still use flat boards. The new version has the splints angled, effectively setting the wings to an angle of 12 degrees above horizontal. The tendency with specimens set on flat boards is for the wings to droop, giving the butterflies an unnatural look. This need not happen, however, if the specimen has been set properly when fresh, and dried for a sufficiently long period. Nevertheless, with the raised boards the specimen does have an 'alive' look about it, and if the wings do droop slightly, they do not droop below the flat position. The standard length for setting-boards is 300 millimetres and the standard centre height is 25 millimetres.

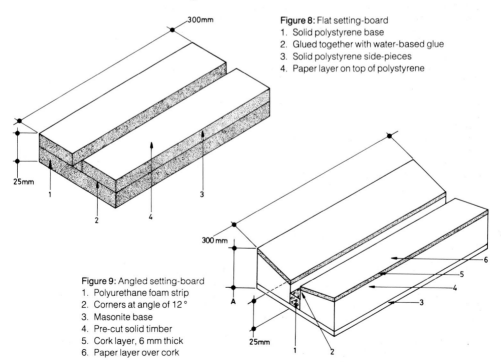

Figure 8: Flat setting-board
1. Solid polystyrene base
2. Glued together with water-based glue
3. Solid polystyrene side-pieces
4. Paper layer on top of polystyrene

Figure 9: Angled setting-board
1. Polyurethane foam strip
2. Corners at angle of 12°
3. Masonite base
4. Pre-cut solid timber
5. Cork layer, 6 mm thick
6. Paper layer over cork

I would suggest first building some flat boards, from smooth polystyrene. Use them for practising your setting techniques on old tattered specimens. Once this art has been mastered, then spend some time carefully building your final raised boards. (See sketches on page 25). The sizes given are approximate and the width of the centre gap must vary from board to board. Charaxes require a large gap to accommodate the thick body, while the small blues only need a fine gap of two millimetres or so.

SETTING

Before reading this section, study the sketches below, which will make the following paragraphs easier to follow. (See also photograph on page 144.)

Take the pinned butterfly and place it in the centre of the gap in the setting-board; push the pin into the polystyrene foam just enough to support it, then hold the board up to eye level and check that the pin is square to the base and ends of the board (Fig. 7). When this is established, push the pin down until the underside bases of the wings are level with the top of the cork surface on the board.

Clear plastic sheeting of the type used for covering books can be cut into strips and used to hold the wings down on to the setting-boards. Take two strips, and with two or three glass-headed dressmaking pins, pin the ends to the top of the board. Hold the strips up and blow gently to open the wings of the butterfly. When they are more or less flat, lower the strips on to the wings to hold them down. With a fine pointed instrument in your right hand and the end of the strip in your left hand (reverse directions if you are left-handed), place the point carefully on to the leading-edge vein on the left forewing near its base, moving the wing slowly upwards under the strip until it is in a position where the trailing edge is square to the split in the board (Fig. 10.1). Now take a dressmaking pin, push it through the plastic into the cork just off the edge of the wing to hold it in position; two or more pins may be required. Deal with the right wing in the same way, making sure that the trailing edges of both forewings are in an apparent straight line, both square to the centre slit of the board (Fig. 10.2). The hindwings are then both set in the same way. Leave a small V-shaped gap on the outside of the wings where the hindwing slips under the fore-

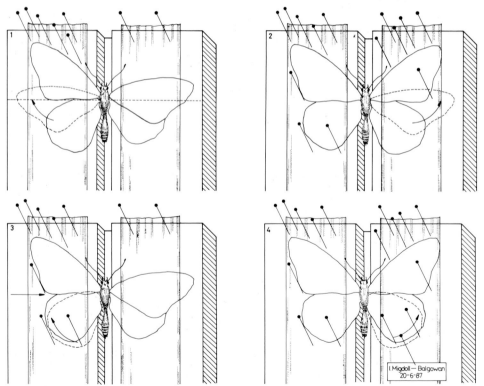

Figure 10: The four stages of setting a butterfly

wing. Have a look at a photograph of a set specimen and this will give an indication of the size of the 'V' (photograph **64e**, page 58, for example).

The antennae are also set: place them in a 'V' that faces forward, as far as possible parallel to the contours of the leading edges of the forewings. Often the antennae will not stay in place. If this happens, take one or two pins and hold them in the required position.

When setting the first forewing, the whole body sometimes tends to twist sideways on the pin. Should this happen, to steady the insect place one pin on each side of the 'waist' where the thorax and abdomen join.

Specimens should be left to dry for at least two weeks although some of the larger ones can take up to a month, depending on the temperature and humidity. The best way to test a set butterfly to see if it is dry, is to take a pin and very carefully push it sideways against the abdomen. If the abdomen is stiff and the body tries to turn with it, then the butterfly is ready to come off the board.

Keep your setting-boards in a sealed drawer or cupboard where insects can't get at them. It is best to sprinkle a little naphthalene around them or to fill a small flat container with this insect-repelling chemical and leave it close by. When the specimens are dry, remove the pins, taking great care not to damage the scales or antennae.

The next and most vital step with any collection is to place on the pin a 'locality label' on which must be noted the date caught, the place caught (preferably in detail) and the name of the collector. If the butterfly was bred from eggs laid by a female caught in the wild, then write 'bred' and the locality where the female was caught. The label should be as small as possible so as not to divert attention away from the butterfly.

It is often desirable to have a specimen showing its undersides; in this case setting is done in the normal way but with the specimens being pinned upside down with their hindwings being set above the forewings where they meet.

STORAGE OF BUTTERFLIES

I have seen collections stored in many ingenious ways. Shirt-boxes are very good, and cheap, and these can be obtained from men's outfitting shops. Cover the boxes with wallpaper and seal all loose corners. A layer of cork or polystyrene inside is all that is required, in addition to an adequate supply of naphthalene. The insides can be painted with a P.V.A. paint, but ensure the paint is completely dry before using the box to store specimens, otherwise they will absorb moisture and start to relax.

Thick cardboard, of the type laminated on both sides, can be purchased in sheet form, cut to size and made into flat boxes using brown sticky paper for all the joints. These boxes are ideal for stacking. The more industrious collectors build a hinged box from wood and masonite, the lid and base both cork-lined to take specimens. When constructing this type of box, ensure that the base and lid are deep enough to allow butterflies to be pinned in both sections without them touching each other when the box is closed.

CABINETS

The ultimate method for butterfly storage is the glass-topped drawer. In their normal form these fit into a cabinet in units of 10 or 20 drawers each. Some have a glass front to seal out moisture. Drawers and cabinets are easily made – if you have the necessary specialized machinery and tools. If these are not available, then a cabinet-maker should be approached to cut timber to size. Then the drawers can be built at home, one or two at a time as required.

The dimensions given in the sketches on page 28 are only guidelines. If larger drawers are required, then the thickness of the wooden parts must be increased to cope with the extra mass of the glass. The only tools that are needed are a pair of large clamps, big enough to accommodate the length of the drawer. When all the necessary materials are gathered together, assemble in the following way:

Take a left and a right side piece, slot the glass into the pre-cut grooves and do the same with the masonite sheet. Cover the ends of both sides with glue, place the front and back pieces in their positions and clamp tightly, taking care to see that the glass is sliding in the slot. When the glue has dried, remove the clamps and run a liberal amount of fresh glue around the underside of the masonite base. The drawer lid is now cut off (be sure to mark the two halves before cutting in half).

Pre-cut masonite strips (three millimetres thick) are now glued inside the base. Measure from the base to the lip, add six millimetres, and this will be the lip that the lid will fit on to, ensuring an air-tight fit. Cork or polystyrene is then fitted on to the base, leaving a gap at the back at least 6 to 10 millimetres wide. This gap is filled with naphthalene flakes, and must be checked every few months and topped up.

The cabinet can be built from chipboard, and adding a veneer to match the drawers will give it a professional touch.

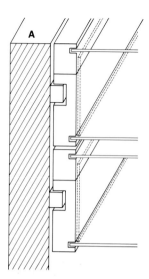

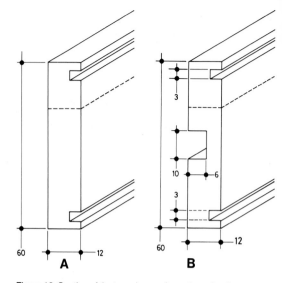

Figure 11: Section showing side of cabinet (A) and two drawers

Glass above and masonite below; front of drawer and top of cabinet not shown. Small handles can be purchased from hardware shops or, alternatively, large brass rivets can be polished and glued into pre-drilled holes. The dotted line shows a masonite strip glued into position; each side of the drawer has such a strip, fitted from corner to corner. They ensure an air-tight seal when the lids are in position.

Figure 12: Section of the two pieces of wood required to construct drawer

A Front and back pieces
B Side pieces

The small slots top and bottom are for the glass and masonite; the larger slot is for the drawer-runner. Sizes (in mm) are only guidelines and can be increased. Care must be taken, however, to allow for the thickness of the cork base and the length of the pins. Allow at least 4 mm more for the thickness of the saw-blade when 'splitting' the top from the bottom (dotted line).

Small strips of hardwood are used for runners on the drawers. They must be glued and nailed carefully, making sure the small gap between each drawer is level and uniform.

COLLECTIONS

The size of a butterfly collection naturally varies from one collector to the next, depending as much on the tastes of the collector as on the availability of time and money. In most cases, however, a male and a female of each species will be taken and displayed, both upperside and underside. Most collectors will display a 'series' to include colour-pattern variants and, depending on the size of the butterfly, may run a row of males and females from the bottom of the drawer to the top. Medium to large specimens give a run of about 10 to 15. The smaller butterflies usually only need half a drawer length, and small-butterfly drawers can be split into two halves, top and bottom, to allow a second series to be run above the first. 'Split' the drawer by pinning a length of black cotton or string across the cork.

Butterflies that fly all year round, and have wet- and dry-season forms can be laid out with wet-season forms at the bottom of the row, progressing to the dry-season forms higher up the series. This could have, for example, a representative specimen for each month of the year. In the case of those species which are not seasonally dimorphic, there may be geographical differences, which should be adequately covered by the series.

It is important, however, to stress the necessity not to over-collect. Only catch what is required, checking each specimen for its condition before killing, and releasing those which are old and tattered.

When breeding butterflies, it is important to release those you do not wish to keep, into the same area from which the egg, larva, pupa or female was taken originally. Remember, it is of no use to any butterfly to be released many kilometres from the nearest suitable food-plant or locality in which it can find others of its kind to breed with.

CHAPTER 7
BREEDING BUTTERFLIES IN CAPTIVITY

Breeding butterflies in captivity can be very rewarding whether the aim is to unravel life-history details or simply to breed out perfect specimens. There is the additional benefit that day-to-day familiarity with all stages of a butterfly's life-cycle can improve one's field knowledge to the extent that eggs, larvae and pupae can be instantly recognized in the wild, along with the larval host-plants. Most butterflies have very specific host-plant requirements and although the larvae of common and widespread species such as the painted lady, *Vanessa cardui* (page 173) may feed happily on dozens of different plants (which is why they are common and widespread) others will eat only one or two different plants and sometimes only one. There are, fortunately, many common plants readily available to breeders which are accepted by the larvae of several species of butterfly.

There can be many a slip between egg and the adult of course, but if a few basic rules are kept in mind the breeding and rearing of butterflies can be relatively easy.

'Breeding' can mean rearing from any stage in the life-cycle. The 'no-fuss' way is to find pupae in the wild, wait a few days for the adult to emerge, and that's that. This is not as easy as it sounds, since larva often walk away from their food-plants just before pupation and pupate in the most obscure places. Their colours, too, are nearly always designed to blend with their surroundings, making them extremely difficult to find. With experience of the habits of the different species, however, it does become easier as one learns exactly where to look.

Finding larvae is not as difficult, but it can be very time-consuming, as the food-plants have to be recognized before the search begins. There are a few tricks to finding larvae, one of which is to look for their frass on the leaves of the host-plant or close by. Provided the frass is fresh, the larvae should be found. Look for fresh signs of eating – nibble marks on the edges and surface of leaves. If these are still green where they have been eaten, not brown and dry, the chances are the larvae are nearby. Here again, knowledge of the particular species' food-plants and habits is a great advantage.

Eggs, too, can be found in the wild in many different situations, depending on the species. Some lay on the uppersides of the leaf, others on the undersides. Eggs may be deposited at the very apex of a fresh young leaf, or in a leaf axil; others are laid on flower-buds, while females of such species as the brown playboy, *Virachola antalus* (page 181) lay their eggs on the outside of large seed-pods. In this latter case the caterpillar will eat through the pod to feed on the seeds within and is out of sight of predators all through its larval life. Still other butterfly species lay on different types of berries. The larvae of the common black eye, *Gonatomyrina gorgias* (page 193), and related species feed on the fleshy leaves of cotyledons and other succulents but are difficult to find because they live **in** the leaf, between its upper and lower surfaces. The females of such species as the Amakoza rocksitter, *Durbania amakosa* (page 176), lay clusters of small eggs on the rocks near patches of lichen – the larval host-plant. To breed them in captivity is difficult as the lichen-bearing rocks have to be taken home to ensure an adequate supply of food.

I learned a lesson from breeding this particular rocksitter. Firstly, I had too many eggs to start with, about 60, and after the larvae had hatched their appetites were enormous. Food had to be provided in the form of lichen-covered rocks, but the nearest convenient source was about 40 kilometres distant. The rocks had to be dug out of the ground, carried to the car, then up the stairs to my flat. After several weeks and several trips for food, the larvae finally pupated. I neglected to check on them for a few days, and to my horror discovered that they had hatched and broken themselves to pieces trying to fly out of the specially constructed mesh-boxes which had been designed to contain the rocks and the larvae. The lessons learned were: firstly, never try to breed more than you can handle, and secondly, check your breeding-boxes regularly at all stages. Incidentally, conservation ethics also demand that you return the 'borrowed' rocks to their original locations in the veld.

The drawback to collecting eggs, larvae and pupae in the wild is that the rate of success is often low. Many eggs, larvae and pupae fall victim to a variety of parasites: eggs will not hatch as their insides have been eaten out; larvae will suddenly die and maggots or newly hatched parasitic flies will crawl out of their bodies; and pupae will also play host to a similar array of wasps and flies (photograph **213b**, page 135). The best method is to catch a gravid (pregnant) female, and to induce her to lay her unparasitized eggs for captive breeding. A gravid female will almost certainly have mated and therefore her eggs will be fertile when laid.

Some species are easier to breed than others and for your first attempts the following species may not prove too difficult: *Princeps demodocus* (citrus swallowtail or Christmas butterfly); *Princeps dardanus cenea* (mocker swallowtail); *Danaus chrysippus aegyptius* (southern milkweed butterfly); *Princeps nireus lyaeus* (green-banded swallowtail); or one of the more common charaxes such as *Charaxes brutus natalensis* (white-barred charaxes) or even *Catopsilia florella* (African vagrant). The appropriate food-plants for each species can be found listed with the butterfly descriptions from page 145.

Do remember, however that there are legal restrictions on the collecting of plant material in South Africa. Make sure that you are familiar with the various provincial nature conservation ordinances, or, if appropriate, municipal ordinances or bye-laws.

BREEDING-BOXES AND EGG-LAYING

There are two schools of thought as to the type of container the female should be placed in for egg-laying. The first type is a square box cage with fine mesh all round, each side measuring about 30 centimetres. The female is introduced into this box together with a cutting of the larval food-plant in a small bottle of water to keep it fresh. The cage is then hung under the trees, away from direct sunlight but in a bright place. The other type of container is a small plastic box, about 12 centimetres square, which is lined with a few leaves not only on the bottom, but also on the lid where you can use a thin strip of tape to hold the leaves up. In this way the female is in close contact with her food-plant even if she walks on the lid. Keep the box in a bright warm position, but not in the sun; close to a light-bulb is often enough.

Each method has its merits, and I have tried both over the years. The former was a little frustrating, as the females seemed to spend most of their time flying about the cage, with little time seemingly devoted to egg-laying, although some were laid. The small plastic box is more easily handled and, in my view, eggs are more readily laid in this situation. Perhaps the concentration of food or its smell induces her to lay. Patience may be required as two or three days usually pass before the female feels at home and starts to lay.

Females kept in containers must be fed twice a day. This can be done as follows. Make up a solution of half a teaspoon of sugar or honey, and dissolve it in a cupful of water. Soak a small piece of cotton-wool and place this on a surface that the butterfly can get a grip on – a flat stone for example. Holding the wings together, take a pin and place it in the middle of the coiled proboscis. Pull the pin forward and uncoil the tongue, at the same time lowering the female on to the stone and her uncoiled tongue on to the cotton-wool. She should start to feed almost immediately, and will become so engrossed that you will be able to let her wings go. Let her drink freely. When enough has been taken she will fly, so make sure that all windows are closed. If she is a little reluctant to feed, hold her proboscis down gently on the cotton-wool for a minute or so. It is surprising how quickly butterflies learn to feed and at subsequent feeding-times often the proboscis will be out ready to drink as soon as the wings are held together!

CARE OF EGGS

Eggs should be removed from the boxes each day. Do not pick them off the leaves, but break the leaves off and transfer them to smaller boxes. After two or three days the eggs will darken, and after a further few days they will hatch.

CARE OF LARVAE

Allow the young larvae to eat the egg-cases which may constitute part of their diet, and without which they often will not survive. After this they will rest for a short period before starting to eat the food-plant provided. Do not place too much food in the container at this stage – one leaf for two or three caterpillars is enough. After a day has elapsed it will be possible to see if they have been feeding; small sections from the edge of the leaf may be nibbled out, although some eat the leaf surface first. The best way is to look for their frass. With larvae of this size, it will look like a sprinkling of pepper.

Fresh food must be provided as it is required, either when the larvae have nearly finished the supply, or when it is drying out and becoming unpalatable. You should check the food situation at least twice a day. Do not handle larvae with your fingers as their internal organs can be damaged if they are accidentally squeezed. It is preferable to use a small paint-brush to transfer them to new food. When they are larger, you can lay the new food on top of the old, wait for the larvae to crawl on to it, then lift the new food and larvae into a clean breeding-box.

Do not feed the larvae on leaves which are too fresh and tender, as this can lead to digestive disorders, diarrhoea, dehydration and death. Give them a portion of food-plant that looks 'average', not too old and dry, but not too new and fresh. Each new food-plant must be inspected carefully for small spiders and other insects that may be lurking within the leaves, as these can worry or kill small caterpillars.

Different species will take different lengths of time to pass from egg to adult, but most will pass through five instars before pupating. A few points to remember about caterpillars are as follows:
☐ keep an absorbent paper on the bottom of the breeding-box, to soak up any excess moisture from the frass and the food. (Too humid conditions can lead to the development of fungus and mould, which can be fatal.)

☐ do not make holes in the container for air, as the oxyen given off by the food-plant is adequate and the larvae will find the holes and escape.

☐ as the larvae get bigger, reduce their numbers per container.

☐ in the final two stages, do not keep more than four or five larvae together.

(Caterpillars of the genus *Iolaus* are prone to cannibalize the smaller members in the containers, and larvae of such species are best kept one to a box).

Large quantities of food are consumed by the larvae in the final two instars, so make sure that fresh food is always at hand. It can be picked, wrapped in plastic bags and kept in the refrigerator. An adequate supply of good food will produce normal-sized butterflies, but poor food and poor conditions will produce under-sized runts, which are of no use in a collection.

Be especially careful with larvae during the time they pause to shed their skins. You will notice that they sit with their backs slightly hunched, and often walk off the food-plant to the side of the box. During this time they sit on a silken mat which they have woven. Do not move them off this mat to place them on fresh food; just leave them, or if they are on a leaf or twig, place this on top of the fresh food. In their own time they will move off to start feeding again. It is important for the caterpillar to have some part of the old skin attached to this silken pad, because when the skin splits, it is able to pull itself out. Without this attachment, the skin may remain only half off and an incomplete skin change will result in the death of the caterpillar.

When gathering food-plants, try not to collect near busy roads or road-junctions, as the oil and rubber dust found on the plants can often prove fatal to larvae. Aerial crop-spraying that has taken place in the vicinity may have deposited poison on the leaves, so do not use food-plants from areas where you suspect that such contamination might have occurred.

Beware of household insecticides and insect repellents, particularly aerosols, as they are deadlier than most people imagine; spraying even two rooms away can mean the loss of caterpillars despite their being in small sealed boxes. The short time the boxes are open for food changes is often sufficient for the poisons to enter and do their work. Volatile solid insect-repellents that are suspended in cupboards and kitchens are only doing what they are designed for, and that is to kill insects – so beware! Caution other members of the family not to use sprays. This is quite often the cause of unsuccessful breeding, with one member of the family unknowingly thwarting the efforts of another. Smoking while cleaning and changing boxes should be avoided because nicotine is a potent poison to insects. If you have been smoking, wash your hands prior to handling larvae. Some pipe-smoking collectors put their habit to good use: they carry a long pin with them while in the field and, as the specimens are caught and trapped in the folds of the net, the pin is dipped into the concentrated nicotine at the base of the pipe bowl, the butterfly is pricked on the side of the thorax and dies within seconds. This method obviates having to squeeze the thorax to kill the specimen.

ALTERNATIVE FEEDING METHODS

A more natural method of rearing caterpillars is to do so out-of-doors – if suitable food-plants are growing nearby. Sleeve a branch on the food plant with a nylon stocking, or some similar·item of fine mesh material. Larvae are placed in this sleeve which is then tied at both ends. The arrangement should be checked daily and only moved if the leaves are nearly finished. However, if two or three larvae per sleeve are kept with a good supply of food, they will feed and go through to pupation with no trouble at all. The pupae are 'harvested' in due course and brought inside to hatch in breeding-cages.

Similarly, potted plants indoors can be covered with a sleeve; no real work is involved, except to observe progress on a daily basis. Alternatively a wire frame can also be bent over a pot-plant, a fine wire mesh placed over this and the whole wired to the top of the pot. Try to keep the mesh away from the foliage, because caterpillars can wander for hours on it before finding their way back to the leaves.

LARVAL FOOD-PLANT SUPPLY

Planting different food-plants in your garden can be a great asset. Plan ahead of time, cultivate the trees and shrubs for a year or two, and when they are big enough employ the sleeving method to rear your larvae.

When driving around your neighbourhood, look for potential food-plants in vacant plots, or growing at the sides of the roads. It is surprising how many there can be within a short walking distance of a suburban home. Certainly there is nothing more frustrating than driving many kilometres each day to collect food-plants for that special butterfly, only to discover a few days after the adults have emerged that the plant is growing almost on your doorstep. Go for walks with a notebook and write down where food-plants are situated or, if possible, take a cutting or a young plant and transfer it to your own garden.

CARE OF PUPAE

When the caterpillar is ready to pupate, it will seek a suitable place within the confines of the breeding-box. Some will pupate on the twigs and leaves, making it an easy task to lift them out to pin their supporting twig or leaf on to the sides of a breeding-box. Others will pupate on the sides of their boxes, and these must not be removed but left to hatch there. If this is inconvenient, however, and the box is required for further breeding, detach the pupa carefully in the following way. Look for a silken girdle which may be supporting it (see page 13), and cut this first on both sides. The silken mat at the tail end can be scraped off the side of the box, and will leave the pupa free. Glue the remains of the pad on to a twig using the least amount of glue possible and making sure none gets on to any part of the pupal case. Pupae which were previously supported by a silken girdle can be left to hang head down; although this might differ from their normal attitude, it apparently has no ill-effects.

In the warmer parts of the country, pupae will hatch within the normal period of time for that particular species, and if it is of a species with continuous broods this may only be a matter of five to 20 days. With species which have only one brood a year, and with conditions as near 'normal' as possible, the butterfly may remain in the pupal stage for many months and will emerge only at the time of the year when its kind normally fly. In this case the pupa has entered a stage of arrested development known as diapause, a strategy evolved to help the species through an unfavourable season of the year. A full year may pass before such an 'overwintering' pupa hatches.

Store pupae in a warm place, away from cold draughts. Spraying once a week with a fine mist spray will prevent them from dehydrating, and keep them in good condition – after all, in nature they do get wet in the rain!

EMERGENCE

To watch a butterfly emerge is a fascinating experience and particularly rewarding after all the work of rearing it. It is not easy to forecast the time of hatching in order to observe it. Most butterflies seem to emerge early in the morning as the sun is rising, but others appear during the night, presumably to avoid detection as they are very vulnerable at this stage, and to be ready for their maiden flight when temperatures rise in the morning.

A day or so before hatching, dark patches will become visible through the pupal case overlying the eyes. A few hours later, the veins in the wings will be visible, followed by the colour pigments. These are the signs of imminent emergence. The pupal case seems to become more and more transparent and soon all the features of the butterfly can be seen – legs, eyes, antennae and proboscis. Do not try to 'help' the butterfly by pulling, pinching or squeezing; it will merely become distressed and die on the threshold of its new life.

The butterfly now starts to pump its 'blood' (or haemolymph) towards the back of the thorax. This will expand and split the pupal case, and a few moments later the butterfly will pull itself out and immediately hang upside down on the nearest convenient place, usually on the pupal case itself. The wings are pumped up by the butterfly's haemolymph being forced into the veins. A coloured fluid is also ejected from the anus around this time, when the wings are full size; this is uric acid waste from the pupal phase. The whole fascinating process of emergence takes only three to five minutes, but drying of the wings takes a further one to two hours.

When the wings are completely hard, the specimens required can be killed and prepared for setting. It is advisable to insert the thorax pin first, then a few hours later when the wings have dried out further, to pin them properly on the setting-board.

When breeding any butterfly it is important to make entries of all your observations in a notebook. In this, you should describe the larvae in as much detail as possible, noting the number of days between each instar, the number of days from hatching to pupa, and the number of days from pupa to adult. At the end, make an entry to record the ratio of males and females hatched. If you are artistically inclined, make sketches with as much detail as possible. If you have a camera take photographs, as the various stages make some of the most perfect models for the photographer.

1a *Danaus chrysippus aegyptius* form *liboria* ♂ upperside

1b *Danaus chrysippus aegyptius* form *liboria* ♂ underside

1c *Danaus chrysippus aegyptius* final instar larva

2 *Amauris niavius dominicanus* ♂ upperside

3a *Amauris ochlea ochlea* ♀ upperside

3b *Amauris ochlea ochlea* ♀ underside

4a *Amauris albimaculata albimaculata*
♀ upperside

5a *Melanitis leda helena*
perfectly camouflaged ♂ among dead leaves

5b *Melanitis leda helena*
♂ upperside

4b *Amauris albimaculata albimaculata*
♀ underside

6a *Bicyclus safitza safitza*
mating pair

6b *Bicyclus safitza safitza*
♀ upperside

7 *Henotesia perspicua*
(above) ♀ underside; (below) ♂ upperside

8 *Aeropetes tulbaghia* ♂ upperside

9b *Paralethe dendrophilus*
final instar larvae

9a *Paralethe dendrophilus*
♀ upperside

10a *Dira oxylus* ♂ upperside

10b *Dira oxylus* ♂ underside

11 *Dira swanepoeli swanepoeli*
(above) ♂ upperside; (below) ♀ underside

12 *Dingana dingana dingana*
♂ upperside

14a *Torynesis orangica* ♂ upperside

13 *Dingana bowkeri bowkeri*
(above) ♀ upperside; (below) ♂ upperside

14b *Torynesis orangica* ♂ underside

16a *Coenyra hebe* ♀ upperside

15 *Tarsocera cassina*
(above) ♀ underside; (below) ♂ upperside

16b *Coenyra hebe* ♀ underside

18a *Stygionympha vigilans* ♂ upperside

17 *Pseudonympha machacha*
(above) ♀ upperside; (below) ♂ underside

18b *Stygionympha vigilans* ♂ underside

37

19a *Bematistes aganice aganice*
♂ underside

19b *Bematistes aganice aganice* ♀ upperside

20a *Acraea horta* 4th instar larva

20b *Acraea horta* pupa

20c *Acraea horta* ♂ underside

20d *Acraea horta* ♂ upperside

21a *Acraea neobule neobule* ♂ upperside

21b *Acraea neobule neobule* ♀ upperside

22 *Acraea cerasa cerasa*
(above) ♀ upperside; (below) ♂ upperside

23 *Acraea admatha*
(above) ♂ upperside; (below) ♀ upperside

24 *Acraea satis*
(above) ♀ upperside; (below) ♂ upperside

25a *Acraea igola* ♀ underside

26a *Acraea rahira rahira* final instar larva

26b *Acraea rahira rahira*
(above) ♀ upperside; (below) ♂ upperside

25b *Acraea igola* ♂ upperside

27a *Acraea eponina eponina* ♀ upperside

27b *Acraea eponina eponina* ♀ underside

28 *Acraea cabira*
(above) ♀ upperside; (below) ♂ upperside

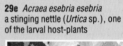

29e *Acraea esebria esebria*
a stinging nettle (*Urtica* sp.), one
of the larval host-plants

29a *Acraea esebria esebria*
egg-cluster typical of the genus

29b *Acraea esebria esebria*
♂ underside

29c *Acraea esebria esebria* ♂ upperside

29d *Acraea esebria esebria* ♀ upperside

30a *Acraea acrita acrita* ♂ upperside (w.s.f.)

31a *Acraea natalica natalica* mating pair

31b *Acraea natalica natalica* ♂ upperside

30b *Acraea acrita acrita*
(above) ♂ upperside; (below) ♀ upperside (d.s.f.)

32a *Acraea oncaea* ♂ underside

32b *Acraea oncaea* ♀ upperside

33a *Acraea aglaonice* ♂ upperside

33b *Acraea aglaonice* ♀ upperside

34a *Acraea zetes acara* ♂ upperside

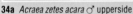

34b *Acraea zetes acara* ♂ underside

35a *Acraea anemosa*
(above) ♀ underside; (below) ♂ upperside

35b *Acraea anemosa* ♂ upperside

43

36a *Acraea petraea* final instar larva

36b *Acraea petraea*
pupa shortly before emergence of adult

36c *Acraea petraea* ♀ upperside

36d *Acraea petraea* ♂ upperside

37a *Pardopsis punctatissima* ♂ upperside

37b *Pardopsis punctatissima* ♂ underside

38a *Stonehamia varanes varanes* ♂ upperside

38b *Stonehamia varanes varanes*
'dead-leaf' camouflage of underside;
shape of tail identifies this as a ♂

39a *Charaxes candiope* egg

39b *Charaxes candiope* 4th instar larva

39c *Charaxes candiope* pupa. Right: one of the larval food-plants, *Croton sylvaticus*

39d *Charaxes candiope* ♂ upperside

40a *Charaxes jasius saturnus* ♀ upperside

40b *Charaxes jasius saturnus* ♀ underside

41a *Charaxes brutus natalensis* pupa

41b *Charaxes brutus natalensis* ♂ underside

41c *Charaxes brutus natalensis* ♀ upperside

41d *Charaxes brutus natalensis:* one of the larval host-plants, *Trichilia dregeana*

47

42a *Charaxes xiphares penningtoni* ♂ upperside

42b *Charaxes xiphares penningtoni* ♀ upperside

43 *Charaxes bohemani*
(above) ♀ upperside; (below) ♂ upperside

44b *Charaxes cithaeron cithaeron* larva shortly before pupation

44c *Charaxes cithaeron cithaeron* pupa

44a *Charaxes cithaeron cithaeron*: one of the larval food-plants, *Chaetachme aristata*

44d *Charaxes cithaeron cithaeron* newly emerged adult ♀ (underside)

44e *Charaxes cithaeron cithaeron* ♀ upperside

44f *Charaxes cithaeron cithaeron* ♂ upperside

49

45a *Charaxes zoolina zoolina*
d.s.f.: (above) ♂ upperside; (below) ♀ upperside

46a *Charaxes jahlusa jahlusa* ♂ underside

46b *Charaxes jahlusa jahlusa* ♂ upperside

46c *Charaxes jahlusa jahlusa* ♀ upperside

45b *Charaxes zoolina zoolina* w.s.f.: (above) ♂ upperside; (below) ♀ upperside

47a *Charaxes achaemenes achaemenes* ♂ upperside

47b *Charaxes achaemenes achaemenes* ♀ upperside

48a *Charaxes ethalion ethalion* ♀ underside

48b *Charaxes ethalion ethalion* ♀ upperside

48c *Charaxes ethalion ethalion* ♂ upperside

51

49a *Euxanthe wakefieldi* final instar larva

49b *Euxanthe wakefieldi* ♂ upperside

49d *Euxanthe wakefieldi:* the larval host-plant, *Deinbollia oblongifolia*

49c *Euxanthe wakefieldi* ♀ upperside

51a *Cymothoe coranus* ♂ upperside

50a *Cymothoe alcimeda trimeni* ♂ upperside

50b *Cymothoe alcimeda trimeni* ♂ underside

50c *Cymothoe alcimeda trimeni*
two variants of ♀ upperside markings

51b *Cymothoe coranus* ♀ upperside

52a *Euphaedra neophron neophron*
final instar larva

52c *Euphaedra neophron neophron*
newly emerged adult ♂

52b *Euphaedra neophron neophron* pupa

52d *Euphaedra neophron neophron* ♀ upperside

53c *Pseudacraea boisduvalii trimenii*
♂ upperside

53a *Pseudacraea boisduvalii trimenii* final instar larva

53b *Pseudacraea boisduvalii trimenii* pupa

53e *Pseudacraea boisduvalii trimenii*
♀ upperside

53d *Pseudacraea boisduvalii trimenii* ♂ underside

54a *Pseudacraea eurytus imitator*
final instar larva

54b *Pseudacraea eurytus imitator* ♂ underside

54c *Pseudacraea eurytus imitator*
(above) ♀ upperside; (below) ♂ upperside

54d *Pseudacraea eurytus imitator* form *pondo*
♂ upperside (see text)

55a *Pseudacraea lucretia tarquinia* ♂ upperside

55b *Pseudacraea lucretia tarquinia* ♂ underside

56a *Neptis saclava marpessa* mating pair

56b *Neptis saclava marpessa* ♂ upperside

56c *Neptis saclava marpessa* ♂ underside

57 *Neptis goochii* ♀ upperside

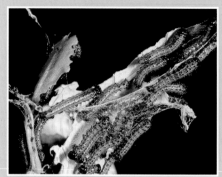

64a *Eunica boisduvali boisduvali* gregarious 2nd instar larvae

64b *Eunica boisduvali boisduvali* final instar larva

64c *Eunica boisduvali boisduvali* pupa

64d *Eunica boisduvali boisduvali* ♀ underside

64e *Eunica boisduvali boisduvali* ♂ upperside

58a *Byblia anvatara acheloia* ♂ underside (w.s.f.)

58c *Byblia anvatara acheloia* ♂ upperside

58b *Byblia anvatara acheloia* ♂ underside (w.s.f.)

59a *Eurytela hiarbas angustata* ♂ upperside

59b *Eurytela hiarbas angustata* ♂ underside

59c *Eurytela hiarbas angustata* form *flavescens*: ♂ upperside (P. & E. Zwart collection)

59d The castor-oil plant, one of the larval food-plants of *Eurytela hiarbas angustata*

61c *Hypolimnas misippus*
pupa

61a *Hypolimnas misippus*
final instar larva

61b *Hypolimnas misippus*
larva just before pupation

61f *Hypolimnas misippus* ♂ underside

61g *Hypolimnas misippus* ♂ upperside

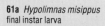

60a *Eurytela dryope angulata* ♂ underside

60b *Eurytela dryope angulata* ♂ upperside

61e *Hypolimnas misippus* newly emerged adult ♀ (underside)

Hypolimnas misippus adult ♀ emerging from pupal case

Hypolimnas misippus form *misippus* ♀ upperside

62a *Hypolimnas deceptor deceptor* ♂ upperside

62b *Hypolimnas deceptor deceptor* ♂ underside

63c *Hypolimnas anthedon wahlbergi* pupa   **63a** *Hypolimnas anthedon wahlbergi* form *wahlbergi* ♂ upperside

63b *Hypolimnas anthedon wahlbergi* form *mima* ♀ upperside

66a *Protogoniomorpha parhassus aethiops* ♂ upperside

66b *Protogoniomorpha parhassus aethiops* ♂ underside   **66c** *Protogoniomorpha parhassus aethiops* ♀ upperside

67a *Protogoniomorpha anacardii nebulosa*
♂ upperside (w.s.f.)

67b *Protogoniomorpha anacardii nebulosa*
♂ upperside (d.s.f.)

65 *Eunica natalensis*
(above) ♀ upperside; (below) ♂ underside

68c *Catacroptera cloanthe cloanthe* ♂ underside

68a *Catacroptera cloanthe cloanthe* ♂ upperside

68b *Catacroptera cloanthe cloanthe* ♂ underside

63

69a *Junonia natalica natalica* ♂ underside

71a *Junonia tugela tugela* ♂ upperside

69b *Junonia natalica natalica* ♂ upperside

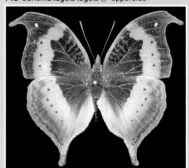

71b *Junonia tugela tugela* ♀ upperside

69c *Junonia natalica natalica* ♀ underside. Right: one of the larval host-plants, *Asystasia gangetica*

71c *Junonia tugela tugela* ♂ underside

70a *Junonia terea elgiva* ♂ upperside

70b *Junonia terea elgiva* ♂ underside

72a *Junonia octavia sesamus* ♂ upperside (d.s.f.)

72b *Junonia octavia sesamus* form *natalensis* ♂ upperside (w.s.f.)

72c *Junonia octavia sesamus* ♀ upperside (rare form intermediate between w.- & d.s.f.)

72d *Junonia octavia sesamus* ♂ upperside (intermediate form)

65

73a *Junonia archesia* ♂ upperside (w.s.f.)

73b *Junonia archesia* ♂ upperside (d.s.f.)

74a *Junonia oenone oenone* 3rd instar larva

74c *Junonia oenone oenone* ♀ underside

74d *Junonia oenone oenone* ♂ upperside

74b *Junonia oenone oenone* newly emerged adult ♂

75a *Junonia hierta cebrene* ♂ upperside

75c *Junonia hierta cebrene* ♀ upperside

75b *Junonia hierta cebrene* ♂ underside

76a *Junonia orithya madagascariensis*
♂ upperside

76b *Junonia orithya madagascariensis*
♀ upperside

77a *Vanessa cardui* ♂ underside   **77b** *Vanessa cardui* ♀ upperside

78 *Antanartia hippomene hippomene*
(above) ♀ underside; (below) ♂ upperside

79 *Antanartia schaeneia schaeneia*
(above) ♀ underside; (below) ♂ upperside

80a *Lachnoptera ayresii* ♀ upperside   **80b** *Lachnoptera ayresii* ♂ upperside

81a *Phalanta phalantha aethiopica*
♂ upperside

81b *Phalanta phalantha aethiopica* pupa

81c *Phalanta phalantha aethiopica*
♂ underside

82a *Libythea labdaca laius* ♂ upperside

82b *Libythea labdaca laius* ♂ underside

83a *Alaena amazoula amazoula* ♂ upperside

84a *Pentila tropicalis tropicalis* ♂ underside

83b *Alaena amazoula amazoula* ♀ underside

84b *Pentila tropicalis tropicalis* ♂ upperside

84c *Pentila tropicalis tropicalis* ♀ upperside

83c *Alaena amazoula amazoula* ♂ underside

85a *Durbania amakosa natalensis*
larvae and pupa

85b *Durbania amakosa natalensis* newly emerged ♀

86a *Durbania limbata* ♂ upperside

85c *Durbania amakosa natalensis* ♀ upper- and underside

86b *Durbania limbata* ♀ upperside

86c *Durbania limbata* ♂ underside

85d *Durbania amakosa natalensis* ♀ upper- and undersides

71

87a *Teriomima zuluana* ♀ upperside

87b *Teriomima zuluana* ♀ underside

88a *Baliochila aslanga* ♂ underside

87c *Teriomima zuluana* ♂ underside

88b *Baliochila aslanga* ♀ underside

89a *Cnodontes penningtoni* ♂ upperside

89b *Cnodontes penningtoni* ♂ underside

90b *Cyclyrius pirithous*
mating pair

90a *Cyclyrius pirithous* ♂ underside

90c *Cyclyrius pirithous* ♀ upperside

91 *Deloneura millari millari*
(above) ♀ upperside; (below) ♂ underside

73

92a *Lachnocnema bibulus* ♀ underside

92b *Lachnocnema bibulus* ♂ underside

92c *Lachnocnema bibulus* ♀ upperside

93a *Thestor protumnus aridus* ♂ underside

93b *Thestor protumnus aridus* ♀ upperside

94a *Thestor brachycerus* ♂ upperside

94b *Thestor brachycerus* ♀ underside

95a *Virachola diocles*
final instar larva

95b *Virachola diocles* pupa

95d *Virachola diocles* ♂ upperside

95c *Virachola diocles*
♀ underside

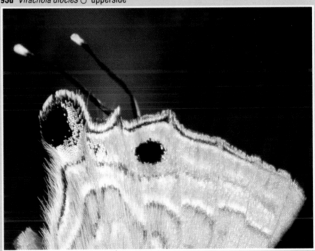

95e *Virachola diocles* detail of hair-tails and eye-spot on
hindwing underside used as false 'antennae'
and 'eye' to deceive predators

75

96a *Virachola dariaves* ♀ upperside

96b *Virachola dariaves* ♂ upperside

96c The larvae of *Virachola dariaves* feed on fruits such as these dune soap-berries (*Deinbollia oblongifolia*)

98b *Virachola dinochares* ♂ underside

98a *Virachola dinochares* ♂ upperside

97a *Virachola antalus* final instar larva

97b *Virachola antalus* pupa

97c *Virachola antalus* ♀ upperside

97d *Virachola antalus* ♂ underside

97e *Cardiospermum grandiflorum*, one of the many larval food-plants of *Virachola antalus*

77

99a *Myrina silenus ficedula* 3rd instar larva

99b *Myrina silenus ficedula* pupa

99c *Myrina silenus ficedula* ♂ upper- and underside

99d *Myrina silenus ficedula* (above) ♀ upperside; (below) ♂ upperside

99e A climbing fig, one of the many *Ficus* species used as food-plants by the larvae of *Myrina silenus ficedula*

100a *Myrina dermaptera dermaptera* larvae and pupae found below a piece of bark

100e *Myrina dermaptera dermaptera* (above) ♀ upperside; (below) ♂ upperside

100b *Myrina dermaptera dermaptera* larvae with ants

100c *Myrina dermaptera dermaptera* pupa

100d *Myrina dermaptera dermaptera* ♂ underside

101a *Hypolycaena philippus philippus* ♂ upperside

102a *Hypolycaena buxtoni buxtoni* ♀ upperside

101c *Hypolycaena philippus philippus* ♀ underside

102b *Hypolycaena buxtoni buxtoni* ♂ upperside

101b *Hypolycaena philippus philippus* ♀ upperside

102c *Hypolycaena buxtoni buxtoni* ♂ underside

103b *Hemiolaus caeculus caeculus*
♂ upperside

103a *Hemiolaus caeculus caeculus*
final instar larva

104a *Stugeta bowkeri bowkeri*
final instar larva

104b *Stugeta bowkeri bowkeri*
pupa camouflaged on bark

104d *Stugeta bowkeri bowkeri* ♀ underside

104c *Stugeta bowkeri bowkeri*
green pupa on twig

104e *Stugeta bowkeri bowkeri* ♂ upperside

81

105a *Iolaus silas* final instar larva

105b *Iolaus silas* pupa

105c *Iolaus silas* ♂ upperside

105d *Iolaus silas* ♀ upperside

105e *Iolaus silas* ♀ underside

106a *Iolaus pallene* pupa

107a *Iolaus sidus* final instar larva

106b *Iolaus pallene* ♀ upperside

107b *Iolaus sidus* pupa

107c *Iolaus sidus* ♀ underside

106c *Iolaus pallene* ♀ underside

107d *Iolaus sidus* ♀ upperside

83

108a *Iolaus mimosae mimosae* ♂ upperside

108b *Iolaus mimosae mimosae* ♂ underside

110a *Iolaus diametra natalica* ♀ upperside

110b *Iolaus diametra natalica* ♀ underside

111a *Iolaus alienus alienus* ♂ upperside

111b *Iolaus alienus alienus* ♀ upperside

112a *Iolaus aemulus aemulus* pupa

112b *Iolaus aemulus aemulus* ♀ underside

109 *Iolaus aphnaeoides* (above) ♀ upperside; (below) ♂ underside

112c *Iolaus aemulus aemulus* ♀ upperside

113a *Aphnaeus hutchinsonii* ♂ upperside

113b *Aphnaeus hutchinsonii* ♂ underside

114a *Spindasis natalensis* (above) ♀ upperside; (below) ♂ underside

114b *Spindasis natalensis* ♂ underside

115a *Spindasis mozambica* ♀ upperside

115b *Spindasis mozambica* ♀ underside

116a *Spindasis ella* ♂ upperside

116b *Spindasis ella* ♂ underside

119a *Axiocerses tjoane* ♀ upperside

119b *Axiocerses tjoane* ♀ underside

117 *Chloroselas pseudozeritis pseudozeritis*
(above) ♀ underside; (below) ♂ upperside

119c *Axiocerses tjoane* ♂ upperside

118 *Desmolycaena mazoensis*
(above) ♀ underside
(below) ♂ upperside

119d *Axiocerses tjoane* ♂ underside

120b *Axiocerses amanga* ♀ upperside

120a *Axiocerses amanga* ♂ underside

120c *Axiocerses amanga* ♀ underside

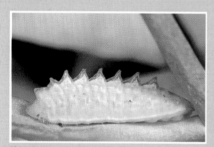

121a *Leptomyrina hirundo* final instar larva

121b *Leptomyrina hirundo* ♀ underside

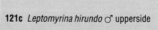

121c *Leptomyrina hirundo* ♂ upperside

122a *Gonatomyrina lara* ♂ underside

122b *Gonatomyrina lara* ♀ upperside

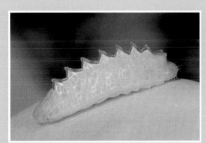

123a *Gonatomyrina gorgias gorgias* final instar larva

123c *Gonatomyrina gorgias gorgias* ♂ underside

123b *Gonatomyrina gorgias gorgias* ♂ upperside

125b *Capys penningtoni* pupa removed from protea head

125b *Capys penningtoni* pupa removed from protea head

125a *Capys penningtoni* final instar larva removed from protea head

125c *Capys penningtoni* newly emerged adult ♂ (underside)

125d *Capys penningtoni* ♀ upperside

125e *Capys penningtoni* ♀ underside

124 *Capys alphaeus alphaeus*
(above) ♀ upperside; (below) ♂ underside

90

126a *Phasis thero thero* ♂ upperside

126b *Phasis thero thero* ♂ underside

127a *Tylopaedia sardonyx sardonyx* ♂ upperside

128 *Argyraspodes argyraspis*
(above) ♀ underside
(below) ♂ upperside

127b *Tylopaedia sardonyx sardonyx* ♂ underside

130a *Anthene lemnos lemnos* ♂ upperside

131a *Anthene amarah amarah* ♂ upperside

130b *Anthene lemnos lemnos* ♀ upperside

131c *Anthene amarah amarah* ♀ upperside

130c *Anthene lemnos lemnos* ♀ underside

131b *Anthene amarah amarah* ♀ underside

129a *Anthene definita definita* ♂ upperside

129b *Anthene definita definita* ♀ upperside

132c *Anthene butleri livida*
♂ upperside

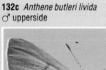

132a *Anthene butleri livida* ♂ underside

132d *Anthene butleri livida*
♀ upperside

132b *Anthene butleri livida* ♀ underside

133a *Cacyreus lingeus* ♂ upperside

134a *Cacyreus marshalli* ♂ underside

133b *Cacyreus lingeus* ♀ upperside

133c *Cacyreus lingeus* ♀ underside

134b *Cacyreus marshalli* ♀ underside

134c *Cacyreus marshalli* ♂ upperside

135a *Tuxentius melaena melaena* ♂ underside

136a *Tarucus sybaris sybaris* ♂ upperside

135b *Tuxentius melaena melaena* ♂ upperside

136b *Tarucus sybaris sybaris* ♀ underside

136c *Tarucus sybaris sybaris* ♀ upperside

137b *Tarucus thespis* ♀ upperside

137a *Tarucus thespis* ♂ upperside

137c *Tarucus thespis* ♂ underside

138a *Lampides boeticus* ♀ underside

138b *Lampides boeticus* ♂ underside

138c *Lampides boeticus* ♂ upperside

138d *Lampides boeticus* ♀ upperside

139b *Harpendyreus noquasa* ♂ underside

139a *Harpendyreus noquasa* ♂ upperside

139c *Harpendyreus noquasa*
bilateral gynandromorph upperside;
left half ♂, right half ♀

140a *Eicochrysops messapus mahallakoaena*
♂ underside

140b *Eicochrysops messapus mahallakoaena* ♂ upperside

140c *Eicochrysops messapus mahallakoaena* ♀ upperside

141a *Eicochrysops hippocrates* ♂ upperside

141b *Eicochrysops hippocrates* ♀ upperside

142a *Cupidopsis cissus* ♂ upperside

142b *Cupidopsis cissus* ♀ upperside

142c *Cupidopsis cissus* ♂ underside

143a *Freyeria trochylus* ♀ underside

143b *Freyeria trochylus* ♂ upperside

144a *Azanus jesous jesous* ♂ underside

144b *Azanus jesous jesous* ♀ underside

144c *Azanus jesous jesous* ♂ upperside

144d *Azanus jesous jesous* ♀ upperside

145a *Oraidium barberae* ♂ upperside

145b *Oraidium barberae* ♀ underside

145c *Oraidium barberae* (left) ♂ underside; (right) ♀ underside

146a *Zizula hylax hylax* ♂ upperside

146b *Zizula hylax hylax* ♂ underside

147b *Lycaena clarki* ♀ upperside

147a *Lycaena clarki* ♂ upperside

147c *Lycaena clarki* ♀ underside

148a *Aloeides thyra* ♂ upperside

148b *Aloeides thyra* ♀ upperside

149 *Aloeides pallida grandis*
(above) ♀ upperside
(below) ♂ underside

150 *Aloeides simplex*
(above) ♀ upperside
(below) ♂ upperside

101

151a *Aloeides penningtoni* ♂ upperside
(material from Balgowan, Natal)

151b *Aloeides penningtoni* ♂ underside
(material from Balgowan, Natal)

153a *Aloeides taikosama* ♂ upperside

153b *Aloeides taikosama* ♀ underside

152a *Aloeides barklyi* ♂ upperside

152c *Aloeides barklyi* ♀ underside

152b *Aloeides barklyi* ♀ upperside

154a *Aloeides pierus* ♂ upperside

154b *Aloeides pierus* ♀ upperside

155a *Chrysoritis chrysantas* ♂ upperside

155b *Chrysoritis chrysantas* ♂ underside

156a *Poecilmitis pyramus* ♂ upperside

156b *Poecilmitis pyramus* ♀ upperside

103

157a *Poecilmitis lycegenes* newly emerged adult ♂

157b *Poecilmitis lycegenes* ♂ underside

157c *Poecilmitis lycegenes* ♀ upperside

158a *Poecilmitis thysbe* ♂ upperside

158b *Poecilmitis thysbe* ♀ underside

159a *Poecilmitis natalensis* ♀ upperside

159b *Poecilmitis natalensis* ♀ underside

160a *Poecilmitis nigricans nigricans* ♂ upperside

160b *Poecilmitis nigricans nigricans* ♀ upperside

161a *Poecilmitis uranus* ♂ upperside

161b *Poecilmitis uranus* ♀ upperside

162a *Lepidochrysops variabilis* ♀ upperside

162b *Lepidochrysops variabilis* ♀ underside

163a *Lepidochrysops ignota* ♂ upperside

163b *Lepidochrysops ignota* ♂ underside

166a *Lepidochrysops plebeia plebeia*
♂ upperside

166b *Lepidochrysops plebeia plebeia* ♀ upperside

165 *Lepidochrysops ortygia*
(above) ♀ underside
(below) ♂ upperside

164 *Lepidochrysops tantalus* ♀ uppersides above, ♂ uppersides
below, to show variation within one colony

167a *Lepidochrysops patricia* ♂ underside

167b *Lepidochrysops patricia* ♂ upperside

167c *Lepidochrysops patricia* ♀ upperside

168 *Lepidochrysops letsea*
(above) ♀ underside; (below) ♂ upperside

169a *Pinacopteryx eriphia eriphia* ♂ upperside

169b *Pinacopteryx eriphia eriphia* ♂ underside (w.s.f.)

171d *Cassia* sp.; the larvae of *Catopsilia florella* feed on several species of this genus

171b *Catopsilia florella* ♂ undersides

171a *Catopsilia florella* final instar larva

171c *Catopsilia florella* ♀ upperside

170a *Colias electo electo* ♂ underside

170b *Colias electo electo* ♂ upperside

170c *Colias electo electo* ♀ upperside

170d *Colias electo electo* form *aurivillius* ♀ upperside

Eurema hecabe solifera ♂ upperside

172b *Eurema hecabe solifera* form *bisinuata* ♂ underside

109

173a *Eurema brigitta brigitta* ♂ underside

174a *Eurema desjardinsii marshalli* ♂ upperside (w.s.f.)

174b *Eurema desjardinsii marshalli* ♀ upperside

173b *Eurema brigitta brigitta* form *zoe* ♂ upperside

173c *Eurema brigitta brigitta* form *zoe* ♀ upperside

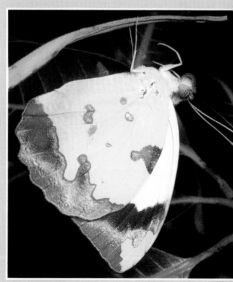

175a *Eronia cleodora cleodora* ♂ underside

110

176a *Eronia leda* ♂ underside

176b *Eronia leda* ♀ upperside (d.s.f.)

176c *Eronia leda* ♀ underside

176d *Eronia leda* ♂ upperside (d.s.f.)

Eronia cleodora cleodora ♂ upperside

175c *Eronia cleodora cleodora* ♀ upperside

111

177a *Nepheronia argia varia* ♂ upperside

177b *Nepheronia argia varia* form *aurora* ♀ upperside

177c *Nepheronia argia varia* ♀ underside

177d *Nepheronia argia varia* form *varia* ♀ upperside

178a *Nepheronia buquetii buquetii* ♂ upperside

178b *Nepheronia buquetii buquetii* ♀ upperside

179a *Nepheronia thalassina sinalata* ♂ upperside

179b *Nepheronia thalassina sinalata* form *sinalata* ♀ upperside

180a *Colotis amata calais* ♂ upperside

180b *Colotis amata calais* ♀ upperside

181a *Colotis doubledayi angolanus* ♂ upperside

181b *Colotis doubledayi angolanus* ♂ underside

182a above left: *Colotis vesta argillaceus* ♂ underside
182b above: *Colotis vesta argillaceus* ♀ upperside

182c *Colotis vesta argillaceus* ♀ underside

183 *Colotis celimene amina*
(above) ♀ upperside; (below) ♂ upperside

184a *Colotis erone* form *jobina* ♀ upperside (d.s.f.)

184b *Colotis erone* form *natalensis* ♀ upperside (w.s.f.)

184c *Colotis erone* form *erone* (w.s.f.)
♀ upperside

184d *Colotis erone* form *erone* (w.s.f.)
♂ upperside

184e *Maerua* sp., one of the larval
food-plants of *Colotis erone*

115

185a *Colotis ione* final instar larva

185g *Colotis ione* form *xanthosana* ♀ upperside (w.s.f.)

185b *Colotis ione* pupa

185d *Colotis ione* ♂ upperside (w.s.f.)

185c *Colotis ione* form *ione* ♂ underside (w.s.f.)

185f *Colotis ione* form *ione* ♀ underside (w.s.f.)

116

Colotis ione form *pepita* ♀ upperside (w.s.f.)

Colotis ione ♀ upperside (aberrant form in P. & E. Zwart collection)

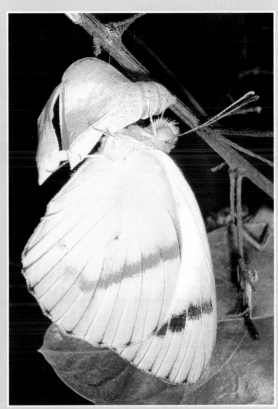

185e *Colotis ione* form *pepita* newly emerged adult ♀ (w.s.f.)

185j *Colotis ione* ♂ upperside (melanistic aberration in P. &. E. Zwart collection)

186c *Colotis regina* ♂ underside

186a *Colotis regina* ♂ upperside (w.s.f.)

186d *Colotis regina*
♀ emerging from pupa

186b *Colotis regina* ♀ upperside

187a *Colotis danae annae* ♂ upperside (w.s.f.)

188a *Colotis aurora dissociatus* ♂ upperside (w.s.f.)

187b *Colotis danae annae* ♀ upperside (w.s.f.)

188b *Colotis aurora dissociatus* ♀ upperside (w.s.f.)

188c *Colotis aurora dissociatus* ♀ underside (d.s.f.)

187c *Colotis danae annae* ♀ underside

119

189a *Colotis antevippe gavisa* pupa

189b *Colotis antevippe gavisa* ♂ upperside (w.s.f.)

189d *Colotis antevippe gavisa* ♀ underside

189c *Colotis antevippe gavisa* ♀ upperside (w.s.f.)

190a *Colotis evenina evenina* ♂ upperside (w.s.f.)

190b *Colotis evenina evenina* ♀ upperside (w.s.f.)

191a *Colotis pallene* ♂ upperside (w.s.f.)

191b *Colotis pallene* form *absurda* ♀ upperside

192a *Colotis agoye agoye* ♂ upperside

192b *Colotis agoye agoye* ♀ upperside

193a *Colotis evagore antigone* ♂ upperside (w.s.f.)

193b *Colotis evagore antigone* ♀ upperside (w.s.f.)

194a *Colotis eris eris* ♂ upperside

194b *Colotis eris eris* ♀ upperside

195a *Colotis subfasciatus subfasciatus* ♂ upperside (w.s.f.)

195b *Colotis subfasciatus subfasciatus* ♀ upperside (w.s.f.)

196a *Belenois thysa thysa* larva

196b *Belenois thysa thysa* ♀ emerging from pupa

196c,d,e *Belenois thysa thysa*: three stages in wing expansion after emergence of adult female

196f *Belenois thysa thysa* ♂ underside

196g *Belenois thysa thysa* ♀ upperside (d.s.f.)

196h *Belenois thysa thysa* ♀ upperside (w.s.f.)

123

197a *Belenois zochalia zochalia* ♂ underside

197b *Belenois zochalia zochalia* ♂ upperside (w.s.f.)

197c *Belenois zochalia zochalia* ♀ upperside

197d *Belenois zochalia zochalia* ♀ upperside

198a *Belenois aurota aurota* ♂ underside

198b *Belenois aurota aurota* ♀ upperside

198c *Belenois aurota aurota* ♀ underside

199b *Belenois creona severina*
♂ upperside

199c *Belenois creona severina* ♀ upperside

199a *Belenois creona severina*
♀ underside

125

200b *Belenois gidica* ♀ upperside (w.s.f.)

200a *Belenois gidica* ♀ underside

200c *Belenois gidica* ♂ upperside (w.s.f.)

201a *Dixeia charina charina* ♀ upper- and underside

201b *Dixeia charina charina* ♂ upperside

201c *Dixeia charina charina* ♀ upperside

202a *Dixeia doxo parva* ♂ upperside

202b *Dixeia doxo parva* ♀ upperside

203a *Dixeia pigea* ♀ underside

203b *Dixeia pigea* form *rubrobasalis* ♀ upperside

203c *Dixeia pigea* ♂ underside

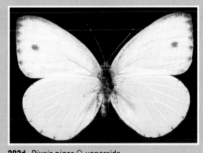

203d *Dixeia pigea* ♀ upperside

204a *Dixeia spilleri* ♂ upperside

204b *Dixeia spilleri* ♂ underside

204c *Dixeia spilleri*: nine females showing range of variation in upperside colouration

205a *Appias epaphia contracta* ♀ upperside (d.s.f.)

205c *Appias epaphia contracta* ♂ upperside (w.s.f.)

205d *Appias epaphia contracta* ♀ upperside (w.s.f.)

206a *Pontia helice helice* ♂ underside

206b *Pontia helice helice* ♂ upperside

206c *Pontia helice helice* ♀ upperside

129

207a *Leptosia alcesta inalcesta*
the minute pupa with a
matchstick head for scale

207b *Leptosia alcesta inalcesta* newly emerged adult ♀

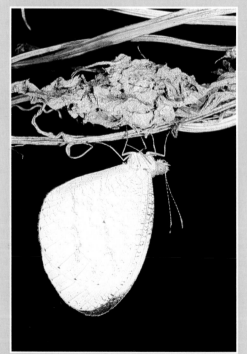

207d *Leptosia alcesta inalcesta* ♀ upperside

207c *Leptosia alcesta inalcesta* ♂ underside

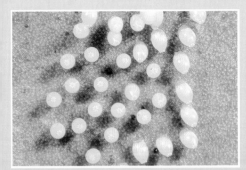

208a *Mylothris rueppellii haemus* eggs

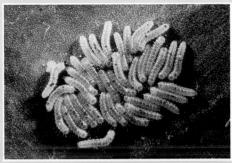

208b *Mylothris rueppellii haemus* day-old larvae

208c *Mylothris rueppellii haemus* final instar larvae

208e *Mylothris rueppellii haemus* ♀ upperside

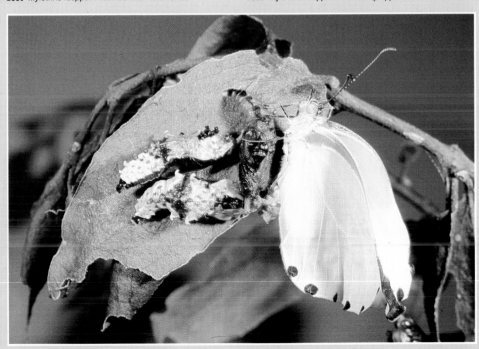

208d *Mylothris rueppellii haemus* ♀ emerging from pupa

209a *Princeps dardanus cenea* egg and (right) newly emerged larva eating eggshell (**209b**)

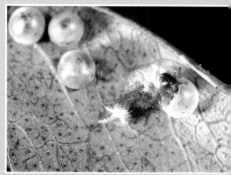

209e *Princeps dardanus cenea* newly emerged adult ♂

209f *Princeps dardanus cenea* newly emerged adult ♀

Princeps dardanus cenea 3rd instar larva

209d *Princeps dardanus cenea* pupa

Princeps dardanus cenea form *cenea* ♀ upperside

Princeps dardanus cenea form *trophonius* ♀ upperside

209i *Princeps dardanus cenea*: asymmetrical marbled gynandromorph (upperside)

210a *Princeps echerioides echerioides* ♂ upperside

210b *Princeps echerioides echerioides* ♀ upperside

210c *Vepris* sp., one of the
several larval food-plants of *Princeps echerioides echerioides*

211a *Princeps euphranor* ♂ underside

211b *Princeps euphranor*
♀ upperside

212a *Princeps constantinus constantinus* ♂ upperside

212b *Princeps constantinus constantinus* ♂ underside

213a *Princeps demodocus demodocus*: final instar larva in defence position with osmeterium extruded

213b *Princeps demodocus demodocus* final instar larva with pupae of parasitic wasp

213c *Princeps demodocus demodocus* pupa

213e *Princeps demodocus demodocus* ♀ upperside

213d *Princeps demodocus demodocus* newly emerged adult ♂

135

214a *Princeps nireus lyaeus* ♂ upperside

214b *Princeps nireus lyaeus* ♂ underside

214c *Princeps nireus lyaeus* ♀ upperside

214d *Princeps nireus lyaeus* ♀ underside

215a *Princeps ophidicephalus zuluensis* ♂ upperside

215b *Princeps ophidicephalus zuluensis* ♀ upperside

216a *Graphium morania* ♂ upperside

216b *Graphium morania* ♂ underside

217a *Graphium leonidas leonidas* ♂ upperside

217b *Graphium leonidas leonidas* ♂ underside

137

218a *Graphium policenes* 3rd instar larva

218b *Graphium policenes* final instar larva
just before pupation

218c *Graphium policenes*:
pupa a few minutes before emergence of adult

218d *Graphium policenes*: newly emerged adult

218e *Graphium policenes* ♂ upperside

219 *Graphium colonna* ♂ upperside

220a *Coeliades forestan forestan* ♂ upperside

221a *Celaenorrhinus mokeezi mokeezi* ♀ upperside

220b *Coeliades forestan forestan* ♂ underside

221b *Celaenorrhinus mokeezi mokeezi* ♀ underside

222a *Tagiades flesus* ♂ upperside

222b *Tagiades flesus* ♂ underside

223 *Sarangesa motozi*
(above) ♂ upperside; (below) ♀ underside

224 *Netrobalane canopus* ♀ upperside

225a *Spialia spio* ♂ upperside

225b *Spialia spio* ♂ underside

226a *Metisella metis paris* ♂ underside

226b *Metisella metis paris* ♂ upperside

226c *Metisella metis paris*
♂ upper- and underside

M. metis paris specimens were collected at Balgowan, Natal

140

228a *Kedestes callicles* ♂ underside

227 *Kedestes macomo* ♂ underside

228b *Kedestes callicles* ♀ upperside

229 *Leucochitonea levubu* ♂ upperside

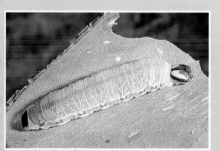

230a *Moltena fiara* final instar larva

230c *Moltena fiara*: larval food-plant
Strelitzia nicolai (Natal wild banana)

230b *Moltena fiara* ♂ upperside

141

231a Far left: *Artitropa erinnys* larva 'wrapped' in food-plant leaf
231f Left: *Artitropa erinnys*: *Dracaena* sp., one of the larval food-plants

231b *Artitropa erinnys* final instar larva

231c *Artitropa erinnys* pupa

231e *Artitropa erinnys* ♀ upperside

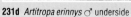

231d *Artitropa erinnys* ♂ underside

142

232a *Gegenes hottentota hottentota* ♂ underside

232b *Gegenes hottentota hottentota* ♂ upperside

232c *Gegenes hottentota hottentota* ♀ upperside

above right:
netting specimens with the aid of butterfly-net handle
extensions
below right: catching with a standard length net

above left: a butterfly trap with bait in a small container at the 'open' end
above right: triangular paper envelope used for transporting specimens in the field
right centre: pinning the specimen before positioning on the setting-board
below left: nipping the thorax to kill the specimen
below right: pinning the wings into position on the setting-board

DESCRIPTIONS OF BUTTERFLY SPECIES

Danaus chrysippus aegyptius (Schreber, 1759)   DANAINAE

southern milkweed butterfly; African monarch/suidelike melkbosskoenlapper
Wingspan: ♂ 50-70; ♀ 50-70 mm   **no. 1: p. 33**

The milkweed butterfly, so well known and so widely distributed in southern Africa, has for years mistakenly been considered to be the nominate race of the butterfly originally described by Linnaeus in 1758. The subspecies found throughout the subcontinent, however, is the one illustrated on page 33 and was described in 1759. Although it is also known as the African monarch, the name 'southern milkweed butterfly' is used here to draw attention to the fact that we are dealing with the southern African subspecies in this account.

This black-bordered orange-brown butterfly normally has a broad black apex to the forewing enclosing several white spots, as in form *liboria* portrayed in photographs **1a** and **1b** (page 33). There are, however, many forms of this very common species. The hindwing, on rare occasions, has a diffuse white patch, while in other forms the black apical patch is reduced to a black border on the margins of the wings. The male and female are almost identical but the female has only three black spots on the hindwing to the male's four; the fourth spot in the male is a scent-patch made up of a cluster of androconia (see pages 9 and 250) and is the large black spot on the hindwing upperside in photograph **1a** and the large white-centred black spot on the hindwing underside in photograph **1b**.

This species is distributed widely through the Old World. It is distasteful to predators and serves as a model which is mimicked by the females of the palatable species *Hypolimnas misippus* (see pages 167 and 247). Its eggs are laid singly and are longitudinally ribbed. The larvae are smooth and ringed with yellow and black bands (photograph **1c**). They often possess fleshy tubercles which grow from the head and back. The smooth pupa is always suspended by the tail and often has gold spots.

The southern milkweed butterfly has a slow, relaxed flight which makes it relatively easy to net. It is also easy to breed. Larvae and eggs are found singly on the food-plants, or eggs can be obtained from a gravid female.

Larval host-plants: *Asclepias* spp. (milkweeds). Larvae also utilize various species of *Ceropegia*, *Stapelia* and *Huernia*, also in the family Asclepiadaceae.

Amauris niavius dominicanus Trimen, 1879   DANAINAE

friar/monnik   **no. 2: p. 33**
Wingspan: ♂ 80-85; ♀ 80-85 mm

This very conspicuous butterfly with its black and white markings on both wings is as large as many swallowtails. The male and female are similar, but the female has a larger white patch on the hindwings than the male and she does not possess the 'sexual badge' or scent-patch on the hindwing characteristic of the male. The male's scent-patch can be seen as a long feather-shaped dark-brown patch lying parallel to the inner margin of the hindwing. The veins of the wing are outlined in black, giving this butterfly a very delicate appearance. The friar (photograph **2**, page 33) is unpalatable to vertebrate predators and serves as a 'model' for several other butterflies, being mimicked, for example, by one of the female forms of *Princeps dardanus cenea* (namely form *hippocoonides*) as well as by *Hypolimnas anthedon wahlbergi* form *wahlbergi* (photograph **63a**, page 62). (See page 247 for a discussion of mimicry, as well as the section on the subfamily Danainae on page 16).

If not disturbed before netting, this gently flying insect may be easily caught. The friar can be found in most forested areas along the Natal coast north to the mountainous eastern regions of the Transvaal. It is on the wing all year round, but is more common during the warmer months and also in April and May.

Larval host-plant: *Gymnema sylvestre*.

Amauris ochlea ochlea (Boisduval, 1847)   DANAINAE

novice/outannie   **no. 3: p. 33**
Wingspan: ♂ 55-60; ♀ 60-65 mm

Amauris o. ochlea is very similar to A. dominicanus but is only about two-thirds of its size. The male possesses a large brownish scent-patch or 'sexual badge' on the hindwing close to the anal angle and parallel to the inner margin. The female lacks the sexual badge and may thus be distinguished from the male. Both sexes have black wings with white markings, the females being slightly more brown-black.

The Natal coastal forests and thornveld seem to be the novice's favourite haunts but it also occurs in the eastern Transvaal. As it flies between the branches of trees and shrubs, however, it seems to scratch the surfaces of its wings and consequently perfect specimens are not easily found. The wing surfaces have a shiny appearance when held in the sunlight and this makes it a very difficult subject for the photographer. It is on the wing all year round, more so in the later summer months and the autumn months of April and May.

This unpalatable butterfly serves as a 'model' for Hypolimnas deceptor, the deceptive mimic, and the reader is invited to compare photograph **3a** (page 33) with photograph **62a** (page 61). (See also page 247).

Larval host-plants: Tylophora anomala; Cynanchum chirindense.

Amauris albimaculata albimaculata Butler, 1875   DANAINAE

layman/ouheks   **no. 4: p. 34**
Wingspan: ♂ 55-60; ♀ 65-70 mm

The layman is a predominantly black butterfly with white (or occasionally very pale yellow) spots on the forewing in both sexes. The hindwing has a yellowish patch against which the wing-veins are outlined conspicuously in black. The male may be recognized by the large, oval, dark-brown scent-patch or 'sexual badge' on his hindwing near the anal angle. The forewings of the male are more angular towards the apex than those of the female, which are rounded.

The layman can very easily be mistaken for its close relative Amauris echeria (not illustrated in this book), but can be distinguished from it by inspecting the palps (see diagram on page 9); in A. albimaculata each palp has an elongate white stripe while in A. echeria it has a white dot. (These features, however, are not readily visible from above). In addition, the male's forewing spots are always pure white while those of A. echeria are more often tinged with orange-yellow. In photograph **4a** (page 34), however, the female's forewing spots are, as is often the case, slightly yellowish. Still another useful distinguishing feature is the hue of the underside of the abdomen; in albimaculata it is whitish, while in echeria it is dark.

It can be found as far south-westwards as the Mbashe (Bashee) River in Transkei, extending along the coast north-eastwards to Port St. Johns and to the coastal thornveld and forests of Natal; it also occurs in the north-eastern forests of the Transvaal and as far west as the Soutpansberg. As is also the case with the novice, the layman's wings tend to get scratched in the forest environment in which it flies.

The layman is unpalatable to vertebrate predators and is mimicked by three palatable butterfly species: these are the false chief Pseudacraea lucretia tarquinia (compare photographs **4a**, page 34, and **55a**, page 56), the mocker swallowtail Princeps dardanus cenea form cenea (photograph **209h**, page 133), and the female of the white-banded swallowtail Princeps echerioides (photograph **210b**, page 134). (See also page 247).

Larval host-plants: Tylophora anomala; Cynanchum chirindense.

Melanitis leda helena (Westwood, 1851)   SATYRINAE

twilight brown; evening brown/skemerbruintjie   **no. 5: p. 34**
Wingspan: ♂ 60-65; ♀ 65-70 mm

This southern African subspecies of M. leda has for years been erroneously identified as M. l. africana Frühstorfer, 1908, a subspecies strictly confined to West Africa. The common name aptly describes the flying hours of this well-camouflaged butterfly. During the daylight hours it sits concealed amongst the dead leaves and debris under bushes and trees, its undersides blending in perfectly with the background (photograph **5a**, page 34). The underwing patterns of no two butter-flies, it seems, are ever exactly the same.

It is seasonally dimorphic, the winter (dry-season) form perhaps being the more beautiful. The upperside of the forewing has a comma-shaped black eye-spot just below the apex, enclosing two white spots, one above the other, all three in turn surrounded by a buff-orange colour. The hindwing also shows one, two or three small black eye-spots, each with a white centre. The orange in the male is more marked, although the extreme variations from different localities or different seasons make this an unreliable feature for separating the sexes.

The twilight brown may be found flying throughout the year. It is sometimes attracted to baited traps (see page 22) suspended close to the ground in shady areas, where it prefers to fly.

When disturbed, it flies up immediately and is easily recognizable, darting down quickly after an erratic short flight. If the specimen is to be collected, watch where it lands and sneak up to it slowly, as it tends to fly into the thick undergrowth on subsequent disturbance.

It is found in all southern African rain-forests and most places where thick bush occurs, as well as in cane-fields, sugar-cane being one of its recorded larval food-plants. Alien bluegum plantations also often harbour specimens, and it has been reported from the Orange Free State in this environment.

Larval host-plants: *Cynodon* spp.; *Setaria sulcata* (bristle-grass – this species is, however, not found in South Africa).

Bicyclus safitza safitza (Hewitson, 1851)   SATYRINAE

common bush brown/swartbosbruintjie   **no. 6: p. 34**
Wingspan: ♂ 40-43; ♀ 45-48 mm

The common bush brown is the most common brown butterfly in Africa and is found almost anywhere where forests and thick vegetation occur. In South Africa it is found in the eastern forests and wooded areas from the eastern Cape through Transkei and the eastern parts of Natal to the eastern and northern Transvaal. The male is dark brown while the female is slightly lighter. Both have eye-spots on the upperside of the forewing but these are indistinct; there are more eye-spots present on the forewing underside (and often the hindwing), where they are also more prominent.

It flies throughout the year, more so in the warmer months; the summer forms, incidentally, are more distinctively marked than the winter forms.

The male possesses two hair-pencils near the base of the costa of the hindwing, the outer one being almost black, the inner creamy yellow. In both sexes there is a sharp delineation on the undersides of the wings which separates the lighter outer margins from the darker inner part; this successfully gives the butterfly a dry-leaf appearance when it is settled on or near the ground with its wings folded over its head. Its flight is weak and floppy and it seldom flies long distances.

Larval host-plants: Various species of grass. *Ehrharta erecta* may, however, be used to rear the larvae in captivity.

Henotesia perspicua (Trimen, 1873)   SATYRINAE

eyed bush brown; marsh patroller/moeraswagter   **no. 7: p. 35**
Wingspan: ♂ 40-43; ♀ 45-48 mm

This satyrine resembles the previous species, *Bicyclus safitza*, but is more reddish-brown. Although it frequents similar situations it prefers the wetter forests and is found commonly along river-banks and around dams. Eye-spots are prominent on the wings of both sexes. There are two on each forewing, one large and one small; both are formed like bull's-eye targets, complete with white centre and rings of black, dark brown or orange. The smaller spot is near the apex. The hind-wings also possess a row of three (sometimes two) small eye-spots. The undersides of the wings are lighter in both sexes, with a thin dividing line down the centre of the fore- and hindwings which is bordered on its outer edge by a band of light yellow-brown. There are two eye-spots on the outer half of the underside of the forewing and six or seven smaller ones on the outer half of the hindwing. It is worth noting, however, that although the summer forms are decorated heavily on their undersides with these eye-spots, in the winter forms they are reduced to mere dots.

The eyed bush brown occurs along the Natal coast northwards through Mozambique and westwards into the northern Transvaal.

Larval host-plants: Various species of grass. *Ehrharta erecta* makes a suitable larval food-plant when the species is being reared in captivity.

147

Aeropetes tulbaghia (Linnaeus, 1764)   SATYRINAE

Table Mountain beauty; mountain pride/bergnooientjie   **no. 8: p. 35**
Wingspan: ♂ 70-75; ♀ 75-80 mm

This strikingly beautiful butterfly, formerly known as *Meneris tulbaghia*, is a strong flier and usually frequents the higher and more mountainous areas of our country, except in the arid west. It prefers rocky areas and on hot days may be seen resting on the shady side of rocks or banks. A fast and vigorous flier for its size, it has a reputation for eluding even the most skilled of collectors. It frequently feeds at the flowers of red-hot pokers and from a distance can look almost like a small hummingbird. It may be taken rather easily when feeding. If it is found flying in numbers, it is often better to wait at the flowers rather than to run kilometres over the mountain slopes flourishing a net.

The male and female are dark brown with two broken orange bands across the forewing upperside parallel to the outer margin and one on the hindwing; the female is easily distinguished from the male as she has a third short band across the forewing cell. Between the hindwing band and the outer edge of the hindwing are several eye-spots with white-dotted centres surrounded by exquisitely beautiful mauve and black rings. The species normally flies only during the summer from December to March.

Larval host-plants: Various species of grass, including *Ehrharta erecta* and *Hyparrhenia hirta* (thatch-grass).

Paralethe dendrophilus (Trimen, 1862)   SATYRINAE

bush beauty/bosprag   **no. 9: p. 35**
Wingspan: ♂ 45-50; ♀ 55-65 mm

The bush beauty is a most handsome and variable butterfly with four subspecies recognized in South Africa. The forewings are dark brown shading to orange-brown at the base and have several white or yellowish spots in the apical half of the wing; in some subspecies (for example, *dendrophilus* and *albina*) some of the spots in mid-wing appear to be 'smudged' outwards to the edge of the wings (photograph **9a**, page 35). The hindwings are orange with a dark scalloped border on the outer margin and, in all subspecies, have five to seven small eye-spots ('ocelli') of varying sizes parallel to the dark-brown outer margin. The undersides are mottled in various shades of brown with white spots or blotches and darker eye-spots. Although males and females are similar, the female is larger, having a greater wingspan and a noticeably larger abdomen.

This species will only be found flying in rain-forests in the eastern parts of South Africa, from the eastern Cape through Transkei and the Natal Midlands to the northern Transvaal. Its usual emergence period commences about the end of December and may continue as late as May.

It is easily caught when flying in open glades in its forest habitat. When disturbed it flies off rapidly, then settles on the side of a tree-trunk. Females lay their eggs in flight, scattering them amongst the grass on the forest floor (see page 16). Females placed alive in envelopes will often lay many hundreds of eggs, one or two every minute. With patience, larvae can be reared indoors using several containers with growing grass; while one or two are being used for food, the others are left to regenerate out of doors. The larvae feed mostly at night and are very slow-growing. When disturbed in the later stages of their development, they drop off the grass stems and feign death by lying curled up on the ground for many hours. The containers must be covered well because the larvae tend to wander off the food-plants. From egg to adult takes almost one year.

Larval host-plants: Various species of grass are utilized, including *Ehrharta erecta* and *Panicum deustum* (buffalo-grass).

Dira oxylus (Trimen, 1881)   SATYRINAE

Pondoland widow/Pondoland-weduwee   **no. 10: p. 35**
Wingspan: ♂ 55-60; ♀ 60-65 mm

The slopes of Mt. Currie near Kokstad are favourite haunts of this graceful satyrine, one of the largest species in the genus *Dira*. When on the wing in January and February it can be found in large numbers, flying and gliding over the hillslopes. It appears to be an easy catch but if given the slightest clue of danger flies off very rapidly and may elude even the most agile collector.

The male and female are both dark brown and have a set of three ocelli or eye-spots in the apex of each forewing. They also possess four or five eye-spots on each hindwing – these having a small dot in the centre surrounded by successive rings of black, brown and then orange. The female is slightly larger than the male, and the background colour of the apex on her forewing is lighter.

The Pondoland widow ranges from Stutterheim to localities near East London, inland towards Queenstown and northwards to Kokstad.

Larval host-plants: Various species of grass including *Ehrharta erecta*. This grass is also suitable for breeding the larvae in captivity.

Dira swanepoeli (Van Son, 1939)   SATYRINAE

Swanepoel's widow/Swanepoel-weduwee   **no. 11: p. 36**

Wingspan: ♂ 45-50; ♀ 55-60 mm

March 7, 1939 was a memorable day for David Swanepoel. Nearly 300 metres to the west of the Mountain Inn near Louis Trichardt in the Soutpansberg he found this lovely butterfly for the first time, flying slowly about in the grass. It was described later the same year by Dr. G. van Son of the Transvaal Museum.

Its ground colour is slightly lighter than that of *D. oxylus* and it has two prominent ocelli in the apex of each forewing. The hindwings also each have five or six ocelli bordering the outer margin. The female is larger than the male, is lighter in colour and has a heavier abdomen – markedly so in the case of a gravid female.

It may be found flying in various localities in the Soutpansberg and on the Blouberg throughout the month of March. The population on the Blouberg inselberg has developed in isolation from the Soutpansberg population for a considerable period of time and has in consequence evolved characteristic features which justify its recognition as a distinct subspecies, *D. swanepoeli isolata*. The subspecies portrayed in photograph **11** (page 36) is *D. swanepoeli swanepoeli*.

Larval host-plants: *Ehrharta erecta* and various other species of grass.

Dingana dingana (Trimen, 1873)   SATYRINAE

Dingaan's widow/Dingaan-weduwee   **no. 12: p. 36**

Wingspan: ♂ 45-48; ♀ 45-48 mm

Flying in September, October and November, Dingaan's widow is found from the Natal Midlands (mostly on the higher slopes) northwards to Barberton, Pilgrim's Rest and Haenertsburg in the Transvaal. Although it is found in the Transvaal Drakensberg, for some inexplicable reason it has not yet been recorded from the Natal Drakensberg.

The species is easily identified by the orange band on the apex of the forewing, which also contains two black ocelli which merge and are centred by two small white dots. In the subspecies *clara* from the Wolkberg near Haenertsburg, the forewing band is predominantly white and not orange. The photograph on page 36 is of subspecies *dingana*.

It flies mostly on the flats between the mountain peaks, preferring to settle on the rocky outcrops. The warmer parts of the day seem to be its favourite time to fly.

The map shows the approximate distribution range of both subspecies of Dingaan's widow.

Larval host-plants: *Ehrharta erecta* and various other species of grass.

Dingana bowkeri (Trimen, 1870)   SATYRINAE

Bowker's widow/Bowker-weduwee   **no. 13: p. 36**

Wingspan: ♂ 40-42; ♀ 40-45 mm

A hillslope a few kilometres north of Mooi River provided two fellow collectors and myself with one of our most memorable collecting days. We had stopped to explore what appeared to be a promising slope. After an hour or so, I stumbled over a rock, and with the thump of my feet disturbed my first specimen of Bowker's widow. It was freshly emerged, without a scratch on its fragile wings. I thumped on the ground once more and, almost miraculously, more and more butterflies rose from the grass. They were emerging from their pupal cases in their hundreds.

Bowker's widow is a little smaller than *D. dingana* and is much darker. In the apex of the forewing there is a semicircle of white patches, above which there is a single small dark ocellus. In the female the hindmost dots have a slight orange suffusion. The hindwings are bordered with four or five small

149

dark ocelli ringed with orange.

In Natal it flies near Giant's Castle and other areas of the Drakensberg range. It is also found in the Cape from the Kammanassie Mountains, Cradock and Richmond to Aliwal North, as well as in the Lydenburg district in the Transvaal, and near Harrismith and Golden Gate in the Orange Free State. It is on the wing from December to the end of February.

There are three recognized subspecies; the photograph on page 36 is of the nominate subspecies *bowkeri* from Natal. The map shows the presumed range of all three subspecies.

Larval host-plants: Various species of grass.

Torynesis orangica Vári, 1971   SATYRINAE

Golden Gate widow/Golden Gate-weduwee   **no. 14: p. 36**
Wingspan: ♂ 42-50; ♀ 48-53 mm

This butterfly was discovered in the Golden Gate Highlands National Park in the Orange Free State. It has since been found in the hills behind Clarens, and other localities undoubtedly await discovery in this part of the country.

The Golden Gate widow is distinctive with its elongate wings, two fused ocelli in the apex of the forewing and several ocelli on the outer border of the hindwing. The male is a much darker brown than the female. The veins on the undersides of the wings in both sexes are outlined by a narrow strip of fine white scales, making them stand out clearly; this is particularly marked on the hindwing.

The Golden Gate widow is on the wing from mid-January to mid-February.

Larval host-plants: Presumably, as with most species in this genus, various species of grass.

Tarsocera cassina (Butler, 1868)   SATYRINAE

sand-dune widow/sandduinweduwee   **no. 15: p. 37**
Wingspan: ♂ 35-40; ♀ 40-45 mm

The sand-dune widow is the smallest member of this genus and has an unusual haunt in the sandy coastal strandveld of the south-western Cape lowlands. For its size, it is surprisingly agile when disturbed. It is normally seen feeding at flowers but spends much of its time resting on the ground. It is on the wing from October to early December.

The female is larger than the male, having more rounded wings and a bigger abdomen. Both sexes have a black eye-spot in the apex of the forewing, with two small white dots within.

Recorded localities where it occurs in the south-western Cape extend from Malmesbury and Darling south-eastwards to the Bredasdorp district. It may be found on the slopes and even the summits of low hills in this coastal area.

Larval host-plants: Various species of grass, including naturalized aliens such as *Brachypodium distachyum* and a species of *Lolium*.

Coenyra hebe (Trimen, 1862)   SATYRINAE

Zulu shadefly; Zulu brown/Zoeloeskaduweebruintjie   **no. 16: p. 37**
Wingspan: ♂ 32-36; ♀ 34-38 mm

Male and female Zulu shadeflies are similar in appearance, although the females are often much larger than the males. Both are mid-brown lightening towards the outer margins and there are three narrow darker-brown bands at and parallel to the outer margins of both fore- and hindwings. The apex of the forewing has a lighter brownish-orange patch in which there are two white-centred black ocelli, one above the other. There are several orange-red stripes across the underside of both wings which give this butterfly a very delicate appearance; these stripes are faintly visible on the upperside.

The Zulu shadefly flies rather weakly and is easily caught. It may be sought in the shade of trees and shrubs along open roads and pathways, because these are the situations where it prefers to fly. It is found from Durban northwards along the coast to Zululand and St. Lucia, and north-westwards to the Transvaal Lowveld where in certain localities it will often be found in large numbers. It is on the wing from October to March but can be found in most months of the year.

Larval host-plants: Various species of grass.

Pseudonympha machacha Riley, 1938   SATYRINAE

Machacha brown/Machachabruintjie   **no. 17: p. 37**
Wingspan: ♂ 32-34; ♀ 34-36 mm

The males and females of this species are almost identical. They are mid-brown above with a large orange patch in the apex of the forewing; each orange patch is crowned by two contiguous, small, black, white-centred ocelli. The hindwings each possess a row of three small ocelli. The veins of the undersides of the hindwings are outlined in white.

The Machacha brown was first encountered in the Drakensberg grasslands near Giant's Castle in large numbers at altitudes between 2 750 and 3 050 metres by the late Ken Pennington. It has since been found on most of the higher mountains of Lesotho and there are records from the Cape Province on the mountain of Ben Macdhui on the Lesotho border near Barkly East.

This satyrine has a swift skipping flight, zigzagging close to the ground. It is on the wing from December to the end of February.

Larval host-plants: Various species of grass.

Stygionympha vigilans (Trimen, 1887)   SATYRINAE

hillside brown/rantbruintjie   **no. 18: p. 37**
Wingspan: ♂ 45-47; ♀ 45-48 mm

Geographically this is a variable species, with the size of the orange-red area on the upperside of the forewing varying enormously. In the Cape the orange-red patch is usually small, but towards the north-easterly limits of the species' distribution range, in Lesotho and Natal, it may be quite large. There is sometimes (but not always) a minute ocellus on the underside of the hindwing towards the anal angle.

The hillside brown flies on most mountain peaks right down into the valleys and seemingly favours places with rocky outcrops among the open grasslands. The flight period peak is from November to February, but it may be seen earlier in spring or as late as April if climatic conditions permit.

Larval host-plants: Various species of grass, including *Ehrharta erecta*; in the western Cape, also the reed-like *Restio cincinnatus*.

Bematistes aganice aganice (Hewitson, 1852)   ACRAEINAE

wanderer/swartbontrooitjie   **no. 19: p. 38**
Wingspan: ♂ 60-65; ♀ 70-75 mm

The wanderer is a large black acraea found from the eastern Cape to East Africa. The female is characteristically much larger than the male and has a wide band of white on the hindwing and a narrower, broken band of white across the forewing. The male is similarly banded, but in light yellow-brown instead of white. Both sexes possess a number of black spots in a triangular area at the base of each hindwing next to the body, on both upperside and underside. As in most of the acraeas, the wing veins are dark and prominent.

Wanderers have a leisurely flight and in the heat of the midday sun glide slowly about the tops of the trees for hours on end. I have often caught tattered specimens and released them, only to catch them again in the same area. When set free they seem very unperturbed, merely flap their wings once or twice and fly off again as if nothing serious had ever happened. The males are territorial and will take off from their favourite perches to chase off intruding butterflies.

The wanderer, like other acraeines, is distasteful to predators. It serves as a model for the Batesian mimic, the false wanderer, *Pseudacraea eurytus imitator* (compare photographs **19b**, page 38, and upper **54c**, page 56). It is also a Müllerian co-mimic of *Acraea esebria* (see page 247).

Although they may be seen throughout the year, they are more abundant in the warmer months.

In southern Africa the wanderer is found all along the warmer and wetter eastern side of the subcontinent, from the Mbashe (Bashee) River in Transkei northwards through Natal to the eastern Transvaal, where it confines itself to the wetter forests.

Larval host-plants: *Adenia gummifera* ('slangklimop') and naturalized members of the family Passifloraceae including *Passiflora caerulea* (blue passion-flower) and *P. edulis* (granadilla).

Acraea horta (Linnaeus, 1764)   ACRAEINAE

garden acraea/tuinrooitjie   **no. 20: p. 38**
Wingspan: ♂ 45-50; ♀ 50-53 mm

Acraea horta is the type-species of the genus and is the most common and wide-spread of all the acraeas. It occurs, as its name suggests, in suburban gardens from Cape Town to the northern Transvaal but in its natural state it is associated with forested areas, especially where its most important larval host-plant, the wild peach (*Kiggelaria africana*), occurs. It is absent from the arid west.

The male is reddish – more so than the female whose colour is brick-orange. Both sexes have a clear or translucent apical wing-tip with prominent wing-veins, a small dark bar on the forewing, and hindwings dotted with several black spots. (The translucent or 'hyaline' outer half to the forewing, incidentally, is a feature shared by many acraeas). The margin of the hindwing is chequered with black.

The garden acraea is abundant in the warmer months but can be found throughout the year. The larvae are often found in large numbers on their food-plants. They are distasteful to predators – a characteristic of the subfamily Acraeinae – and are covered with spines (photograph **20a**, page 38); when broken, these spines exude a yellow fluid containing cyanide. The larvae wander off the food-plant to pupate and seem not to worry about concealing themselves when they finally select a site. The pupae are black and yellow with black dots (photograph **20b**) and, although they may be found on or near the food-plant, they can also be found hanging fully exposed from window-sills or letter-boxes. Their conspicuous markings are a good example of 'warning colouration' and they are shunned by vertebrate predators. The adult butterfly is also distasteful to predators, the poisonous ingredients in its body having, it seems, been acquired at the larval stage from its host-plant.

Larval host-plants: *Kiggelaria africana* (wild peach); also various species of *Passiflora*, but not *P. edulis* (granadilla).

Acraea neobule neobule (Doubleday, 1848)   ACRAEINAE

wandering donkey acraea/dwaaleselrooitjie   **no. 21: p. 39**
Wingspan: ♂ 48-55; ♀ 50-55 mm

The wandering donkey acraea is rather similar to the garden acraea but paler overall. The forewings are perhaps more transparent, and the black dots on the hindwings are slightly less numerous. The best distinguishing feature is the small patch of orange on the apex of the fore-wing, lacking in *A. horta*.

It occurs in open grassland and bushveld areas, and although it usually flies singly and is seldom seen in large numbers, on one occasion a few kilometres north of Pretoria I found an aggregation of wandering donkey acraeas feeding on flowers at the side of the road. However, there was not a female amongst them and I must have examined over 100 specimens.

It is a slow flier, and prefers to fly close to the ground. It is also fond of gliding and playing among the trees at the tops of small koppies. Although it is commoner in the summer months, it flies through-out the year in the warmer areas from the eastern Cape and Karoo, northwards to Natal, the Orange Free State and Transvaal. It is not found in rain-forests and appears to frequent only the drier regions of the subcontinent.

This species was formerly known as *Acraea terpsicore neobule*.
Larval host-plants: *Passiflora edulis* (granadilla); *Adenia gummifera* ('slangklimop').

Acraea cerasa cerasa Hewitson, 1861   ACRAEINAE

tree-top acraea/boomtoprooitjie   **no. 22: p. 39**
Wingspan: ♂ 35-40; ♀ 35-40 mm

The common name 'tree-top acraea' very aptly describes this little butterfly. It spends much of its time gliding about the tops of the highest trees, out of reach of even the longest extensions of the net handle, and seldom comes within reach of the collector. The sexes are similar, the outer half of both fore- and hindwing being hyaline (translucent) with no scales and the inner half of each wing being orange-red. There are several black spots on the hindwing and there is usually a black spot in the forewing discal cell, another at the apical end of the cell, and perhaps one or two smaller spots in mid-wing.

It is a coastal species found in some of the Natal forests from Eshowe, Ngoye Forest and Zululand south to Oribi Gorge and Port St. Johns in Transkei.

I recall one day in Eshowe watching *A. cerasa* flying in numbers around the tree-tops, wondering if I was ever going to catch one. A change of weather occurred, clouds formed, and *A. cerasa* left the tree-tops to fly much lower down. I was then able to net several perfect specimens within a short period. The females are normally rather more scarce than the males.

The tree-top acraea is on the wing all year round but is more plentiful during the hotter months.

Larval host-plants: *Rawsonia lucida* (forest peach).

Acraea admatha Hewitson, 1865   ACRAEINAE

rain-forest acraea; forest acraea/reënbosrooitjie   **no. 23: p. 39**

Wingspan: ♂ 47-52; ♀ 47-52 mm

The rain-forest acraea is a beautiful red butterfly and although the sexes are similar, the male is brighter than the female. As in several other acraeas the outer half of each forewing is transparent, the inner half red. The hindwings are also red, and have a scattering of black dots and a black outer margin enclosing a marginal row of red dots (which tend to be more brown in the female).

A. admatha is a rain-forest species found along the east coast of South Africa from Transkei northwards to Zululand and Eshowe. Specimens have also been taken at Woodbush near Haenertsburg in the Transvaal. Like the tree-top acraea, the rain-forest acraea prefers to fly high among the tree-tops. It settles and suns itself there with its wings open, tantalizing the collector. It does, however, appear to fly closer to the ground in the later afternoon, when it descends to feed from flowers.

This butterfly flies all year round, but more so in the warmer months. Specimens from the winter brood are smaller and not as red as those from the summer brood.

Larval host-plants: *Rawsonia lucida* (forest peach); *Cassine tetragona* (climbing saffron); *Maytenus acuminata* (silky bark); *Maytenus heterophylla* (common spike-thorn).

Acraea satis Ward, 1871   ACRAEINAE

Chirinda acraea/Chirinda-rooitjie   **no. 24: p. 39**

Wingspan: ♂ 55-65; ♀ 50-70 mm

This is an unusual species of acraea in that the male and female are so markedly different in colour. The male's forewing is red, with transparent apical and outer marginal zones; his hindwing is also red and has a black border on the outer margin, spotted with red, and an irregular black band across the middle. The female is virtually identical except that where the male is red, she is white – a most unusual contrast which makes her very conspicuous when on the wing. The Chirinda acraea is a slow-flying butterfly and is easily netted if not disturbed by the collector beforehand. It is on the wing during the summer months.

This butterfly was named from Chirinda in the Eastern Highlands of Zimbabwe and was regarded as a rare vagrant to Natal until 1960 when a breeding population was discovered in Gwaliweni Forest in northern Zululand's Lebombo Mountains. Specimens can be found in central Natal, however, and I recall taking a female at Mariannhill near Pinetown whilst collecting with a friend. Within one minute of my catch, a shout from my colleague indicated that he too had netted a female – a rare coincidence indeed. We searched the hills in the vicinity for many weeks thereafter but no other specimen was taken.

Larval host-plant: Unknown.

Acraea igola Trimen, 1889   ACRAEINAE

dusky-veined acraea/vuilvensterrooitjie   **no. 25: p. 40**

Wingspan: ♂ 40-45; ♀ 47-52 mm

This is a distinct species, with a clear (hyaline) apical half to the forewing (photograph **25b**, page 40) bounded on the costal and outer marginal edges of the wing in black. The wing-veins as they pass through the apical patch are heavily marked with dark-brown scales. The basal half of the forewing is red with no spots. The hindwings are red, spotted and bordered in black. There are two forms of females, one red and the other pale yellow; they are equally common.

Flying low over bushes, the dusky-veined acraea is easily caught; however, if it is disturbed it is surprisingly fast and usually flies to the tree-tops to evade danger.

It is found sparingly along the east coast in coastal forests from Port St. Johns in Transkei north to Natal and Zululand; it can be found in all months of the year, but is more scarce during the colder months.

Larval host-plants: *Urera cameroonensis* and other species in the family Urticaceae; *Kiggelaria africana* (wild peach).

Acraea rahira rahira Boisduval, 1833   ACRAEINAE

marsh acraea/moerasrooitjie   **no. 26: p. 40**
Wingspan: ♂ 35-40; ♀ 43-48 mm

The food-plants of the larvae of this yellow-brown acraea are found in, or close to streams, rivers, dams and marshes. The adult butterfly therefore frequents such situations, often in swarms. The male is orange-brown, with all wing-veins ending in black streaks on the outer wing margins, the streaks widening as they approach the margins. Black spots are scattered over both fore- and hindwings. The female is larger than the male, her forewings slightly longer and tapered towards the apex.

The flight of the marsh acraea seems hurried, with much flapping to get from one place to another; it prefers to fly near to the ground, where it may be easily caught. It flies most of the year, being more abundant from September to April and is found in all the moister regions of South Africa, shunning the drier areas in the Karoo and northern Cape.

Larval host-plants: *Conyza canadensis* (a naturalized alien); *Polygonum pulchrum*.

Acraea eponina eponina (Cramer, 1780)   ACRAEINAE

small orange acraea; dancing acraea/kleinoranjerooitjie   **no. 27: p. 40**
Wingspan: ♂ 35-40; ♀ 35-43 mm

This is a small, common and distinctive butterfly. The subspecies *manjaca* Boisduval, 1833 (under which name our small orange acraea was formerly classified) is now considered to be a synonym of *A. terpsicore*, a non-South African butterfly; the local South African race is now accepted as the nominate race, *A. eponina eponina*, and is found in all the eastern districts of the country northwards from East London, through Natal and Swaziland to the eastern and northern Transvaal.

The male is orange with a wide black border on both fore- and hindwings. Enclosed in this border (except on the forewing costa) are orange dots and there is a comma-shaped black bar projecting into the orange of the forewing from the costa. The female is the most variable of all the acraeas in colour pattern, with no two ever the same; the dark apex and dark border remain fairly constant, but the ground colour may be any shade from dark brown to grey, often with white patches on the inner angle of the hindwing; the females in photographs **27a** and **b** (page 40), however, have the orange colouration more typical of the male.

The small orange acraea flies in and out of the long grass at the edge of most of our moist forests. Being a weak flier, it is easily netted. It flies throughout the year but is more plentiful in summer.

Larval host-plants: Various species of *Triumfetta* such as *T. rhomboidea* ('klitsbossie') and *T. pilosa*; *Hermannia* spp.

Acraea cabira Hopffer, 1855   ACRAEINAE

yellow-banded acraea/geelstreeprooitjie   **no. 28: p. 41**
Wingspan: ♂ 38-43; ♀ 40-45 mm

This is a variable little acraea, both in the size of specimens, some of which are very small indeed, and in the extent of the yellow contained within the distinctively wide black borders of their wings. The females often have a slight orange-yellow colour in the base of their wings, and appear to be scarcer than the males.

Yellow-banded acraeas have a slow, weak flight and stay close to the ground. They are consequently easily netted. They may be found on the wing year-round, but are more plentiful in autumn. They inhabit coastal bush in the eastern parts of southern Africa from Port St. Johns (Transkei) northwards through Natal and Zululand to the eastern Lowveld of the Transvaal.

Larval host-plants: *Triumfetta* spp. including *T. tomentosa*; *Hermannia* spp.

Acraea esebria esebria Hewitson, 1861 ACRAEINAE

dusky acraea/kafferbokrooitjie **no. 29: p. 41**
Wingspan: ♂ 55-60; ♀ 45-55 mm

The dusky acraea is a variable species with several named forms. The ground colour above is black and the nominate form has an orange-red or orange-brown patch extending from the forewing through most of the hindwing to the hindwing's inner margin (photograph **29d**, page 41). The commonest form in this country, however is form *protea* (photograph **29c**) in which the wing patches in both sexes are pale yellow-orange, as is the male's subapical forewing bar; the female's subapical bar is white. The veins of the wings of both forms are more or less clearly outlined in black. A few small black spots occur on the basal area of the hindwing near its point of attachment to the body; these are more prominent on the lighter underside (photograph **29b**). The female has a longer tapered forewing than the male.

Form *protea* (**29c**) of the dusky acraea is a Müllerian co-mimic (see page 247) of the male of the wanderer, *Bematistes aganice*. Photograph **19b** (page 38), however, portrays the black-and-white female wanderer and not the black-and-yellow male. It is a woodland species which is found on the fringes of most forests on the eastern side of the country; it flies all year round.

Larval host-plants: *Laportea peduncularis*; *Urera tenax* ('bergbrandnetel'); *Pouzolzia parasitica*.

Acraea acrita acrita Hewitson, 1865 ACRAEINAE

fiery acraea/vuurrooitjie **no. 30: p. 42**
Wingspan: ♂ 45-52; ♀ 45-52 mm

This fiery-red insect is certainly one of our brightest acraeas. As its common name suggests, it is flame-red, although the outer half of the forewing is suffused with orange. There are usually four or five large black spots on the forewing, which also has a black tip to the apex (photograph **30b**, page 42). The hindwings have more black spots than the forewings and have a broad jet-black outer margin normally enclosing a series of distinctive red spots. The female is not quite as bright as the male. Wet-season forms however, tend to have more black colouration, and photograph **30a** (page 42) shows a male with no red spots on the hindwing outer margin; the dry-season male in photograph **30b**, on the other hand, shows the red spots quite clearly.

For many years, only one specimen of the fiery acraea had ever been recorded in South Africa – at Komatipoort. Since then it has been recorded many times south of that original locality, mostly in Zululand at such localities as Kosi Bay, Lake Sibaya, Ndumu and west of Sordwana Bay on the flats below the Ubombo Mountains. David Swanepoel, however, recorded a specimen at Waterpoort north of the Soutpansberg in the Transvaal in July 1985 and I have caught a tattered female at Hluhluwe. It is possible that this species is expanding its range further southwards and westwards.

It is on the wing all year round, the summer forms being a more pronounced fiery red than the specimens caught in the cooler months.

Larval host-plant: *Adenia* sp.

Acraea natalica natalica Boisduval, 1847 ACRAEINAE

Natal acraea/Natalse rooitjie **no. 31: p. 42**
Wingspan: ♂ 55-63; ♀ 55-63 mm

As the name suggests, this acraea was first described from Natal. It is a large conspicuous butterfly, both in colour and the manner in which it flies. Both sexes have a black tip to the apex of the forewing and a black outer margin to the hindwing; the fore- and hindwings are spotted with black and the wing bases are suffused with black. There is a small wedge of contiguous black spots at the apical end of the forewing discal cell. The male is reddish-pink in colour while the female is more brown-red with a broader black band on her hindwing margin.

The flight of the Natal acraea is rapid when disturbed, but when on the wing it seems to have a rather zigzag flight. It flies all over the eastern sides of South Africa from the Kei River in Transkei northwards to most of the wooded parts of Natal and further north to Zululand and the eastern parts of the Transvaal; from there it spreads into the drier savanna veld of the north-western Transvaal.

Larval host-plants: *Adenia gummifera* ('slangklimop'); *Passiflora* spp. (but not granadilla). *Tricliceras longipedunculatum* ('rooihaarbossie').

Acraea oncaea Hopffer, 1855 ACRAEINAE

rooibok acraea/rooibokkie **no. 32: p. 42**
Wingspan: ♂ 40-47; ♀ 40-55 mm

The males of the rooibok acraea are red-brown with the veins on the forewing out-lined in black and a small black tip to the forewing apex; the hindwing has a narrow black band on the outer margin. The females are variable in colour from brown-red to almost grey-black, but always with a white band below the apex of the forewing which serves to distinguish them from the males. Both sexes have many black spots, randomly scattered on both wings. The undersides are more clearly defined: there is a black band on the outer margin of the hindwing enclosing a line of orange spots, while the background colour of the underwings is also orange with several black spots. There is con-siderable variation in the size of specimens of the rooibok acraea, the males often being larger than the females which are sometimes quite small – and vice versa.

This interesting butterfly may be found in the bushveld of the Transvaal and Zululand as well as in the coastal bush of Natal southwards probably to Margate. It is relatively common in suitable habitat and is on the wing all year round, more so in the summer months.

Larval host-plants: *Adenia* spp.; *Xylotheca kraussiana* (African dog-rose); *Tricliceras longipedun-culatum* ('rooihaarbossie').

Acraea aglaonice Westwood, 1881 ACRAEINAE

clear-spotted acraea/vensterrooitjie **no. 33: p. 43**
Wingspan: ♂ 42-47; ♀ 47-53 mm

The specific name of this butterfly – *aglaonice* – is something of a mouthful but I have always referred to it mnemonically as 'a nice glow', for that is what reflects from the wings of a freshly caught specimen. It is a pretty insect, particularly in the case of the male.

Clear-spotted acraeas are red with a pink 'glow'. Below the apex of the forewing is a small clear 'window' (or hyaline area), often covered with a thin layer of scales in the female, but shown to advan-tage in the female in photograph **33b** (page 43). The upperside of the hindwing has a solid black band on the outer margin, while on the underside this band encloses a series of yellow-orange spots. Both sexes have black spots on both fore- and hindwings; these coalesce just behind the clear window on the forewing to form a small but distinct bar. The females are variable and are mostly duller than the males. Female specimens from the northern Transvaal are sometimes almost black-grey with a small central white patch in the hindwing and white patches in the forewing below the apex.

Flying throughout the year, this bushveld species can be found in the coastal scrub of Natal and Zululand and in most areas of the Transvaal bushveld. Beautiful specimens may be found in the bush-veld north of the Soutpansberg in the winter months.

Larval host-plants: Introduced species of *Passiflora*, but not *P. edulis* (granadilla).

Acraea zetes (Linnaeus, 1758) ACRAEINAE

large-spotted acraea/ridderrooitjie **no. 34: p. 43**
Wingspan: ♂ 55-65; ♀ 60-70 mm

This is a large slow-flying acraea. I have never found it in large numbers, but dur-ing the course of a catching day in the thornveld, every now and then a large-spotted acraea flies by and, with luck, may be caught. At the end of the day – if Fortune has smiled – several can be counted in one's catch. It is best not to give them even a hint of your presence for, once disturbed, they fly high up and make a straight fast flight out of the area.

Large-spotted acraeas of the subspecies *acara* resemble the Natal acraea but have proportiona-tely larger black spots on the forewings (compare photographs **31b** and **34a**, pages 42 and 43) and a white patch on the underside of the hindwing which often shows through to the central area of the up-per surface of the hindwing. The underside of the hindwing is surrounded by a heavy black band on the outer margin enclosing a row of whitish spots. The females are more brown-red than the males and appear to be more scarce.

This species is on the wing throughout the year, but less so in the winter months, and is found mostly in thornveld areas from Durban northwards to most parts of Zululand and further north and west into the Transvaal, northern Cape and western Orange Free State.

Acraea zetes acara is the most widespread of the three subspecies of *A. zetes* in South Africa and is the subspecies portrayed in photographs **34a** and **b** (page 43). Note, however, that the subspecies *barberi* occurs in a limited area of the western Transvaal: its males are less heavily marked with black and the females have a large part of the forewing transparent. Subspecies *trimeni* occurs in the north-western Cape and western Orange Free State: the black markings are even more reduced in this sub-species. The distribution map shows the presumed range of all three subspecies in South Africa.

The large-spotted acraea is the model (see page 247) for the normal form of the Batesian mimic Trimen's false acraea *Pseudacraea boisduvalii trimenii*. However, the photograph of the latter species on page 55 (**53c**) is of form *colvillei* which mimics such acraeas as *Acraea admatha* (species 23).

Larval host-plants: *Passiflora* spp. (but probably not the granadilla); *Adenia glauca* ('bobbejaan-gif').

Acraea anemosa Hewitson, 1865   ACRAEINAE

broad-bordered acraea; Christmas-tree acraea/Kersboomrooitjie   **no. 35: p. 43**
Wingspan: ♂ 50-55; ♀ 60-65 mm

The broad-bordered acraea is one of our more attractive acraeas. It is a large red-dish or reddish-brown species and may be easily recognized by looking at the upper surface of the hindwing which has a heavy, broad, black band on the outer margin, and no spots. On the underside of the hindwing however, there is a row of white spots within the black marginal band and there are also scattered white spots within the black patch in the basal area. Both sexes have a black apex to the forewing, and a narrow black bar (with one or two associated black spots) which extends almost half-way across the wing from the forewing costa. The females have a dull orange-brown background colour and are not as brightly coloured as the males.

This species is widespread in all the warm bushveld regions of the Transvaal and northern Natal. It is perhaps more common, however, in the drier regions of the Transvaal. It appears to be fond of flying about the slopes of hills on warm sunny days and is on the wing from September to May. The female is less commonly encountered than the male.

Larval host-plant: *Adenia venenata*.

Acraea petraea Boisduval, 1847   ACRAEINAE

blood-red acraea; crimson acraea/bloedrooitjie   **no. 36: p. 44**
Wingspan: ♂ 45-48; ♀ 45-50 mm

This is a striking red acraea, with a black apex to the forewing and a black band on the outer margin of the hindwings. The sexes are easily distinguished, the male being red with many black markings and spots, and the female brown-red with a white band below the black apical tip of the forewings (photographs **36c** and **d**, page 44). The black dots on the hindwing are confined largely to the basal area and do not extend more than half-way towards the outer margin. The wing-veins on the underside are heavily marked in black.

The larvae (photograph **36a**) can easily be found on the food-plants, and when they are in the first or second instar, one leaf may contain upwards of 60 caterpillars. The pupae (photograph **36b**) can be found everywhere on the food-plant (often the small tree *Xylotheca kraussiana*, the African dog-rose), mostly on the upper surface of the leaves, but also all over the surrounding bush close to the main food-plant. If there is a wall or fence close by, a search will yield a 'harvest' of dozens of pupae. Al-though it is easy to gather the pupae, a large percentage will probably have been attacked by par-asites. It is therefore best to take the smaller caterpillars home and breed them through in captivity – it is worth the extra effort in the long run.

When on the wing, the blood-red acraea is a slow flier and is easily netted. It frequents the coastal forests of Natal and north to Zululand, following the distribution range of the African dog-rose.

Larval host-plants: *Xylotheca kraussiana* (African dog-rose); *Adenia* spp.; *Passiflora* spp. but not *P. edulis* (granadilla).

Pardopsis punctatissima (Boisduval, 1833)   ACRAEINAE

polka dot/polkastippel   **no. 37: p. 44**
Wingspan: ♂ 30-33; ♀ 33-35 mm

The polka dot is unmistakable in flight even from a distance; it is pale orange in colour with a narrow black border on the outer margins of both fore- and hindwings, and a black apical tip to the forewings. The rounded wings are peppered above and below with many black spots, from which characteristic this little butterfly obtains its common name.

The polka dot's flight is low and slow in the grass near rocky outcrops. It can be netted easily. Colonies are localized but widespread. It is on the wing during the warmer months, occurring in the eastern parts of the country from Port Elizabeth through the Transkei to Natal. It also occurs inland from Zululand to parts of the eastern Transvaal.

Larval host-plant: *Hybanthus capensis.*

Stonehamia varanes varanes (Cramer, 1777)   CHARAXINAE

pearl charaxes; pearl emperor/pêreldubbelstert   **no. 38: p. 45**
Wingspan: ♂ 65-70; ♀ 75-80 mm

This lovely butterfly, formerly known as *Charaxes varanes*, has a deep reddish-brown colour on the outer half of the upperside of each wing. It obtains its name, however, from the distinctive, broad, pearly-white basal area of the wings; this colouration also extends over most of its body. The dark orange-brown area on the outer margin of the forewing contains two rows of orange spots, while the lighter orange-brown area on the outer margin of the hindwing contains a row of black crescent-shaped streaks on the outer side of a row of dark-brown spots.

The hindwings have only one tail each. The tails of the female, however, are longer than those of the male and are slightly club-shaped at the end, not tapering. (Photograph **38b**, page 45, shows a male; the apparent 'club' at the tip of the tail is in fact a portion of the tail of the other wing). The undersides of no two specimens are the same; they are beautifully camouflaged to resemble a dead leaf, even to the extent of showing a false midrib. The pattern of the underside includes various shades from light brown through to mottled black. Given this remarkable resemblance to a dead leaf, it seems strange that this butterfly should spend most of its time perched at the ends of branches, often among green leaves, from which vantage-point it chases off any intruders.

The pearl charaxes is found in thick bush and forest, and is widespread from Knysna in the Cape north to Natal and Zululand, and thence into the eastern Transvaal and north-westwards along the Soutpansberg.

Larval host-plants: *Allophylus natalensis* (dune bastard currant); *Cardiospermum* spp.; *Rhus* spp. (wild currants).

Charaxes candiope (Godart, 1824)   CHARAXINAE

green-veined charaxes; green-veined emperor/skelmdubbelstert   **no. 39: p. 46**
Wingspan: ♂ 70-75; ♀ 80-85 mm

The green-veined charaxes is a large, reddish-brown butterfly with the bases of the fore- and hindwings bright yellow. A broad dark-blackish band on the outer margin of the wings contains a row of orange spots or blotches. The green veins near the forewing costa are prominent.

The male is smaller than the female. Both sexes have two tails on the hindwing. The upper tail of the male is much shorter than the lower tail and is sharply pointed; the upper tail of the female is longer and thicker and is only slightly shorter than the lower tail. The undersides at the base of the wings are also suffused with green, particularly near the main wing-veins.

Common in suitably wooded localities, the green-veined charaxes occurs on the eastern side of South Africa from Port St. Johns (Transkei), through Natal and Zululand to the eastern Transvaal, from where it sparingly penetrates to the central bushveld areas of the Transvaal.

It flies all year round in its wooded habitat and is a regular visitor to banana-baited traps.

Note: *All species of* Charaxes *are protected in the Transvaal by the Nature Conservation Ordinance 1983 (Ordinance 12 of 1983) (Transvaal); collecting is allowed only under permit from the Transvaal Nature Conservation Division in Pretoria.*

Larval host-plants: *Croton sylvaticus* (forest fever-berry) and other *Croton* spp.

Charaxes jasius saturnus Butler, 1865   CHARAXINAE

koppie charaxes; koppie emperor; foxy charaxes/koppiedubbelstert

Wingspan: ♂ 65-70; ♀ 75-80 mm   **no. 40: p. 47**

This charaxes, when fresh, is a most beautiful insect. The black outer margins of the uppersides of the wings carry a line of orange dots, which shade to white on the hindwing around the 'tails'. There is also a short row of blue dots near the hindwing tails, enclosed in the broad black band on the outer margin of the hindwing. This broad black band is also present on the forewing and is bordered medially by a lighter orange band. The basal third of both wings is a rich brick-orange colour. The underside has a patchy appearance with dull orange spots and stripes, each edged with a thin silver and white border. A prominent white flare extends across both wings. Both sexes possess two long slender tails on each hindwing. The upper tails of the male are considerably shorter than the lower tails; in the female the upper tail is almost as long as the lower tail.

Flying about the tops of small koppies is a favourite pastime of the aptly named koppie charaxes. It spends much of its time on warm sunny days 'hilltopping' (see page 18), perching on branches and chasing off any intruders. It is attracted to banana-baited traps on occasion but perhaps not as readily as other species of charaxes.

It ranges from the thornveld areas north of Durban and northern Natal through Zululand to the Transvaal bushveld areas where it is relatively common. It flies throughout the year, but is scarce during the winter months.

Note: *All species of* Charaxes *are protected in the Transvaal; see italicized text under* Charaxes candiope *on the previous page.*

Larval host-plants: *Hibiscus* spp.; *Croton* spp. (fever-berry trees); *Afzelia quanzensis* (pod mahogany); *Bauhinia galpinii* (pride-of-De Kaap); *Brachystegia* spp.; *Schotia brachypetala* (weeping boerbean); *Maytenus senegalensis* (red spike-thorn).

Charaxes brutus natalensis Staudinger, 1886   CHARAXINAE

white-barred charaxes; white-barred emperor/witstreepdubbelstert   **no. 41: p. 47**

Wingspan: ♂ 60-70; ♀ 75-80 mm

The white-barred charaxes is a common and distinctive species with its black uppersides and bold white (occasionally light yellowish) wing-band. This band commences at a point on the costa of the forewing and gradually broadens towards the anal margin of the hindwing. The outer margin of the hindwing is serrated, and there are two long slender tails on each hindwing. The undersides are variegated, with dark spots edged in silvery-white on a brownish-red background; there is a tapering silvery-white wing-band corresponding to that on the upperside of the butterfly.

It is found in most coastal and inland forests from the Mbashe (Bashee) River in Transkei to Natal and Zululand, Swaziland and the eastern Transvaal.

The larvae of the white-barred charaxes feed on certain species of the mahogany family Meliaceae. The Persian lilac, which has been introduced to South Africa from India as an ornamental tree, is also a member of this family and has proved to be an acceptable alternative host-plant.

It is on the wing all year round, although more rarely in the winter months, and is a regular visitor to banana-baited traps.

Note: *All species of* Charaxes *are protected in the Transvaal; see italicized text under* Charaxes candiope *on page 158.*

Larval host-plants: *Trichilia emetica* (Natal mahogany); *T. dregeana* (forest mahogany); *Turraea* spp. (wild honeysuckle trees); *Ekebergia capensis* (Cape ash); *Melia azedarach* (the alien Persian lilac or 'syringa').

Charaxes xiphares (Stoll, 1782)   CHARAXINAE

forest king charaxes; forest emperor/boskoningdubbelstert   **no. 42: p. 48**

Wingspan: ♂ 65-70; ♀ 70-80 mm

There are several recognized subspecies of the forest king charaxes in South Africa. The male is smaller than the female and is black above with a shiny, shimmering, broken blue band across both wings, but wider and more continuous on the hindwing. The female's background

159

colour above is black or dark brown with two broken white bands on the forewing, one narrow and one broad; the basal half of each hindwing is light brown. The undersides of both sexes are attractively patterned in various shades of brown. Both sexes have two tails on each hindwing, those of the female being longer than the short stubby tails of the male.

The forest king charaxes is a common forest species which occurs from Swellendam in the western Cape eastwards to the Amatola Mountains, the coastal forests of Transkei and north through Natal to the forests of the eastern Transvaal and the Soutpansberg. It has been reported that monkey dung entices the butterfly down from its tree-top haunts but traps baited with banana are equally effective and, in addition, the insect may often be seen sucking at spots where sap is oozing from trees.

Note: *All species of* Charaxes *are protected in the Transvaal; see italicized text under* Charaxes candiope *on page 158. The form* occidentalis *from Grootvadersbos near Swellendam is protected by the Nature and Environmental Conservation Ordinance 1974 (Ordinance 19 of 1974) (Cape).*

Larval host-plants: *Cryptocarya woodii* (Cape quince); *Chaetachme aristata* (thorny elm); *Scutia myrtina* (cat-thorn).

Charaxes bohemani C. & R. Felder, 1859   CHARAXINAE

large blue charaxes; large blue emperor/bloujuweeldubbelstert   **no. 43: p. 48**
Wingspan: ♂ 65-70; ♀ 75-80 mm

The large blue charaxes is undoubtedly one of the most handsome members of its subfamily. Both sexes are striking: the female is larger than the male, with the basal half of both fore- and hindwings being a spectacular pale violet-blue. This is bordered on the hindwing with a black band extending to the outer margin, and on the forewing with a wide contrasting white band. The rest of the forewing is black although there are two small white patches just below the apex. The male is similar to the female, but lacks the white band on the forewing while the blue scaling on both wings appears more silvery. Both sexes have two tails on each hindwing, those of the females being longer than those of the males.

This species occurs infrequently in the north of Swaziland and in the drier areas of the Transvaal Lowveld south of the eastern reaches of the Soutpansberg. It is more frequently encountered north of the Limpopo River, in Zimbabwe.

The males are prone to flying about the tops of small koppies and ridges, usually between the hours of 10 a.m. and 1 p.m. They are very alert and are easily disturbed by the movements of a would-be collector. The species is on the wing from September to April.

Note: *All species of* Charaxes *are protected in the Transvaal; see italicized text under* Charaxes candiope *on page 158.*

Larval host-plants: *Afzelia quanzensis* (pod mahogany); *Lonchocarpus capassa* (apple-leaf); *Xeroderris stuhlmannii* (wing-bean).

Charaxes cithaeron cithaeron C. & R. Felder, 1859   CHARAXINAE

blue-spotted charaxes; blue-spotted emperor/bosprinsdubbelstert   **no. 44: p. 49**
Wingspan: ♂ 70-75; ♀ 80-90 mm

The blue-spotted charaxes is rather similar to the forest king charaxes, particularly so in the case of the males which also have silver-blue markings on the uppersides, but which are distinguished by having the blue patch on the hindwing strongly suffused posteriorly with white. The females are black with a broad white crescent-shaped band extending across both fore- and hindwings; the forewing bands are continuous, while in the forest king charaxes they are broken and somewhat staggered. The hindwings each have two tails.

This butterfly can be found in all the forests along the eastern coastal zone of southern Africa from East London and Port St. Johns (Transkei) to the Mozambique border. It is not found in the Transvaal. It flies throughout the year although it is more abundant in the summer months. Like many other species of this genus, the blue-spotted charaxes seems irresistibly attracted to baited traps.

Note: *All species of* Charaxes *are protected in the Transvaal; see italicized text under* Charaxes candiope *on page 158.*

Larval host-plants: *Chaetachme aristata* (thorny elm); *Albizia adianthifolia* (flat-crown); *Afzelia quanzensis* (pod mahogany); *Maytenus senegalensis* (red spike-thorn); various other host-plants.

Charaxes zoolina zoolina (Westwood, 1850)   CHARAXINAE

club-tailed charaxes; club-tailed emperor/wit-en-bruindubbelstert   **no. 45: p. 50**
Wingspan: ♂ 40-45; ♀ 50-55 mm

This small and pretty butterfly is interesting in that it is the only charaxes in southern Africa to have distinct summer and winter forms. The summer or wet-season form is greenish white with a broad black border which, in the female, is broken up by several greenish-white spots – large on the forewing, smaller on the hindwing (photograph **45b**, page 50). The underside is more silvery green, broken by several light-brown bands. The winter or dry-season form could at first be taken for a different species as its upperside is orange-brown with a darker orange border (photograph **45a**). The undersides of this form are chestnut-brown and closely resemble dry dead leaves, even to the extent of having a darker brown false midrib. As with so many other butterfly species whose undersides resemble dead leaves, no two specimens are the same. Forms intermediate in colouration between the two seasonal extremes occur rarely, and are prized by collectors.

The sexes are readily distinguishable as the male has a single tail while the female has two; the tails of both sexes are spatulate or club-shaped (photograph **45b**).

The club-tailed charaxes is a fast, elusive insect, preferring the tree-tops where it rests and plays. Traps slung high in trees close to where the food-plant grows will usually produce results, but in the dry northern Transvaal the butterflies come to traps baited with fermenting fruit at ground level.

It flies all year round in wooded areas in the eastern coastal zone of South Africa, from north of the Mbashe (Bashee) River (Transkei) through most of Natal and Zululand to Swaziland and the lowveld of the eastern Transvaal; it also occurs in the Soutpansberg and the far northern Transvaal.

Note: *All species of* Charaxes *are protected in the Transvaal; see italicized text under* Charaxes candiope *on page 158.*
Larval host-plants: *Acacia karroo* (sweet thorn); *A. kraussiana* (coast climbing thorn); *Entada spicata* (spiny splinter-bean).

Charaxes jahlusa (Trimen, 1862)   CHARAXINAE

pearl-spotted charaxes; pearl-spotted emperor/silwerkoldubbelstert
Wingspan: ♂ 45-55; ♀ 50-60 mm   **no. 46: p. 50**

This is the smallest of the charaxes group in South Africa. The male and female are orange to red-brown with several black spots on the forewing. The hindwings have a dark border broken with orange spots near the termen or outer margin; this is bounded on the margin itself by a narrow orange border. The underside of the forewing is flushed with salmon-pink and spotted with black; the hindwing underside is dark brown with pearl-coloured spots and patches. These are particularly attractive in freshly emerged specimens. Both sexes have two tails on the hindwing, those of the male being slightly shorter than those of the female.

Although the pearl-spotted charaxes occurs in bushveld areas in the eastern Cape, north through Natal and Zululand to Swaziland and the Transvaal, it also occurs in the Little Karoo from Ladismith to Oudtshoorn. Two subspecies are recognized in South Africa: *jahlusa* occurs in the Cape and Natal range of the species, and *rex* in the Transvaal. The photographs on page 50 are of the subspecies *jahlusa*.

Although the species flies throughout the year in warmer areas, it is scarce in the winter months.

Note: *All species of* Charaxes *are protected in the Transvaal; see italicized text under* Charaxes candiope *on page 158.*
Larval host-plant: *Pappea capensis* (jacket-plum).

Charaxes achaemenes achaemenes C. & R. Felder, 1867   CHARAXINAE

bushveld charaxes; bushveld emperor/bosvelddubbelstert   **no. 47: p. 51**
Wingspan: ♂ 55-60; ♀ 60-65 mm

In this species, both male and female closely resemble other species of charaxes. The male is similar to the white-barred charaxes, *C. brutus natalensis*, and the female resembles the koppie charaxes, *C. jasius saturnus*. The undersides, however, are noticeably different. The underside of the bushveld charaxes is light brown mottled with dark-brown streaks and patches, and there is a suffused whitish bar across the forewing which extends into the first portion of the hindwing. There are two long slender tails on each hindwing.

The males have a habit of frequenting the tops of koppies during the warmer parts of the day and are easily netted. The females are scarce on the koppies but can be trapped in the bushveld below.

Its flight period extends throughout the year in the bushveld of the Transvaal, Zululand and Natal, and in parts of Transkei.

Note: *All species of* Charaxes *are protected in the Transvaal; see italicized text under* Charaxes candiope *on page 158.*

Larval host-plants: *Pterocarpus rotundifolius* (round-leaved teak); *P. angolensis* (Transvaal teak or kiaat); *Dalbergia boehmii* (large-leaved dalbergia); *Xanthocercis zambesiaca* (nyala tree).

Charaxes ethalion ethalion (Boisduval, 1847) CHARAXINAE

coast charaxes; satyr charaxes/kusdubbelstert **no. 48: p. 51**
Wingspan: ♂ 45-55; ♀ 50-60 mm

There are many and diverse species, subspecies and forms amongst the group of butterflies referred to as the 'black *Charaxes* complex'. *Charaxes ethalion*, the coast charaxes, is an extremely variable member of this difficult group and is well worth looking for.

As with the other black charaxes, the male coast charaxes is smaller than the female. Its upperside is almost entirely velvet-black but a faint blue-green band is evident on the anal angle of the hindwings. The female is also black, with a light (often bluish) band across the forewing, broadening over the hindwing. The outer margin of the hindwing is light red-brown and this is bordered on the inside with a line of small white stripes. Both undersides are dark brown and mottled and have a dead-leaf appearance – but without the false midrib of, for example, the club-tailed charaxes (page 161). There are two tails on each hindwing.

The coast charaxes occurs in coastal forests and woodland from around Oribi Gorge in southern Natal northwards throughout Zululand to the Transvaal, where it is found chiefly along the eastern parts of the Soutpansberg and in the northern part of the Kruger National Park. It is on the wing all year, but more so in the warmer months.

Specimens of black *Charaxes* from the Transkei coast and Port St. Johns were formerly classed as a subspecies of *C. ethalion* but are now considered to warrant specific recognition as *C. pondoensis*.

Note: *All species of* Charaxes *are protected in the Transvaal; see* Charaxes candiope *(page 158).*

Larval host-plants: *Albizia adianthifolia* (flat-crown); *Acacia ataxacantha* (flame-thorn).

Euxanthe wakefieldi (Ward, 1873) CHARAXINAE

forest queen/boskoningin **no. 49: p. 52**
Wingspan: ♂ 65-70; ♀ 80-85 mm

This is probably one of our most sought-after butterflies and also one of our most magnificent. Be warned, however – it is alert, fast and elusive.

At first glance, male and female look the same with their black velvet background colour and bold white markings. The males, however, when viewed from above with lighting from the sides, appear black and green-blue; viewed at a sharp angle from one side, the light markings revert to iridescent white. This colour change is not caused by pigment but is a 'structural colour' created by diffraction of the light rays striking the microscopic sculpturing of the white areas. The phenomenon does not occur in the females.

Although females are scarce, when one is caught and used for breeding she will readily lay a considerable number of eggs. These are large and round, flattened slightly at the top, and are lime-green in colour. The larvae are very attractive – bright green with two cream-white spots on the back, each usually enclosing two smaller green spots (photograph **49a**, page 52). The head possesses two large outer 'horns' and a pair of shorter inner 'horns'. The pupa is jade-green and angular with gold corners.

I have taken specimens north of Durban at La Lucia, Ballito Bay, the Tugela Mouth area, Nkandla Forest and Dukuduku near Mtubatuba, in northern Zululand and in the southern parts of Swaziland. The species has also been recorded from Umkomaas south of Durban. They fly throughout the year, although more so in the warmer months, only the odd specimen being taken in winter. They come to baited traps, but less readily than most *Charaxes* species.

Larval host-plant: *Deinbollia oblongifolia* (dune soap-berry).

Cymothoe alcimeda (Godart, 1819)　　　　　　　NYMPHALINAE

battling glider/alsiewitkoppie　　　　　　　　　　**no. 50: p. 53**
Wingspan: ♂ 42-48; ♀ 48-52 mm

　　　　Two subspecies of this small butterfly occur in South Africa and another in Zimbabwe. The males are creamy white with brown markings, mostly along the outer margins of the wings. In the nominate subspecies *alcimeda* there are two very prominent black bars across the discal cell of the forewing towards the costa, below which on the basal side there is a small circular marking of dark brown. These markings are absent from subspecies *trimeni* (photograph **50a**, page 53). The females are markedly different from the males and are brown-black with a median stripe of white and cream or yellow-orange across both fore- and hindwings, but not reaching the costa of the forewing. There is a pronounced small white bar across the discal cell of the forewing in both subspecies.
　　　　The battling glider is very shy and flies up and away rapidly when disturbed. Although it is often found feeding on damp patches of soil on the side of the road, it also has the habit of sitting and sunning itself high out of reach of the collector. Females are scarcer than the males and are not commonly encountered.
　　　　It is a localized species, but in appropriate habitat often occurs in large numbers. It prefers the wetter forests in the western and eastern Cape, from Caledon and Knysna north and east through Natal and Zululand to the eastern Transvaal. The subspecies *alcimeda* occurs in the western Cape and the subspecies *trimeni* is the form found throughout the rest of the species' South African range. It is on the wing all year round, but is scarce in the winter months.
　　　　Larval host-plant: *Kiggelaria africana* (wild peach).

Cymothoe coranus Grose-Smith, 1889　　　　　　NYMPHALINAE

blond glider; golden glider/corawitkoppie　　　　**no. 51: pp. 52-53**
Wingspan: ♂ 52-58; ♀ 58-65 mm

　　　　The blond glider is very similar to the battling glider but is larger. The male is cream-white above with dark brown on the outer margins of both fore- and hindwings; immediately next to the brown margin is a black zigzag line. The female is larger than the male and is black with a white curving band across both wings. The undersides of both sexes have a light-coloured dead-leaf appearance enhanced by a false 'midrib'. Like the blond glider this species is very alert and, once disturbed, appears to vanish for ever. The best time to net specimens is early in the day while they are drinking from damp soil.
　　　　It may be found flying in the summer months in forested areas from the Mbashe (Bashee) River and Port St. Johns northwards to the warmer and wetter coastal forests in Zululand. It has also been recorded in a small patch of forest on the farm Amo, in the hills south of Malelane and east of Nelspruit.
　　　　Larval host-plant: *Rawsonia lucida* (forest peach).

Euphaedra neophron neophron (Hopffer, 1855)　　NYMPHALINAE

gold-banded forester/skaduweedansertjie　　　　**no. 52: p. 54**
Wingspan: ♂ 55-60; ♀ 60-75 mm

　　　　For the sheer fun and pleasure (not to mention hard work) of collecting butterflies, this spectacular creature is a must; the fun comes from watching a fellow collector being tantalized by the butterfly and the hard work comes if you are doing the collecting; the pleasure of course comes when the specimen has been deposited safely in your collecting envelope.
　　　　The very nature of the environment in which it lives, renders the gold-banded forester a difficult prize to net. It flies in the dense bush of the coastal forests of Zululand, occasionally settling in patches of sunlight to sun itself but it is essentially a shade-loving species and seldom ventures out into the open. If it does, it is very wary and always keeps a metre or two ahead of the stalking collector by giving a few flaps of its wings and simply gliding away.
　　　　The sexes have a similar appearance although the females are considerably larger than the males. The forewings are tinted basally with a gunmetal blue and have a broad golden band bordered on both sides by a broad black band across the lower apex of the forewing. The apex tip is orange-yellow in both sexes but the females also have a small white-gold mark at the tip of the apex.

The larvae are quite different from those of most other butterflies. They possess fine, feather-like, translucent spines which project from the sides of the body and fan out flat on the leaf on which they are feeding or resting, creating the impression of a small flat spider-web (photograph **52a**, page 54). The pupae are smooth, angular and emerald-green, dotted with gold (photograph **52b**).

Larval host-plants: *Deinbollia* spp. (soap-berry bushes).

Pseudacraea boisduvalii trimenii Butler, 1874   NYMPHALINAE

Trimen's false acraea/Trimen-valsrooitjie   **no. 53: p. 55**
Wingspan: ♂ 65-70; ♀ 75-80 mm

This butterfly provides a perfect example of Batesian mimicry (page 247), as it is a palatable species which avoids predation by birds by mimicking the unpalatable large-spotted acraea, *Acraea zetes acara* as well as the tropical species *A. egina*.

It is a beautiful insect. The males of the 'normal' form are blood-red when fresh, with a black apex on the forewing and a broad black outer margin on the hindwings with black spots or blotches radiating outwards from the bases of the wings. The female is more orange-red, with an orange subapical patch below the black tip on the forewing. Trimen's false acraea is polymorphic, however, and exists in two forms. The form portrayed in photograph **53c** (page 55) is not in fact directly comparable with *A. zetes acara*; it is form *colvillei*, in which the apical half of the forewing is almost transparent. It is therefore a mimic of those acraeas which have hyaline apical areas in the forewing, such as *Acraea admatha* (photograph **23**, page 39). It is worth noting, however, that the females of *A. zetes barberi* in the Transvaal also have hyaline forewing patches.

Trimen's false acraea occurs from Port St. Johns in Transkei, northwards into Natal and Zululand and to Entabeni Forest and Louis Trichardt in the northern Transvaal. It prefers the wetter forests, although it can sometimes be found in drier areas.

Net extensions are usually essential for the capture of this butterfly, as it gracefully glides and settles on the tops of the tallest trees. In the late afternoon it often descends to settle lower down or to sport about under the trees. It is also fond of sucking moisture from damp and muddy patches on roads or near streams.

Larval host-plants: *Chrysophyllum* sp. (milk-plum); *Mimusops obovata* (red milkwood) and *Manilkara discolor* (forest milk-berry).

Pseudacraea eurytus imitator (Trimen, 1873)   NYMPHALINAE

false wanderer/skaduweevalsrooitjie   **no. 54: p. 56**
Wingspan: ♂ 65-70; ♀ 62-68 mm

As the name suggests this is another mimic. In this case, it resembles the acraeine butterfly, the wanderer (*Bematistes aganice*), discussed on pages 151 and 247. What makes the mimicry even more remarkable, however, is that just as the coloured wing-patches on the wanderer are yellow for the male and white for the female, so the pattern is repeated in the false wanderer – although some female wanderers are adorned with 'male' colours. The reader is invited to compare the photograph of the female wanderer (**19b**, page 38) with that of the female false wanderer (upper **54c**, page 56); both of these have the typically white female markings.

The male is black or dark brown, with a yellow median band on both wings, roughly at right angles to each other on the fore- and hindwing, and generally being broader on the hindwing. The female is larger with more rounded wings and white median bands, although as stated above females may alternatively carry yellow bands. An unusual male with rusty-red markings was caught in Durban in 1903: this aberration has been named form *pondo* and is portrayed in photograph **54d** (page 56).

It is worth noting that there is an important difference between model and mimic in that there are black spots at the base of both fore- and hindwings of the false wanderer, whereas the model has spots only in the basal area of the *hind*wings.

Flying high in the tree-tops, with the acraea-like habit of gliding, this species may be encountered in the coastal rain-forests of the eastern Transkei from Port St. Johns north to Natal and Zululand. It is on the wing throughout the year, but is more abundant in the warmer months.

Larval host-plants: *Bequaertiodendron natalense* (Natal milk-plum); *Chrysophyllum viridifolium* (forest milk-plum); *Mimusops* spp. (red milkwood trees).

Pseudacraea lucretia tarquinia (Trimen, 1868)

false chief/bontvalsrooitjie
Wingspan: ♂ 60-70; ♀ 60-65 mm

NYMPHALINAE

no. 55: p. 56

The false chief resembles species of the danaine genus *Amauris* both in its flight pattern and habits and is a good mimic of the chief, *Amauris echeria* , and the layman *A. albimaculata albimaculata* (compare photographs **55a**, page 56, and **4a**, page 34). The males and females are black-brown with a broad white or yellow patch on the hindwings. There is a band of around four whitish dots in mid-forewing, two smaller dots towards the apex of the forewing and often a small white tip on the apex which serves to distinguish it from its 'model'. All wing-veins are dusted with black and are clearly visible even against the dark-brown background colour. The hindwing patches are variable in colour – from white to light brown or yellow; the females usually have yellow or yellow-orange hindwing patches.

This species loves to sit and sun itself, usually beyond the reach of even the longest net of the enthusiastic collector. In flight it glides about the tree-tops, settling for short periods before dashing off again to chase away any intruding butterflies.

Flying throughout the year, the false chief is found northwards and eastwards from Port St. Johns to Zululand and to the moist forests of the eastern Transvaal. It is not uncommon in the coastal forests.

Larval host-plants: *Chrysophyllum viridifolium* (forest milk-plum); *Bequaertiodendron magalismontanum* (Transvaal milk-plum); *Mimusops obovata* (red milkwood).

Neptis saclava marpessa Hopffer, 1855

small spotted sailor/spikkelswewer
Wingspan: ♂ 42-45; ♀ 45-48 mm

NYMPHALINAE

no. 56: p. 57

The colloquial name of this attractive little butterfly is apt. It is small and dark brown to black, with three white dots in the subapical area of the forewing, below which is a white patch itself divided by a finely dusted brown vein. On the inner margin there is another white patch. The hindwing has a broad white band from the costa to the inner margin, bordered towards the outer margin of the wing with a series of black and brown markings. The female is slightly larger than the male.

The small spotted sailor has a characteristic flight style, a few rapid flaps of its wings being followed by long-sustained straight glides. It will 'patrol' in the same area for most of the day, resting from time to time on a favourite twig. Day after day it will remain within the same area, guarding its chosen domain and chasing off all intruders.

While it is on the wing in most months of the year, it is uncommon in winter. It prefers wooded areas and may be found flying in glades and near trees along streams. It is found from the Suurberg north of Port Elizabeth to Port St. Johns in Transkei and along the coastal bush areas of Natal and Zululand to the eastern Transvaal and Swaziland. Occasional specimens have been taken in the Magaliesberg.

Larval host-plants: *Acalypha glabrata* (forest false-nettle); *Combretum bracteosum* (hiccup creeper); *Ricinus communis* (castor-oil plant).

Neptis goochii Trimen, 1879

streaked sailor/strepiesswewer
Wingspan: ♂ 32-35; ♀ 32-38 mm

NYMPHALINAE

no. 57: p. 57

The streaked sailor is the smallest member of its genus in South Africa. The sexes are similar although the female is a little larger than the male. The wings are rounded at the apex. The forewing and hindwings are dark brown to black, bordered on the outer margins with three parallel fine lines of white scales. The hindwing has a continuous broad white band while the forewing has a much-broken white band and one or two small white patches in the discal cell.

Like the small spotted sailor, the streaked sailor spends much of its time perched on a twig or leaf, chasing off intruders from its territory which it patrols regularly. It is a wary and elusive butterfly.

It is found in coastal bush from around Durban northwards to Zululand and Mozambique. It tends to be localized in its distribution and is not found in large numbers. Although it is on the wing all year round, it is scarce in the winter months.

Larval host-plant: *Acalypha* sp. (family Euphorbiaceae).

Byblia anvatara acheloia (Wallengren, 1857)

joker/tolliegrasvegter
Wingspan: ♂ 40-45; ♀ 40-48 mm

NYMPHALINAE

no. 58: p. 59

Two very similar *Byblia* species occur in South Africa, the joker (*B. anvatara*) and the common joker (*B. ilithyia*). They are distinctive butterflies and are common within their respective distribution ranges. The joker (portrayed on page 59) is clad in a rich orange base colour while the female is a lighter orange-brown. Both have similar upperside black markings. These consist of a jagged-edged broad black border extending half-way along the forewing costa from the base, another small black patch between this and the apex, and a short black band running parallel to the outer margin to the inner angle of the forewing. This latter band continues all along and parallel to the outer margin of the hindwing. On both wings the veins between the black bands and the chocolate-brown outer margin are heavily outlined in black. There are also small black patches with irregular edges at the basal end of the hindwing costa and forewing inner margin. *Byblia ilithyia* can be readily distinguished from *B. anvatara acheloia* as its orange mid-hindwing area carries a clear row of small black dots.

The joker has distinct summer (wet-season) and winter (dry-season) forms, the former having a darker brown base colour on the undersides; two variants of the darker wet-season form are shown in photographs **58a** and **58b**.

Its habitat is grassland or open savanna, where it generally flies low down, within a metre or two of the ground. It is a slow flier and is easily caught; it is also attracted to banana-baited traps.

Although the common joker occurs over the entire eastern half of South Africa, including the eastern Karoo and Orange Free State, the joker itself only occurs along the eastern fringe of the subcontinent from East London northwards to Natal and western Zululand and thence to the Transvaal Lowveld and northern Transvaal bushveld; it appears to be absent from the coastal strip north of Durban.

This species was formerly known as *Byblia acheloia*.

Larval host-plant: *Tragia durbanensis*; *Dalechampia capensis*.

Eurytela hiarbas angustata Aurivillius, 1894

pied piper/witlintbosvlieër
Wingspan: ♂ 45-50; ♀ 45-50 mm

NYMPHALINAE

no. 59: p. 59

The pied piper is an attractive medium-sized black butterfly with a clearly defined white band across each hindwing; gradually narrowing, this band crosses on to the forewing and stops half-way to the apex. The outer margin of the hindwing has a scalloped edge which is bordered with a narrow red-brown band. The underside is mottled with different shades of light brown and a white band appears in the same position as on the upperside. Although the sexes are similar, the ground colour in the female is blackish-brown rather than black. A named form, *flavescens*, has been caught in Natal on rare occasions; in this butterfly the light band is a yellow-orange colour, rather similar to that of the following species *E. dryope*.

The male pied piper is a territorial butterfly, and sits on a favourite bush or tree guarding its domain. It flies up and down a short beat only a few metres long, changing direction with a quick flap of its wings. It chases off all intruders and stations itself on the same twig or leaf day after day.

The larvae are covered in short spines and the head possesses a V-like projection. The pupae are light green, long and angular, with two flat wing-like projections on each side.

The pied piper may be found flying throughout the year in woodland and forest habitats from the eastern Transvaal to Zululand and Natal and as far south-westwards as Knysna.

Larval host-plants: *Tragia durbanensis*; *Dalechampia capensis*; *Ricinus communis* (castor-oil plant).

Eurytela dryope angulata Aurivillius 1899

golden piper/oranjelintbosvlieër
Wingspan: ♂ 42-48; ♀ 45-50 mm

NYMPHALINAE

no. 60: p. 60

The golden piper is a dark-brown butterfly with a broad orange or rich-gold submarginal band, wider on the hindwing but tapering on the forewing and stopping about two-thirds of the way to the apex. The hindwing has a scalloped outer margin and, as in the pied piper, the scalloping is bordered with a narrow brown band. The female is lighter in colour than the male.

Flying all year round, the golden piper is found in much the same situations as the pied piper and has similar habits; its flight, however, is a little more robust, and it is often found some distance away from the forest edge.

Females are reluctant to lay eggs in captivity, but when they do, I have found that they only lay a small number. These can be easily hatched and the larvae reared if the humidity within the breeding-box is kept to a minimum. This can be difficult with such food-plants as *Ricinus communis*, the castor-oil plant, which tends to lose its moisture rapidly, with resultant condensation on the sides and lid of the breeding-boxes.

Larval host-plants: *Tragia durbanensis*; *Ricinus communis* (castor-oil plant).

Hypolimnas misippus (Linnaeus, 1764)   NYMPHALINAE

diadem (male)/blouglans (manlik)
mimic (female)/na-aper (vroulik)   **no. 61: pp. 60-61**
Wingspan: ♂ 60-65; ♀ 70-75 mm

This fascinating and beautiful butterfly has a very wide distribution throughout the world, occurring all over sub-Saharan Africa and through the greater part of the Indo-Australian region. Not only does it exhibit extreme sexual dimorphism – to the extent that the male (photograph **61g**, page 60) and the female (photograph **61h**, page 61) have different common names – but it provides one of the best examples of mimicry in the animal kingdom. Only the female, however, does the mimicking, the model in southern Africa being the local subspecies of the milkweed butterfly *Danaus chrysippus aegyptius* (photograph **1a**, page 33). The milkweed butterfly is distasteful to vertebrate predators, while *H. misippus* is not; the latter is therefore a Batesian mimic of the former (see page 247). What makes this case of mimicry all the more remarkable is the fact that the female *H. misippus* occurs in four different colour forms, each one corresponding to one of the four female forms of the model.

The male is black-velvet in colour above, with a large white patch in mid-hindwing, another in mid-forewing and a smaller white patch just below the forewing apex. These patches are surrounded by the most vivid violet-blue, which is a 'structural colour' resulting from the diffraction of light by the sculptured surface structure of the scales. A fresh male held at the correct angle in the sun is a beautiful sight. The females have an orange ground colour, black margins on both wings and occur with or without a black apical patch in which there are white markings, depending on the form of the mimic. On the costa of the hindwing there is a single medium-sized brown-black spot which serves to distinguish the mimic from the milkweed butterfly; the latter has four such spots across the male hindwing and three spots in the female. Another distinguishing feature is that the hindwing cell of the mimic is 'open' to the outer margin, while that of the milkweed butterfly is 'closed' at the end. (Such an 'open' cell can be seen very clearly in photograph **62b**, page 61, which shows the closely related *H. deceptor*).

Both sexes are shy and alert. They are strong fliers and should be carefully approached with the net. Diadems and mimics are on the wing all year round, but perhaps more so in the early winter months.

In captivity females may be reluctant to lay for a few days, but when laying begins it seems never-ending. A gravid female will lay upwards of 200 tiny pearl-like eggs. The larvae are easy to rear. However, a word of caution: do not try to raise more than 30 or 40 larvae. They have enormous appetites and unless a suitable food-plant is growing close by, and abundantly, they will eat themselves out of house and home, particularly in the last two larval stages.

Hypolimnas misippus occurs throughout South Africa except for the arid Karoo, Namaqualand and north-west Cape.

Larval host-plants: *Asystasia* spp.; *Portulaca* spp.; *Talinum* spp.

Hypolimnas deceptor deceptor (Trimen, 1873)   NYMPHALINAE

deceptive mimic; scarce diadem/skelmapie   **no. 62: p. 61**
Wingspan: ♂ 65-75; ♀ 70-80 mm

The deceptive mimic is not a common butterfly in South Africa and well merits its alternative common name, the 'scarce diadem'. Few collectors in this country have netted more than a few specimens. In the last ten years or so I have netted only two, perhaps sighting three or four more.

There are several records of clusters of this species roosting together but so far I have not been lucky enough to witness this.

Like the previous species, *H. deceptor* is a Batesian mimic (see page 247); in this case the model is the unpleasant-tasting novice, *Amauris ochlea ochlea* (compare photographs **62a**, page 61, and **3a**, page 33). It is a large black butterfly with two broken transverse white patches on the forewing together with a small white subapical spot or spots; the hindwing carries a single large creamy-white patch and sometimes a series of small white dots or streaks parallel to the outer margin. The female is larger than the male, the apex of her forewing is more rounded and the white patch on her hindwing is larger.

Records show the deceptive mimic can be found on the wing throughout the year, more so during the period from January to June. It inhabits forested areas in the coastal zone from East London northwards through Natal and Zululand to Swaziland and the eastern Transvaal.

Larval host-plant: *Laportea peduncularis.*

Hypolimnas anthedon wahlbergi (Wallengren, 1857) NYMPHALINAE

variable mimic; variable diadem/verneukertjie **no. 63: p. 62**
Wingspan: ♂ 75-80; ♀ 75-90 mm

The variable mimic is a large and variable species with two forms of the southern African subspecies in South Africa, *wahlbergi* and *mima*. Form *wahlbergi* (photograph **63a**, page 62) mimics the friar, *Amauris niavius dominicanus* (photograph **2**, page 33), while form *mima* (photograph **63b**) mimics the layman, *Amauris albimaculata* (photograph **4a**, page 34). This is a case of Batesian mimicry, butterflies of the genus *Amauris* being distasteful to predators while *Hypolimnas* butterflies are potentially palatable. The two forms of the variable mimic are so different that for years they were believed to be separate species; in 1910, however, the results of breeding experiments were published which proved that a female of one form could produce offspring of its own *and* the other form. Form *wahlbergi* is black with two large patches of white on the forewing, one subapical, the other on the inner margin next to the hindwing; the hindwing has a single white patch which covers almost the whole wing from the base, leaving only a black border on the outer margin. Form *mima* is black with a few small white spots on the forewing, a row of small white dots on the hindwing parallel to the outer margin, and a light ochreous-brown patch covering the basal half of the hindwing. The forewings are long and taper slightly towards the apex.

The flight of the variable mimic is slow and deliberate and it can easily be caught on the wing or while feeding on flowers. The females lay readily when captured and the larvae can be reared with ease.

The variable mimic occurs in all the moist forests on the eastern side of South Africa from Port St. Johns in the Transkei northwards through Natal and Zululand to the eastern Transvaal. The species is commoner during the warmer months but is on the wing throughout the year.

This butterfly was formerly known as *Hypolimnas dubius wahlbergi.*

Larval host-plant: *Laportea peduncularis.*

Eunica boisduvali boisduvali (Wallengren, 1857) NYMPHALINAE

brown tree-nymph/Boisduval-boombruintjie **no. 64: p. 58**
Wingspan: ♂ 35-40; ♀ 38-43 mm

This is a small and somewhat sombre mid-brown species. The males are uniformly mid-brown on the upperside, except for a row of tiny black spots near and parallel to the outer margin of the hindwing. The females are similar, but the apical half of the forewing is flushed with darker brown and carries three or four indistinct orange bars or blotches. The undersides of both sexes are an attractive light orange-brown; the apex of the forewing features a row of three or four small black spots while the hindwing is mottled with various shades of brown and has a crescent of dark-brown eye-spots parallel to the outer margin.

The brown-tree nymph is occasionally found in large numbers. I recall a collecting trip to the Dukuduku Forest in Zululand a few years ago. Just before I reached the forest, brown tree nymphs were swarming in countless numbers on both sides of the road. These myriads represent the greatest number of butterflies I have ever seen in one place at one time. Every leaf on every branch was covered with butterflies as were the tree-trunks and the grass. They had obviously just hatched as each specimen was in perfect condition. When I drove off, the windscreen of my car became almost opaque with the body fluids of dozens of butterflies which were struck by the car as they flew over the road. When I returned to the same area a few hours later, not one could be seen; the whole swarm had disappeared. Perhaps all had flown off together in a mass migration to an unknown destination.

The larvae are gregarious in all stages. They pupate on or near their food-plant and apparently hatch synchronously within a few hours of each other.

Brown tree-nymphs are on the wing all year round, but more so in the summer months. They occur in coastal bush from the Mbashe (Bashee) River in the Transkei through Natal and Zululand to the eastern Transvaal.

This species was formerly known as *Sallya boisduvali*.

Note that the photographs of the brown tree-nymph appear on page 58, and not with those of the Natal tree-nymph on page 63.

Larval host-plant: *Sapium integerrimum* (duiker-berry).

Eunica natalensis (Boisduval, 1847)   NYMPHALINAE

Natal tree-nymph/Natal-boombruintjie   **no. 65: p. 63**
Wingspan: ♂ 40-45; ♀ 42-48 mm

A close relative of the brown tree-nymph (*E. boisduvali*), the Natal tree-nymph is very similar but slightly larger, and is mid-brown rather than dark brown above. The male is almost uniform in colour above but has an inconspicuous line of fine black streaks close to the outer margins of both fore- and hindwings; there are also tiny black spots near the apex of the forewing in a row parallel to the outer margin, and a similar row of spots on the hindwing. The female's spots and streaks are bolder and the apical half of her forewing is flushed with dark brown or black and carries three or four smudged orange blotches or bars. The underside resembles that of the brown tree nymph but is more lightly marked.

Natal tree-nymphs are gregarious by nature and often settle on tree-trunks where they may remain motionless for long periods. If disturbed, they fly rapidly away to seek another perch in the darker and more inaccessible parts of the bush.

These butterflies are on the wing all year round when conditions permit, and are found from Port St. Johns northwards through Natal and Zululand to Swaziland and the Transvaal Lowveld.

This species was formerly known as *Sallya natalensis*.

Larval host-plant: *Sapium integerrimum* (duiker-berry).

Protogoniomorpha parhassus aethiops (Palisot de Beauvois, 1805)
NYMPHALINAE

mother-of-pearl/perlemoenvlinder; perlemoenskoenlapper   **no. 66: p. 62**
Wingspan: ♂ 65-75; ♀ 75-85 mm

This species will take pride of place in most beginners' collections. It is white-green, with a pearl-like violet lustre on the upperside of the wings, which are beautifully marked with several ocelli. The forewings are angular with extended backward-curving points on the apex; the hindwings possess a short tail on the outer margin and are sharply pointed at the anal angle. The ocelli on the hindwings are very attractive, particularly the lower one near the anal angle; it is only four to five millimetres in diameter, but has a purple and black centre or 'pupil' surrounded in turn by orange, yellow and black rings.

The female is of a lighter hue and larger than the male. Both sexes are strong fliers and spend much time sunning themselves on the topmost branches of the tallest trees. When they are courting, all dangers seem forgotten and male and female fly low, lazily circling and chasing each other. At this stage they can sometimes be easily caught – two at a time.

They grace our coastal forests from the Mbashe (Bashee) River northwards through Natal and inland to the eastern Transvaal. They can be seen in any month of the year, but appear to be more abundant in the warmer months. The winter form is more darkly marked and the males reflect a decidedly violet-blue sheen in the sunlight at this time of the year.

This butterfly was formerly known as *Salamis parhassus aethiops*.

Larval host-plants: *Asystasia gangetica*; *Isoglossa* spp. including *I. woodii* (buckweed) and *I. mossambicensis*.

Protogoniomorpha anacardii nebulosa (Trimen, 1881)   NYMPHALINAE

clouded mother-of-pearl/newelperlemoen   **no. 67: p. 63**
Wingspan: ♂ 55-65; ♀ 65-70 mm

This butterfly is very similar to *P. parhassus aethiops*, but is more darkly marked and has fewer true ocelli. However, the ocellus near the anal angle of the hindwing is virtually the same as in the mother-of-pearl, with its purple centre surrounded by successive rings of orange, yellow and black. Seasonal changes in wing colour are also evident in the clouded mother-of-pearl, the female having a gold-coffee flush to her upperside in the winter form.

The clouded mother-of-pearl is on the wing in all the months of the year in the drier forests of the eastern parts of South Africa from, according to some reports, Port St. Johns in Transkei, but certainly from Umkomaas northwards to Zululand, Swaziland and the bushveld of the eastern Transvaal. It appears to be less common than the mother-of-pearl.

This butterfly was formerly known as *Salamis anacardii nebulosa*.
Larval host-plants: *Asystasia schimperi; A. gangetica.*

Catacroptera cloanthe cloanthe (Stoll, 1781)   NYMPHALINAE

pirate/seerower   **no. 68: p. 63**
Wingspan: ♂ 50-55; ♀ 55-60 mm

The pirate is one of those butterflies which is often seen but is difficult to catch. It tends to fly singly (rarely more than one or two at a time) on grassy hillsides and the males protect small areas by chasing off any intruding butterflies. Both sexes have an orange ground colour with scalloped edges to the outer margins of the wings, and have a row of black-edged blue eye-spots on the hindwing, slightly in from the outer margin. The scalloping ends at the anal angle of the hindwing in a small tail-like projection. The males have a violaceous-blue suffusion on the basal half of the upper surface of the wings, almost the same colour as methylated spirits. In both sexes the forewings have a series of three black bars extending into the cell from the costa, and one (or two) broken bars extending into the subapical area from the costa (photograph **68a**, page 63).

Always alert and flying close to the ground, the pirate may be found on the wing all year round, usually close to wet areas in grassland, from sea level to hills and mountains.

Its range includes the eastern Cape from George eastwards, and the more hilly or mountainous areas of Natal, Swaziland and the Transvaal.
Larval host-plants: *Justicia protracta; Asclepias* spp.; *Barleria stuhlmannii.*

Junonia natalica natalica (C. & R. Felder, 1860)   NYMPHALINAE

brown commodore/Natal-blaarvlerk   **no. 69: p. 64**
Wingspan: ♂ 45-50; ♀ 50-55 mm

This common species is brown with two broad, wavy-edged, reddish bands with black borders across the forewing cell (not meeting the costa), a cluster of three white spots on a dark brown-black apical patch, a smaller white spot nearer the apex and a row of reddish ocellate spots which runs parallel to the outer margin of the hindwing and on to the posterior part of the forewing. The most prominent ocellus is the last one on the hindwing; it is red with a black central spot sometimes edged on the inner side with blue. The wings are angular, have scalloped outer margins and the undersides have a mottled 'dead-leaf' appearance with a false 'midrib'. The sexes are similar.

Seldom seen flying high, the brown commodore spends much of its time flying and gliding low about the bushes at the edge of forested areas, often stopping to feed on flowers. It is easily caught if not disturbed beforehand.

It ranges from the Port St. Johns area in Transkei northwards throughout Natal to the eastern Transvaal, where it occurs sparingly.
This species was formerly known as *Precis natalica*.
Larval host-plants: *Asystasia gangetica; Ruellia patula; Phaulopsis imbricata.*

Junonia terea elgiva Hewitson, 1864   NYMPHALINAE

soldier commodore/bosblaarvlerk   **no. 70: p. 64**
Wingspan: ♂ 42-47; ♀ 45-50 mm

The soldier commodore is a very distinctively marked butterfly with its brown base colour and curving semicircular orange bands on both wings. The hindwing has several ocelli parallel to the outer margin and touching the outer edge of the orange band. The underside has a 'dead-leaf' appearance, which includes a false 'midrib'. It characteristically settles on open pathways and roads, and relies on its camouflage to escape detection; when disturbed it flies up at the last moment, but usually settles close by, sometimes amongst dead leaves.

It occurs from Port St. Johns through the Natal coastal forests to the eastern Transvaal.
This butterfly was formerly known as *Precis terea elgiva*.
Larval host-plants: *Asystasia gangetica; Ruellia patula; Phaulopsis imbricata.*

Junonia tugela tugela (Trimen, 1879)   NYMPHALINAE

dry leaf; leaf commodore/Tugela-blaarvlerk   **no. 71: p. 64**
Wingspan: ♂ 55-60; ♀ 55-60 mm

Of all the southern African butterflies with 'dead-leaf' underwings, perhaps the aptly named 'dry leaf' is the most realistic. No two specimens are ever the same on the undersides. It possesses not only a false 'midrib', but a false 'leaf-stem' in its hindwing tails, and a false 'leaf-tip' in the extended and bent apex of the forewings. The upperside of the butterfly is dark brown with a broad semicircular orange band from the middle of the forewing costa to the inner margin of the hindwing. There is a small white spot near the apex of each forewing and a row of black dots down the middle of the orange band.

This species flies in the darker areas of its forest habitat, flying low and near to the ground. When it settles on the undergrowth it blends remarkably with its surroundings. Despite its camouflage, however, it is readily disturbed by the clumsy approach of a would-be collector and may fly off rapidly, sometimes high into the trees. It will sit under cut-aways in roads, often in large numbers. It is on the wing all year round, but the winter brood is more plentiful than the summer brood.

The dry leaf occurs in forested areas of Natal from Pietermaritzburg and Karkloof to Kranskop and Eshowe, as well as in most moist forests of the eastern Transvaal.
This species was formerly known as *Precis tugela*.
Larval host-plants: *Plectranthus* spp.; *Englerastrum scandens*.

Junonia octavia sesamus (Trimen, 1883)   NYMPHALINAE

gaudy commodore/rooi-en-bloublaarvlerk   **no. 72: p. 65**
Wingspan: ♂ 50-58; ♀ 55-60 mm

The sexes are virtually identical in this species, the female however having a larger abdomen and wingspan than the male.

The seasonal dimorphism exhibited by the gaudy commodore is so marked that for many years the winter and summer forms were thought to be two separate species (photographs **72a** and **72b**, page 65). Intermediate forms do occur, but are rarely caught (photographs **72c** and **d**). The summer form male (**72b**) is red above with a broad black margin which extends from the middle of the forewing costa round the outer margins of both wings to the anal angle of the hindwing. Parallel to this on both wings is a row of black spots. There is a suffusion of black at the base of both wings. The male of the winter form (**72a**), on the other hand, has a mainly violet-blue upperside with numerous black bands and lines and a row of large red spots parallel to the outer margins of the wings.

It is an easy species to breed, especially as food is readily available – one of its larval host-plants is the common garden flower *Coleus blumei* (the painted nettle). If the gaudy commodore is seen flying in a suburban garden planted with *Coleus*, the chances are that eggs or larvae will be found. The caterpillars are dark grey with spines on all segments of the body. Often a single female may be seen flying in a garden for days on end if suitable food-plants occur. In the natural situation, butterflies of the winter form may often be found congregating together for the night under rocky overhangs by the sides of roads and cliffs, presumably to reduce heat loss. Both seasonal forms play for hours on small koppies during the warmer part of the day.

On the wing all year round, it occurs in bushveld and on the fringes of forested areas from just west of Port Elizabeth in the eastern Cape northwards through Natal and Swaziland to the bushveld of the northern and eastern Transvaal.

This species was formerly known as *Precis octavia sesamus.*

Larval host-plants: *Coleus* spp.; *Plectranthus esculentus* ; *P. fruticosus* ('vlieëbos'); *Rabdosiella calycina.*

Junonia archesia (Cramer, 1779)   NYMPHALINAE

garden inspector/rotsblaarvlerk   **no. 73: p. 66**

Wingspan: ♂ 45-50; ♀ 52-60 mm

    As with the previous species, this is another of our butterflies in which the wet-season and dry-season forms differ markedly. Here again it is possible to believe that they represent two separate species. Both forms are dark brown overall, with a broad curving band across both wings from the forewing costa to the inner margin of the hindwing. In the wet-season (summer) form, however, this band is a light orange-brown, while in the dry-season (winter) form the band is light lilac on the forewing costa, shading to red and orange-red as it sweeps down to the hindwing inner margin. The winter form also has a series of whitish-blue spots parallel to the outer margin of the forewing; these are practically absent in the summer form. The wings of both forms are angular and scalloped and there is a tail-like projection from the outer margin of the forewing near the apex. The underside has the 'dead-leaf' appearance common to many species of this group.

    The garden inspector is found in the eastern areas of South Africa eastwards and north-eastwards from Knysna and Port Elizabeth to most of Natal and thence to the Transvaal bushveld and adjoining parts of the highveld.

This species was formerly known as *Precis archesia.*

Larval host-plants: *Coleus* spp.; *Plectranthus* spp.

Junonia oenone oenone (Linnaeus, 1758)   NYMPHALINAE

blue pansy; black pansy/blougesiggie   **no. 74: p. 66**

Wingspan: ♂ 40-48; ♀ 45-50 mm

    This is another of the familiar day-to-day butterflies in the eastern half of South Africa. It is a distinctive species, black overall but with a prominent large blue spot near the middle of the front part of each hindwing. The forewings have a broken white band from mid-costa to the middle of the outer margin and there are two or three white spots near the apex. In addition to the blue spot, the hindwings have three broken creamy-white lines running parallel to the outer margins. There are two small, inconspicuous, blue-centred, orange-red ocellate spots in each forewing and each hindwing.

    This butterfly is found on most hilltops within its distribution range during the warmer parts of the day. It settles on the rocks and bare ground and it is a common sight to see the males chasing each other off their territories. They settle frequently, their wings opening and closing slowly.

    The blue pansy occurs from the eastern Cape through Transkei and Natal to the Transvaal and Orange Free State. It is absent from the western Cape and the arid Karoo and north-western Cape. It flies throughout the year but is more common in the warmer months.

This species appears in some books under the name *Precis oenone oenone.*

Larval host-plants: *Asystasia gangetica; Barleria stuhlmannii; Adhatoda natalensis.*

Junonia hierta cebrene Trimen, 1870   NYMPHALINAE

yellow pansy/geelgesiggie   **no. 75: p. 67**

Wingspan: ♂ 40-45; ♀ 45-50 mm

    The yellow pansy is an easily recognized species. The base colour is black with bright orange and yellow patches on both fore- and hindwings, and a large blue-violet spot on each hindwing next to the costa. The underside is cryptically coloured in finely mottled light grey-brown, although there is a large orange patch on the forewing with a dark ocellate spot on its lower edge.

    This species is found all over the wetter eastern half of South Africa and extends to Cape Town along the south coast. It is absent from the Karoo, Namaqualand and the north-west Cape. Seldom found in large numbers, it tends to fly singly and may often be seen sitting on the ground sunning itself. Unlike the related *Junonia oenone* it seldom engages in 'hilltopping' (see page 18).

Whilst feeding on flowers it can easily be caught unawares, but given the slightest hint of a collector's presence it will keep ahead of the wildest chase. It also relies on camouflage, when with a quick movement it closes its wings to allow the grey-brown underside to blend into its surroundings.

This species appears in some books under the name *Precis hierta cebrene*.

Larval host-plants: *Adhatoda natalensis*; *Asystasia gangetica*; *Barleria pungens*; *Ruellia cordata*.

Junonia orithya madagascariensis (Guenée, 1865) — NYMPHALINAE

ox-eyed pansy; eyed pansy/padwagtertjie — **no. 76: p. 67**
Wingspan: ♂ 35-40; ♀ 40-45 mm

This is the third and last of our 'pansy' butterflies and the one with the most prominent ocelli. There are two on each wing, relatively large and red with dark spots in the centre and a black border. There is also a large blue patch on the hindwing which spreads to the inner angle on the forewing. This blue has a slight pink tinge if viewed in the sunshine and gives the ox-eyed pansy a place in the line-up of our most beautiful butterflies. The female is larger than the male and her blue markings are slightly less intense.

The ox-eyed pansy is found in the Orange Free State, eastwards to the Natal Midlands and north to the bushveld areas of the Transvaal. The collector often encounters it unexpectedly settled on roads and pathways in its preferred open thornveld habitat. It is a very elusive butterfly and is not found in large numbers – indeed, it appears to be extremely localized in its distribution. It is on the wing in all months of the year, particularly in the warmer areas.

This species appears in some books under the name *Precis orithya madagascariensis*.

Larval host-plants: *Hygrophila* spp.; *Englerastrum scandens*; *Plectranthus* spp.

Vanessa cardui (Linnaeus, 1758) — NYMPHALINAE

painted lady/sondagsrokkie — **no. 77: p. 68**
Wingspan: ♂ 40-45; ♀ 45-50 mm

The painted lady is the most cosmopolitan of all butterflies, occurring world-wide with the exception only of South America and Australasia. Its base colour is orange and the apical third of the forewing is black with several small white patches. There is an irregular broken black band from the basal end of the forewing costa across to the inner margin, and the outer margin is bordered in blackish-brown. The hindwing is mid-brown basally and orange towards the outer margin; there are three rows of black spots parallel to the outer margin. The underwings are cryptically and beautifully marked in orange, white, black and brown and there is a series of eye-spots parallel to the outer margin.

It is found in all parts of our country – even in arid Namaqualand – and in almost every suburban garden. On rare occasions it has been known to migrate in vast numbers, usually following population 'explosions'.

This species was formerly known as *Cynthia cardui*.

Larval host-plants: Many species of host-plant have been recorded, from families as varied as the Asteraceae (formerly Compositae), Boraginaceae, Urticaceae, Malvaceae and Fabaceae (formerly Leguminosae). Nettles of the genus *Urtica* and thistles of the genus *Carduus* are good examples of typical larval host-plants.

Antanartia hippomene hippomene (Hübner, 1806) — NYMPHALINAE

short-tailed admiral; yellow admiral/bosnooientjie — **no. 78: p. 68**
Wingspan: ♂ 42-45; ♀ 44-47 mm

The short-tailed admiral is basically brown above with a broad orange band bisecting the forewing obliquely from the mid-costa to the inner angle. The apical portion of the forewing is black with a scattering of small white spots. The hindwing is brown and has a broad orange band along the anterior half of the outer margin as far as the upper tail. Immediately posterior to this band, towards the anal angle, are two dark eye-spots. Each hindwing has two short pointed tails, the upper one being longer than the lower one. The underside is intricately and richly patterned in shades of brown and yellow and the upperside forewing band of orange is mirrored below in lighter orange.

The short-tailed admiral usually flies close to the ground. It suns itself on road edges but always remains alert and ready to dart back to the safety of the undergrowth. It is not an abundant butterfly in its forest habitat but is sometimes attracted to flowers in gardens adjacent to forested areas.

It occurs in the wetter forests of the southern and eastern Cape from Knysna and Grahamstown through Transkei to Natal. It flies throughout the year, but is more plentiful in autumn.

Larval host-plants: *Laportea peduncularis; Pouzolzia parasitica; Australina acuminata.*

Antanartia schaeneia schaeneia (Trimen, 1879)　　　NYMPHALINAE
long-tailed admiral/langstertbosnooientjie　　　**no. 79: p. 68**
Wingspan: ♂ 40-45; ♀ 45-49 mm

The long-tailed admiral is slightly larger on average than the short-tailed admiral and has considerably longer tails on its hindwing; the anal angle at the junction of the outer and inner margins is sharply pointed and also tail-like. The lower of the tails is shorter than the upper and is more sharply pointed. In colour pattern the two species are alike although the long-tailed admiral's hindwing eye-spots are perhaps less clearly visible and the orange border on the hindwing is narrower.

Like the short-tailed admiral, this butterfly species is very shy and wary, seldom flying high above the ground. It is found in the wetter forests of the eastern Cape from Kingwilliamstown and Bathurst north-eastwards through Transkei to Natal, and thence to the eastern Transvaal rain-forests.

It flies throughout the year, but is more abundant in the summer months.

Larval host-plants: *Laportea* spp.; *Boehmeria nivea; Pouzolzia parasitica.*

Lachnoptera ayresii Trimen, 1879　　　NYMPHALINAE
blotched leopard/vaalkolluiperd　　　**no. 80: p. 68**
Wingspan: ♂ 45-50; ♀ 50-55 mm

Although discovered at Pinetown in Natal in 1874, the blotched leopard is now scarce in this area. It is an orange butterfly with blackish markings along the edge of the forewing costa, a dark apex and a line of small dark spots parallel to the outer margin of the forewing. On both fore- and hindwings there are two thin black lines parallel to the outer margin, the outer line following the contour of the margin, the inner line clearly scalloped. The male has an obvious large grey scent-patch on the costal margin of the hindwing; the female has a black patch in almost the same situation.

Both sexes are robust on the wing and fly and glide around the edges of their rain-forest habitat. They are very elusive butterflies, and once danger from a collector's net has been sensed, they will fly rapidly into the trees for safety. The males select individual territories and ward off any male intruders who dare to enter their chosen areas.

The blotched leopard is on the wing all year round in most of the wetter forests from Port St. Johns in Transkei northwards to Natal (Eshowe, Karkloof, etc.); it also occurs in the Transvaal rain-forests.

Larval host-plant: *Rawsonia lucida* (forest peach).

Phalanta phalantha aethiopica (Rothschild & Jordan, 1903)　　　NYMPHALINAE
poplar leopard; African leopard/populierluiperd　　　**no. 81: p. 69**
Wingspan: ♂ 42-45; ♀ 45-47 mm

The poplar leopard is a widely distributed butterfly found in the wetter eastern half of South Africa; it occurs from around Bathurst in the eastern Cape north-eastwards through Transkei to Natal, the Transvaal and the northern Orange Free State.

The male and female are both orange with delicate black markings on both wings, including three black lines along the outer margins, the innermost line being boldly scalloped. The underside is streakily orange-brown and there is a prominent black spot near the inner angle of the forewing.

This butterfly, it seems, is always on the move; even when sitting on a twig or leaf it opens and closes its wings every few seconds. In flight it constantly changes its direction and height.

It is on the wing throughout the year but in colder areas is seen only during the warmer months.

Larval host-plants: *Populus alba* (white poplar – a naturalized alien); *Salix* spp. (willows); *Trimeria grandifolia* (wild mulberry); *Dovyalis rotundifolia* (dune sour-berry); *Maytenus* spp. (spike-thorns and koko-trees).

Libythea labdaca laius Trimen, 1879		LIBYTHEIDAE
snout butterfly/snuitvlinder; snuitskoenlapper		**no. 82: p. 69**
Wingspan: ♂ 43-48; ♀ 47-50 mm		

The snout butterfly is the only member of the genus *Libythea* and family Libytheidae in southern Africa. It is a small predominantly brown butterfly with somewhat angular wings – the apical area of the forewing being 'stepped' out from the outer margin. There are usually two or three small white dots in the apical angle and the centre of the forewing has orange streaks radiating out from the base. The hindwing has an oblique discontinuous orange band. The male and female are similar in appearance although the latter is browner and slightly larger.

It is essentially a woodland butterfly, preferring the moister eastern forests and coastal bush. Its habitat ranges from the Mbashe (Bashee) River in Transkei north-eastwards to Durban, Zululand and the eastern Transvaal. It is a strange creature in that it never seems to be consistent in its choice of habitat; one year it will be in abundance in a particular locality and the next year there will be no sign of it at all. It is usually seen sitting on a twig or branch, high out of reach of the collector. Often it flies off for no apparent reason, never to be seen again. Occasionally it may be found with wings closed on the bark of its larval food-plant tree.

It is on the wing from early December to the advent of winter.

Larval host-plant: *Celtis africana* (white stinkwood).

Alaena amazoula (Boisduval, 1847)		LYCAENIDAE
yellow Zulu/geel Zoeloe		**no. 83: p. 70**
Wingspan: ♂ 20-25; ♀ 25-28 mm		

This miniature version of a butterfly is a delight to observe with its orange ground colour and contrasting black wing-veins and outer margins. The black markings are heaviest at the apex and along the outer margins of the wings. The undersides are a lighter ochreous-yellow with the veins and outer margins narrowly and equally outlined in black. The male is slightly smaller than the female and its black markings are stronger.

The yellow Zulu inhabits rocky koppies where it may be found flying in and out of long grass, seldom more than one metre above the ground. Its flight is slow and weak and it seems to require considerable wing action to get from place to place. It rests for prolonged periods and is often reluctant to move even when disturbed. To find it, look down on to the grass, where it may perhaps be seen settled on a stem with its wings closed, looking like a small leaf. Its larvae feed on various species of lichen which grow on the rocks in suitable localities and the females will often be found close by, looking for a suitable rock on which to lay their eggs. The females appear to be scarcer than the males.

Small, localized colonies of *Alaena amazoula* inhabit the slopes of stony koppies from the eastern Cape to Natal, Zululand and the Transvaal. The race prevalent in the Transvaal has been described as a separate subspecies, *ochroma*; it is, however, very similar to the subspecies *amazoula* whose photographs appear on page 70. The map portrays the distribution of the species as a whole.

Larval host-plants: Various species of rock lichen.

Pentila tropicalis tropicalis (Boisduval, 1847)		LYCAENIDAE
spotted buff/spikkelgeelvlerkie		**no. 84: p. 70**
Wingspan: ♂ 32-34; ♀ 32-38 mm		

This variable small butterfly is a pale ochreous-buff colour above and below. The male has a fairly prominent broad blackish edge to the apex of the forewing but this may be less well developed in some specimens. There is a distinct black dot at the apical end of the forewing cell, a smaller one at the end of the hindwing cell and there may be other scattered spots on both wings. The females are generally less marked with black and may lack the apical black edge completely. In both sexes the undersides are finely and richly flecked and spotted with black.

The spotted buff is a very weak flier and seems to struggle to fly even against the slightest breeze. It is probably for this reason that it flies within the protected clearings of forest and coastal bush, seldom venturing into the open. When found, it is easily netted, but sometimes it flies at considerable heights beyond the reach of a net. Occasionally groups may cluster at the end of a small branch or twig, perhaps for courtship and mating.

It is found commonly along the coastal forests from Port St. Johns in Transkei northwards to Natal and Zululand and beyond to Mozambique. It is usually on the wing from October to May.

Larval host-plants: Various species of tree lichen.

Durbania amakosa Trimen, 1862   LYCAENIDAE

Amakoza rocksitter/Amakoza-klipsitter   **no. 85: p. 71**
Wingspan: ♂ 25-28; ♀ 28-35 mm

An inexperienced collector going to a known locality of the Amakoza rocksitter at the correct time of the year, may search and find nothing. If he should think, however, of the species' common name and then look very carefully at the rocks and boulders, his luck might change. For this variable little butterfly rests only on rocks and is also reluctant to fly. When it does fly, it does so weakly and for only short distances, flitting from rock to rock in search of a mate. It characteristically sits sunning itself virtually from the moment it emerges from the pupa.

The Amakoza rocksitter is a small dark-brown butterfly with a semicircular band of orange on each wing. In the males these tend to be reduced to curving series of orange dots, but in the females the orange markings coalesce to form a continuous broad band. The underside is rock-coloured – richly speckled in tiny brown and white dots with a lichen-like orange crescent on each forewing. The males are normally much smaller than the females.

Including the nominate race *D. amakosa amakosa* there are six subspecies of this variable butterfly currently recognized in southern Africa. The orange wing-bands vary in colour, shape and width with each subspecies. The subspecies portrayed on page 71 is *natalensis*. The wings in all cases are characteristically elongate and rounded.

The eggs are laid on rocks among lichen or in crevices and the larvae have specially adapted mouthparts for nibbling on lichen. They pupate on the side of the rocks, usually a few centimetres above soil level, concealed behind the grass which grows close by. The pupae are smooth but the hairy remnants of the last larval skin often remain, half-covering the pupa. From egg to adult, the entire life-cycle of this butterfly is spent on the rocks.

It occurs on mountain slopes amongst rocky outcrops from the Suurberg Mountains north of Port Elizabeth north-eastwards to the Natal Midlands, and from Pinetown and Pietermaritzburg northwards to the eastern Transvaal. It is on the wing from November to January.

Larval host-plants: Various species of rock lichen.

Durbania limbata Trimen, 1887   LYCAENIDAE

Natal rocksitter/Natal-klipsitter   **no. 86: p. 71**
Wingspan: ♂ 25-28; ♀ 32-35 mm

The Natal rocksitter has the same habits as the Amakoza rocksitter, spending its life associated with rocks on ridges and koppies. Although they are similar in general appearance, the Natal rocksitter is the darker species – almost black in fact – and the crescent-shaped bands on all four wings are blood-red in colour. The undersides again are richly covered with brown speckling and there is a reddish crescent-shaped band on each forewing; this band is bordered on the inside with black. The female is much larger than the male and, typical of the genus, the wings are elongate and rounded.

It flies later in the year than *D. amakosa* – in March and April as opposed to November, December and January – and is on the wing for only a month or so. It is confined to small colonies in the Natal Midlands above Balgowan and in numerous localities near Rietvlei between Mooi River and Greytown, sometimes sharing the same habitat with *Durbania amakosa*. I believe there are many more localized colonies of the Natal rocksitter in similar locations, waiting to be found by collectors who are prepared to venture away from the established collecting spots. Records also indicate that they occur occasionally in the hills and mountains around Harrismith in the Orange Free State.

Larval host-plants: Rock lichen.

Teriomima zuluana Van Son, 1949   LYCAENIDAE

Zulu buff/Zoeloegeelvlerkie   **no. 87: p. 72**
Wingspan: ♂ 23-27; ♀ 25-30 mm

This scarce lycaenid has only a few known localities in Zululand. It appears to be associated with gallery forest along certain rivers in Zululand (as well as on the shores of False Bay in the St. Lucia Game Reserve where the species was first discovered in 1930). Agricultural development and habitat destruction have severely affected this butterfly.

It is a small insect, butter-yellow above and below with rounded fore- and hindwings. The apices of the forewings in both sexes are black on the upperside and angular. On the underside of the butterfly there are fine black spots scattered along the edge of the forewing costa, round the apex and half-way down the outer margin, as well as along the edge of the anal angle of the hindwings.

It is a weak, slow flier and flies high amongst the trees, settling for long periods on tree-trunks where it typically opens and closes its wings. The eggs are laid on the lichen on the tree-trunks.

The Zulu buff is on the wing from October to May.

Larval host-plants: Tree lichens.

Baliochila aslanga (Trimen, 1873)   LYCAENIDAE

common buff/Natal-boomgeelvlerkie   **no. 88: p. 72**
Wingspan: ♂ 25-28; ♀ 26-30 mm

The common buff seems to be a gregarious butterfly and when conditions are right several can be taken in the same spot. It sits in small groups on bushes or on the low branches of trees although on occasion only solitary specimens are seen. It flies slowly and lazily in large circles, usually returning to the same branch.

It is mainly orange-yellow in colour, with rounded hindwings and forewings, and has a dark-brown area at the apex of the forewing. The male has further dark-brown markings along the forewing costa to the base but these are only just present in the female. The underside of the hindwing in both sexes is dark brown mottled lightly with orange and with a faint dark crescent-shaped band; the forewing underside is similarly brown but there is an extensive orange-yellow patch extending forward from the inner margin to the centre of the wing. When the butterfly is at rest on a tree-trunk this underside pattern renders it inconspicuous although it may give itself away by slowly opening and closing its wings.

The common buff is found in the coastal bush of Natal and Zululand and is on the wing during the warmer months of the year. Its eggs are laid singly or in clusters on lichens on the bark of trees.

Although the species name is usually spelt *'aslauga'*, Trimen originally used the spelling *'aslanga'*, which is the form followed here.

Larval host-plants: Tree lichens.

Cnodontes penningtoni Bennett, 1954   LYCAENIDAE

Pennington's buff/Pennington-boomgeelvlerkie   **no. 89: p. 73**
Wingspan: ♂ 24-27; ♀ 24-28 mm

Pennington's buff is rather similar in appearance to the common buff and has the same habits. It occurs in the coastal bush of Zululand and throughout the bushveld of the eastern Transvaal and parts of the northern and central Transvaal. It has a slow, weak flight and is easily netted. Although it is said to be rare, I believe it to be more common than some people think. Collectors, regrettably, have the habit of returning to the same collecting localities again and again and may be reducing certain local populations. In Zululand, where colleagues and I have found new collecting localities, Pennington's buff always seems to crop up in reasonable numbers.

It is the same colour and shape as *Baliochila aslanga*, both sexes being orange-yellow above with a dark-brown apical area tapering off along the edge of the outer margin of the forewing to the inner angle. There is also a dark-brown bar extending half-way across the forewing from the mid-costa. In *B. aslanga* the markings on the costa differ in extent between the sexes, but this is not the case with Pennington's buff. The underside of the forewing is similar to the upperside, but the hindwing underside is entirely mottled in brown with some orange.

This species is on the wing in the summer months from September to April.

Larval host-plants: Unknown – perhaps tree lichens.

Cyclyrius pirithous (Linnaeus, 1767)   LYCAENIDAE
common blue/gewone bloutjie   **no. 90: p. 73**
Wingspan: ♂ 23-26; ♀ 23-27 mm

The common blue was formerly placed in the genus *Syntarucus* along with four other southern African 'blues'. However, this complex genus has been surrounded with controversy for years and on its revision by Dr. L. Vári of the Transvaal Museum in 1986, *Syntarucus* was reduced to subgeneric level as a subgenus of *Cyclyrius*. The other four members of the group are *C. brevidentatus*, *C. pulcher*, *C. babaulti* and *C. jeanneli*. *Cyclyrius pulcher* (the 'beautiful blue') is distinctly different from the others, the male being of a lighter blue shade and the female having more white enclosed in the fore- and hindwings.

As far as the common blue is concerned, only the male is in fact blue, and then only on his uppersides. The female is dark blackish-brown with white-fringed black spots on the forewing and with a suffusion of blue at the bases of the wings. Both male and female undersides are attractively mottled in brown with whitish streaks and there are two eye-spots at the margin near the anal angle of the hindwing. These are associated with a flimsy antenna-like tail which projects from the margin between the eye-spots. When the wings are up and closed, the butterfly keeps its true antennae hidden and moves its hindwings gently back and forth. Potential bird predators are misled into believing that the 'eyes' and 'antennae' on the hindwings are the part of the butterfly to be seized – and the butterfly escapes with the loss of only a fragment of wing. (See also page 246).

The common blue can be found in all regions of South Africa and at all times of the year when conditions permit. It is not uncommon in suburban gardens as a result of the widespread ornamental planting of one of its larval food-plants, the blue-flowered *Plumbago auriculata*.

The name *Syntarucus telicanus* used in older publications is a synonym of *C. pirithous*.

Larval host-plants: *Plumbago auriculata* (plumbago); *Indigofera* spp.; the flowers or buds of lucerne; *Vigna* spp.; *Burkea* spp.; *Melilotus* spp.

Deloneura millari millari Trimen, 1906   LYCAENIDAE
Millar's buff/Millar-geelvlertjie   **no. 91: p. 73**
Wingspan: ♂ 32-35; ♀ 34-36 mm

Millar's buff! – a name to set the heart of any butterfly-collector aflutter. This elusive insect inhabits the coastal forests of Natal and Zululand and there are recent records from as far to the south-west as East London in the eastern Cape. Another subspecies, *D. m. dondoensis* is found in Mozambique.

My first specimen was caught a kilometre or two north of Umhlanga Rocks on the Natal Coast. It was an accidental find – with my net in one hand and a long stick in the other I was tapping branches when something orange and brown came out of the foliage; with a quick and lucky sweep of the net I had captured my first *millari*, a female. I returned to the same spot for many days thereafter but found no more. Several years later, whilst collecting with three friends on the flats on the eastern side of the Ubombo Mountains in Zululand, a similar incident occurred. When a branch of a tree was tapped, several Millar's buffs flew out. Within two minutes we had collected 19 specimens. In the following weeks these flats were visited again and again, and each time on the same tree more specimens of this unusual species were caught.

Millar's buff is similar to the common buff but larger. It is orange-brown above with the forewing costa and apex broadly bordered in dark brown to black. Both wings are rounded with an angular tip to the apex. The sexes are similar in size and colour although the female's forewing costa markings are a lighter brown than the male's. The upperside forewing markings are repeated on the underside except that the dark-brown markings are replaced by heavy brown speckling; the underside of the hindwing is entirely speckled in brown.

This species is on the wing from October to April.

Larval food: Uncertain. Some authorities claim the larvae feed on tree lichens, others that they are carnivores feeding on leaf-hoppers of the family Cicadellidae (formerly known as the Jassidae).

Lachnocnema bibulus (Fabricius, 1793)　　　　　　LYCAENIDAE

woolly-legs/wolpootjie　　　　　　　　　　　　　　**no. 92: p. 74**
Wingspan: ♂ 22-25; ♀ 22-26 mm

The woolly-legs is a small, dark, brown-grey butterfly, the male being unicoloured above and the female slightly lighter with diffuse white markings in the central areas of both wings. The undersides of the wings are cryptically coloured in various shades of brown in the male, and browns flushed with white in the female. Both sexes at rest with their wings folded vertically above them are very inconspicuous; the female in particular bears a strong resemblance to a bird-dropping! When settled, this species is easily recognizable by its small 'woolly' legs covered thickly with fine hairs.

This relatively common species occurs all along the eastern seaboard from Port Elizabeth through Transkei, Natal and Zululand to the bushveld of the northern and eastern Transvaal. It can be found flying in all months of the year but is more common in summer.

It may often be found flying in rapid circles about the tops of small bushes and trees, often in groups of five or six. It is not easily netted unless caution is exercised or unless it is caught unawares while sitting on the end of a branch or twig. The males are often found 'playing' on the tops of koppies.

The larvae of the woolly-legs are not vegetarian but carnivorous and have been recorded as feeding on plant-sucking bugs. They are also associated with ants.

Larval food: Plant bugs of the families Psyllidae (psyllids), Cicadellidae (leaf-hoppers) and Membracidae (tree-hoppers).

Thestor protumnus (Linnaeus, 1764)　　　　　　LYCAENIDAE

Boland thestor (subspecies *protumnus*)/Bolandskollie
Karoo thestor (subspecies *aridus*)/Karooskollie　　　　**no. 93: p. 74**
Wingspan: ♂ 28-37; ♀ 30-40 mm

There are 23 species of the genus *Thestor* presently recognized in southern Africa south of the Zambezi and Cunene rivers. They are rather drab butterflies as a group, with the dominating colours ranging from light orange to dark brown. Most of them are rather difficult to identify and the locality of origin of a specimen can often be of great assistance in finalizing an identification.

Thestor protumnus has two subspecies, each with its own common name; subspecies *protumnus* occurs in the south-west Cape, from Piketberg and Saldanha Bay to Franschhoek and Somerset West; subspecies *aridus* (photographs **93a** and **b**, page 74) occurs throughout the Karoo from Vanrhynsdorp in the west to Grahamstown in the east, and north to the Orange Free State. Males of both forms have a burnt-orange base colour with a broad border to the outer margins of the fore- and hindwings. The fringe of cilia (fine hairs) along the outer margins is chequered in white and brown. There are black spots on the outer half of the forewing and smaller spots on the hindwings of some specimens. The hindwing undersides are cryptically speckled in light brown with two faint brown bands; the forewing undersides are orange with a brown marginal band and black spots mirroring those on the upperside. The females are larger than the males, with more rounded wings; they also have more orange colouration and fewer black spots on the upperside of the forewing. Both sexes have very short antennae.

The flight pattern of *Thestor protumnus* is erratic and fast although the female is slower and more fluttery than the male. It seems to spend much of its time on bare patches of soil or small stones. Although it is alert and flies off at the slightest hint of danger, it often returns to the same spot afterwards.

The species is on the wing from September to early January.

Larval food: Apparently soft scale insects of the family Coccidae. In the later stages of larval development the larvae are associated with ants and may possibly feed as scavengers or on the immature stages of the ants. The full details of the complex life-cycle of this species have not yet been clarified.

Thestor brachycerus (Trimen, 1883)　　　　　　LYCAENIDAE

seaside thestor/strandskollie　　　　　　　　　　**no. 94: p. 74**
Wingspan: ♂ 28-33; ♀ 28-40 mm

The seaside thestor is a predominantly dark-brown butterfly with the fringe of cilia around the outer margins of both wings attractively chequered in dark brown and white – a characteristic common to most members of the genus. On the forewing there is an indistinct bar of fused black-

179

ish spots curving half-way across the wing towards the inner margin; on the basal side of this bar is a small greyish patch, more prominent in the female, and then another indistinct black spot. The hindwing has a similar indistinct crescentic row of contiguous blackish spots parallel to the outer margin but situated near the centre of the wing. The females are larger than the males, have more rounded wings and their markings tend to be more bold. As with all thestors, the undersides of the wings are cryptically patterned in light browns and greys with darker-brown spots. When the butterfly has settled and folded its wings it is almost indistinguishable from its background.

The seaside thestor flies weakly and slowly for short distances and is easily observed or netted. It is on the wing from late November to early February, often in large numbers. Its distribution range is restricted to the southern Cape coastal strip from Knysna in the east to around Stilbaai in the west.

Larval food: Unknown. The caterpillar is probably carnivorous – on plant-bugs – and is certainly associated with ants in its early developmental stages (see page 18).

Virachola diocles (Hewitson, 1869)   LYCAENIDAE

orange-barred playboy/skaduspelertjie   **no. 95: p. 75**
Wingspan: ♂ 24-32; ♀ 25-37 mm

The orange-barred playboy exhibits sexual dimorphism to a marked degree. The male has a bright orange hindwing, flushed with brown basally, and an orange patch extending into the centre of the forewing from the middle of the forewing inner margin; the rest of the forewing is black. The female is larger and is grey-brown in colour above. The outer margin of the male's forewing is straight, not curved, giving the wing an angular appearance. Both sexes have antenna-like tails on the outer margin of the hindwing near the anal angle; at the base of each tail is an eye-spot. The orange-barred playboy typically sits with its head down and its tail up, the false eyes and antennae encouraging would-be predators to attack the 'wrong end' (see also the common blue, page 178).

It is a coastal bush and forest insect, found from Port St. Johns in Transkei northwards through Natal to the forests of the eastern Transvaal. Its flight is rapid – particularly in the case of the male – and it tends to settle high in the trees and out of reach of collectors without extensions to their net-handles.

With experience and knowledge of their food-plants, one may readily find the larvae of the orange-barred playboy in the berries and fruits of the appropriate species. The female lays her eggs on the berries and seed-pods and the newly hatched larvae eat into the fruits and spend their larval life encased and out of danger, generally also pupating in the empty shells. Sometimes they walk off the food-plant, in which case they will pupate close to the fruits on nearby twigs and branches; captive-bred specimens in such circumstances will wander all over the inside of the breeding-box, seemingly distressed, not being able to find a convenient place to pupate. Here I have experimented by breaking some polystyrene 'foam' into small pieces and leaving it within the box. Remarkably, the larvae burrowed into the polystyrene to a depth of approximately 10 millimetres and pupated, leaving behind a small trail of polystyrene frass (faecal and other detritus). The polystyrene apparently passed through their alimentary tracts with no ill-effects. As their mouthparts are specially designed to nibble and chew through hard seed-pods, captive-bred larvae must be kept in boxes made of hard plastic. This species is unusual in that the metamorphosing butterfly in the pupa is able to produce a high-pitched squeaking noise when disturbed, by rubbing its harder parts against the pupal case.

Orange-barred playboys are on the wing throughout the year.

This species was formerly known as *Deudorix diocles*.

Larval host-plants: The seed-pods and fruits of *Bauhinia galpinii* (pride-of-de Kaap); *Millettia grandis* (umzimbeet); various *Acacia* spp.; *Baphia racemosa* (Natal camwood); *Prunus persica* (peach).

Virachola dariaves (Hewitson, 1877)   LYCAENIDAE

black-and-orange playboy/swart-en-oranjespelertjie   **no. 96: p. 76**
Wingspan: ♂ 23-25; ♀ 30-33 mm

The black-and-orange playboy is one of the rarer members of its genus in South Africa. It is similar to the orange-barred playboy, but smaller. The male is very distinct with its bright-orange hindwings bordered on the outer margins with a thin black line. The upperside of his forewing is jet-black and lacks the orange patch characteristic of *V. diocles*. The female closely resembles the female *V. diocles*, but is smaller and slightly darker brown. Both sexes have an antenna-like hair-tail near the anal angle of the hindwing, associated with an eye-spot to confuse predators.

It is generally considered to be rare and local, but it is also widespread and is found from the Natal forests and the coastal areas of Zululand, to Swaziland and the forests of the eastern Transvaal.

Black-and-orange playboys rest overnight on the lower branches of trees and bushes. As the day warms up, however, they play around the tops of the trees, often well out of reach of the collector's net, to descend again in the late afternoon. They are on the wing from September to April and May.

This species was formerly known as *Deudorix dariaves*.

Larval host-plants: The seed-pods of *Brachystegia* spp. have been recorded in East Africa; in South Africa the larvae presumably feed on the fruits and seed-pods of similar trees. They have been bred out in captivity on the berries of *Deinbollia oblongifolia* (dune soap-berry).

Virachola antalus (Hopffer, 1855)   LYCAENIDAE

brown playboy/bruin spelertjie   **no. 97: p. 77**
Wingspan: ♂ 25-28; ♀ 27-35 mm

This butterfly is the most common and widespread member of its genus in South Africa – and the least colourful. The male is dark brown, in fact resembling the females of the previous two species, and the female is a slightly lighter shade of brown with a suffusion of grey in the central areas of both wings. The undersides are a lighter brown with grey mottling. Both sexes possess the hair-like tails and eye-spots on the underside of the hindwings characteristic of this group of butterflies (see account for *V. diocles* on page 180).

The brown playboy is a fast and elusive flier and is most easily captured when feeding on flowers. Its eggs are laid on the outside of the seed-pods of several plant species. On hatching, the larvae gnaw their way inwards, feeding within the protection of the pod until they are ready to pupate; they may pupate within the pod or outside the pod. When larvae are found they can be collected for rearing, provided fresh seed-pods or fruits are available.

This species may be found flying throughout the year, but more so in the summer months. It occurs widely through South Africa and although it is absent from the more arid central Karoo and northern Cape it does occur also in Namaqualand.

This species was formerly known as *Deudorix antalus*.

Larval host-plants: The fruits and seed-pods of several species of plant including trees of the genera *Acacia*, *Schotia*, *Syzygium*, *Cassia* and *Prunus*. *Cardiospermum grandiflorum* (balloon-vine).

Virachola dinochares (Grose-Smith, 1887)   LYCAENIDAE

apricot playboy; red playboy/appelkoosspelertjie   **no. 98: p. 76**
Wingspan: ♂ 25-29; ♀ 25-32 mm

The apricot playboy is one of the commoner members of the playboy genus *Virachola* and like most of its congeners is strongly sexually dimorphic. The males have a beautiful orange-red ground colour above with a narrow black margin to the costa and outer margin of the forewing, widening at the apex. Both wings are suffused basally with brown. The females, like others of the genus, are a drab grey-brown, although when fresh they can exhibit a pinkish flush on the outer marginal area of the hindwing. Both sexes have a small lobe at the anal angle of the hindwing and an antenna-like hair-tail close to it. The undersides of the wings are mid-brown with a cryptic pattern of reddish streaks. There are two eye-spots on the underside of each hindwing on either side of the hair-tail (one on the lobe). The false eye-spots and false antennae are used to deceive predators (page 246).

Like other playboy species, the apricot playboy lays its eggs on the fruits and seed-pods of a wide variety of plant species from trees to herbs. In the fruits of two *Syzygium* trees off Stamford Hill Road in Durban, for example, I have found the larvae of *V. dinochares* year after year. They are easy to spot as they leave a tell-tale trail of frass adjacent to a small hole in the fruit. The larvae, when ready, crawl out of the fruit, and pupate in the bark of the tree; they often tunnel into the cork-like bark, reversing in and leaving only the top of the pupal case visible. They may also pupate within the pod or fruit where they have spent their larval life.

The species is on the wing throughout the year but is more abundant in autumn. It is found from Umkomaas south of Durban, northwards through the thorn- and bushveld of Zululand to the Transvaal.

This species was formerly known as *Deudorix dinochares*.

Larval host-plants: The fruits and berries of *Syzygium* spp.; *Acacia* spp.; *Combretum* spp.; *Prunus persica* (peach); *Vigna sinensis* (cow-pea).

Myrina silenus (Fabricius, 1775)   LYCAENIDAE

fig-tree blue/vyeboombloutjie   **no. 99: p. 78**
Wingspan: ♂ 30-35; ♀ 32-38 mm

The fig-tree blue is an enchanting butterfly fit to grace any collection. Fast-flying and elusive, it is fairly common and widespread. There are three recognized subspecies in southern Africa: *deserticola* is found in South West Africa/Namibia; *penningtoni* is found in Namaqualand from Citrusdal north to Springbok; and *ficedula* occurs from Graaff-Reinet in the eastern Cape eastwards through Transkei, Natal and Zululand to the Transvaal bushveld. The map shows the combined distribution ranges of the two South African subspecies.

The species is one of the most striking members of its family. The basal two-thirds of the upperside of the forewing are a metallic deep blue, bordered along the costa and across the wing to the inner angle with blackish-brown; the apical area and a broad strip along the outer margin, tapering to the inner angle, are chestnut-brown. The hindwings are similar but with more blue and less brown; the brown is confined to the margins and to the long, somewhat crooked tail which adorns each hindwing. The undersides have a 'dead-leaf' appearance and are orange- and chestnut-brown with a false 'midrib'.

The larvae are easy to find on the food-plants. On one occasion I found almost 100 larvae in about as many minutes on a *Ficus* hedge. Imagine my disappointment when, after careful feeding and rearing, I only obtained one adult! Parasites were the problem, and in the final stages one larva after another died with maggots of a parasitic fly emerging from their bodies.

Pupae can also be found at the bases of the trees on which they breed. Clear away the grass and leaves and search carefully at the base of the tree-trunk where larvae have been feeding; they will sometimes be found just under the surface of the soil surrounding the tree if it is dry and sandy. Fig-tree blues seem to prefer certain hedges and trees year after year. Finding the 'right' tree can be a problem, but once one is found it can be a source of supply of pupae for season after season.

In flight fig-tree blues are very fast and fly straight from one place to the next, seldom stopping to allow a collector to net them. They often gather on certain trees or koppies to play. This is usually the best place to net them – but be careful not to break their tails. They are on the wing in the warmer months from September to May.

The photographs on page 78 are of the subspecies *ficedula*.

Larval host-plants: *Ficus* spp. (figs) including *F. sur* (broom-cluster fig), *F. cordata* (Namaqua fig), and *F. pumila* (alien to South Africa).

Myrina dermaptera dermaptera (Wallengren, 1857)   LYCAENIDAE

lesser fig-tree blue/kleinvyeboombloutjie   **no. 100: p. 79**
Wingspan: ♂ 26-30; ♀ 30-34 mm

Although smaller than *Myrina silenus*, to my eye the lesser fig-tree blue is more beautiful. The forewing of the male is a lovely metallic turquoise basally with the costal margin and the outer half of the wings pitch-black; the hindwing is metallic turquoise with a broad black border to the costa, a narrow black border along the outer margin and a brownish-black band along the inner margin which continues on to the long, streamer-like tail. The female is larger than the male and has less extensive blue markings – indeed in some specimens the blue is almost obliterated by dark grey-brown; the 'black' on her hindwings has a brownish tinge. The undersides of both sexes are mid-brown and, unlike the fig-tree blue, there is no false 'midrib'.

The lesser fig-tree blue is a high-flying butterfly. On occasion several specimens will be seen playing and sunning themselves on the topmost branches of certain trees. It is scarce and local.

It is a well-known fact among collectors that the best specimens are obtained from pupae. Certain fig-trees will yield a 'harvest' from one year to the next and here again the trick is to find the right tree. 'My' tree was in Umgeni Road in Durban – a huge fig-tree with a circumference of perhaps six or seven metres and an estimated age of more than 100 years. I had driven past this tree many times and one day stopped on impulse to look for pupae. The first thing I spotted was a ball of old newspaper wedged into a crevice in the trunk of the tree; I pulled this out to look behind and found over 25 pupae in a hollow no larger than the palm of my hand, with perhaps 15 to 20 more in the folds of the crumpled newspaper! Over the next few days I collected many more pupae – not a moment too soon, for two weeks later the tree was felled and removed to allow for widening of the road.

Pupae can also be found in debris around the base of the tree-trunk. Both larvae and pupae may be found in association with ants (photograph **100b**, page 79).

This species has a more coastal distribution than the fig-tree blue and occurs from East London north-eastwards through eastern Natal and Zululand to Swaziland, the eastern Transvaal bushveld and the Soutpansberg.

It is on the wing throughout the year, but is more numerous in January and February with another major emergence in July and August.

Larval host-plants: *Ficus* spp. (figs), including *F. thonningii* (common wild fig).

Hypolycaena philippus philippus (Fabricius, 1793)   LYCAENIDAE

purple-brown hairstreak/persbruinstertbloutjie   **no. 101: p. 80**
Wingspan: ♂ 23-27; ♀ 25-30 mm

The purple-brown hairstreak is a small and delicate butterfly which exhibits a strong degree of sexual dimorphism. The male is a breathtakingly handsome little insect and when tilted to the right angle in the sunlight reflects a beautiful mauve sheen from almost the entire upper surface of his wings. The female is larger and has uniformly mid-brown forewings. Her hindwings are also brown but are lighter along the inner margin and carry two short rows of clear whitish blotches positioned parallel to the outer margin and near the anal angle. Both sexes have two hair-tails and two eye-spots on each hindwing near the anal angle. The underside pattern is cryptic, being light grey-brown with deeper-brown streaks over the wings roughly parallel to the outer margins. The eye-spots also appear on the underside and, as in the case of the playboys (see *Virachola diocles* on page 180), the combination of eye-spots and hair-tails is intended to deceive potential predators.

The flight of the purple-brown hairstreak is surprisingly slow as most butterflies with its wing shape are capable of rapid flight.

It is a common species, occurring from East London north-eastwards to Natal and Zululand, Swaziland and the Transvaal in coastal bush and bushveld. It is on the wing all year round but is scarce in the colder months.

Larval host-plants: *Clerodendrum glabrum* (resin-leaf); *Ximenia americana* (small sour-plum); the berries and fruits of numerous trees including *Deinbollia oblongifolia* (dune soap-berry).

Hypolycaena buxtoni buxtoni Hewitson, 1874   LYCAENIDAE

Buxton's hairstreak/Buxton-stertbloutjie   **no. 102: p. 80**
Wingspan: ♂ 23-27; ♀ 26-30 mm

Buxton's hairstreak is somewhat similar to the purple-brown hairstreak. The males are mostly mauve above with a suffusion of brown along the costal and inner margins of both wings; there is a fine white border around the margins of the hindwings. The females are often much larger than the males and are brownish-black above with a diffusely edged broad white band on the forewing (not quite reaching the costa) and two narrower white bands near the outer margin of the hindwing (again not reaching the costa). The female also has two eye-spots on the upperside near the anal angle of the hindwing. Both sexes have two long, thin and fragile hair-tails on each hindwing near the anal angle. The undersides of both sexes are white with fine brown lines running parallel to the outer margins. There are two eye-spots on each hindwing at the base of the hair-tails, used as in *Virachola diocles* (see page 180) to deceive predators into attacking the wrong end of the butterfly.

The hair-tails can be up to 10 millimetres long and great care must be taken not to break them during capture.

Buxton's hairstreak may be found flying in all months of the year, but more so in the spring and late summer. It occurs from Kei Mouth in the eastern Cape, north-eastwards through the coastal areas of Natal and Zululand to Mozambique.

Larval host-plants: Possibly the same as for the previous species, *Hypolycaena philippus*.

Hemiolaus caeculus caeculus Hopffer, 1855 — LYCAENIDAE

azure hairstreak/Venda-stertbloutjie — **no. 103: p. 81**
Wingspan: ♂ 27-30; ♀ 30-35 mm

The male azure hairstreak is a bright violet-blue above, with a narrow black band along the forewing costal margin, broadening out over the apex and continuing as a broad black band down the outer margin. There is a similar brownish-black broad band along the costal margin of the hindwing while the inner margin of the hindwing carries the broad brown wing folds which envelop the abdomen when the butterfly is at rest. The female is similar but the blue area is less extensive and paler, while the black is replaced by mid-brown. Both sexes have two circular dark spots on each hindwing near the anal angle. The undersides of both sexes are a light coffee-brown with several bold red streaks traversing the wings from top to bottom. These red lines are wider in the wet-season form and narrower in the dry-season form. There are two hair-tails on each hindwing in both sexes; the one at the anal angle is thicker than in the previous species. The hair-tails and eye-spots are used to deceive predators (see *Cyclyrius pirithous*, page 178).

This species inhabits open bush, savanna and woodland in the dry and arid parts of the eastern Transvaal and is abundant in the foothills of the northern parts of the Soutpansberg. Specimens have also been collected on occasion in northern Natal and Swaziland.

It flies weakly, spending much of the day fluttering in and out of the small bushes on which it breeds. This environment makes it a difficult insect to catch and great care must be taken to avoid ripping the collecting-net. The azure hairstreak is on the wing throughout the year, the autumn broods often being the more abundant.

This species was formerly known as *Iolaus caeculus*.

Larval host-plant: *Olax dissitiflora* (bastard sour-plum).

Stugeta bowkeri (Trimen, 1864) — LYCAENIDAE

Bowker's tailed blue/Bowker-stertbloutjie — **no. 104: p. 81**
Wingspan: ♂ 30-34; ♀ 32-36 mm

There are three described subspecies of this beautiful butterfly in South Africa. The nominate race, *S. bowkeri bowkeri*, extends from Namaqualand and the northern Cape across the Karoo to the eastern Cape, Transkei and Natal (but is absent from the south-west Cape); subspecies *henningi* occurs in the southern Transvaal and Orange Free State; and subspecies *tearei* occupies the remainder of the Transvaal. The distribution range of the species as a whole is provided on the accompanying map. The photographs on page 81 are of the nominate subspecies.

Male and female Bowker's tailed blues are similar although the females are slightly larger. The forewing is pale blue above, although the blue is suffused with white towards the outer margin. There is a narrow black border to the costa broadening along the outer margin, the black extending irregularly into the wing from the apical area. The hindwing is also largely blue, the black being concentrated at the junction of the costa and the outer margin, although there is also a narrow black border to the outer margin (fringed with white cilia). There are three dark spots and two hair-tails at the anal angle of each hindwing. The undersides of both sexes are light brown and white and are traversed by irregular red-brown bands; there are two eye-spots at the anal angle of each hindwing, used as in the common blue, *Cyclyrius pirithous* (page 178), to deceive predators (see also photograph **104d** on page 81).

This rather variable lycaenid tends to sit within the branches of small trees and shrubs where it flits tantalizingly from branch to branch, making an impossible target for the collector; many a net has been torn in frustration in the pursuit of Bowker's tailed blue.

Its eggs are laid on the undersides of the leaves of the larval food-plant. The larvae tend to 'plough' through the surface of the leaves, leaving a small tell-tale trail behind them. In the later stages of development the larvae are very difficult to detect; they eat out a section of the leaf and then fill the resulting space with their bodies, fitting snugly against the eaten edge of the leaf. On completion of the larval phase, they trek down the trunks of the trees to pupate. They are masters of disguise and the pupal cases normally assume the exact colour of the bark to which they are attached; if lichen or moss is present, the pupal cases will match their colours. Pupation usually takes place within one metre of the ground, and the larvae will sometimes leave the tree-trunk to pupate on blades of grass close by.

Bowker's tailed blue is on the wing all the year round but is more plentiful in the warmer months from August to April.

This species was formerly known as *Iolaus bowkeri.*

Larval host-plants: *Ximenia caffra* (large sour-plum); various species of mistletoe of the families Loranthaceae and Viscaceae including *Moquiniella rubra, Tapinanthus oleifolius,* and *Viscum rotundifolium.*

Iolaus silas Westwood, 1852   LYCAENIDAE

sapphire/saffier   **no. 105: p. 82**

Wingspan: ♂ 30-34; ♀ 32-36 mm

The aptly named sapphire would truly be the jewel of any collection. Both male and female are extraordinarily beautiful and attract immediate attention both in the wild and in the collector's cabinet. The males are a bright metallic-blue above with a black apical area on the forewing which extends as a broad border along both costa and outer margin. The hindwing costa and outer margin are also bordered in black and the inner margin wing folds and a small patch near the base of the costa are brownish. There are two red spots near the anal angle. The female's blue colouration is tinged with violet and is less extensive than the male's because of the proportionately larger size of her dark-brown (not black) apical patch. There is a suffusion of white in mid-wing between the blue and the dark brown. Her hindwing costa is light brown and the outer margin is narrowly black, bordered on the inside with an orange band. Both sexes have two hair-tails on each hindwing.

The underside of this species, however, provides a dramatic contrast to the upperside: it is snow-white. A thin red stripe crosses the hindwing from the costa to the anal angle, parallel to the outer margin, broken and black as it approaches the single eye-spot at the anal angle. The undersides of the hair-tails are dark like the antennae. Although these white undersides might seem to be imprudently conspicuous, the sapphire is remarkably well camouflaged when at rest on a glossy leaf.

The sapphire is seldom found in large numbers, and is often seen playing about the tree-tops; long net extensions are usually required for a capture when it is on the wing.

Its pupae and larvae are easily found on the mistletoes which are its food-plants. Larvae in the early stages are however difficult to detect. They seem to 'plough' through the leaf, gathering on their backs the fluff from the leaf's surface and thus acquiring effective camouflage. In the later developmental stages they are easier to find. They pupate on the tops of the leaves or on twigs, and the pupae look very much like brown or green mistletoe berries.

The sapphire may be found on the wing in all months of the year in the warmer regions. It is found in coastal bush, woodland and forests from Addo and Somerset East in the eastern Cape northeastwards to Natal and Zululand, Swaziland and most of the Transvaal bushveld.

This species is listed in some publications as *Argiolaus silas.* The subspecies *silarus* formerly assigned to *I. silas* has recently been raised to species rank in its own right.

Larval host-plants: *Phragmanthera usuiensis; Moquiniella rubra; Erianthemum dregei.* (All are semiparasitic mistletoes of the family Loranthaceae).

Iolaus pallene (Wallengren, 1857)   LYCAENIDAE

saffron; scarce sapphire/geelsaffier   **no. 106: p. 83**

Wingspan: ♂ 35-38; ♀ 37-42 mm

Members of the genus *Iolaus* are, for the most part, iridescent blue butterflies; the exception is *Iolaus pallene,* the saffron, whose alternative English common name – 'scarce sapphire' – is rather misleading as there is not a vestige of blue on its wings. It is a very beautiful species nonetheless, the male being a rich butter-yellow above and the female a slightly lighter yellow. Both sexes have a thin black border to the outer margins of both wings. The forewing apex is tipped with greyish black and the hindwing anal angle is flushed with a light pink-red. The undersides of both sexes are also rich yellow with narrow black borders to the outer margins and a deeper ochreous flush to the anal angle of the hindwing. A long black line traverses the forewing from mid-costa and there is a much shorter black line parallel to it in the basal area. A similar black line traverses two-thirds of the hindwing from mid-costa, almost meeting a short black line from the midpoint of the inner margin at right angles. Both sexes have two long black hair-tails on each hindwing.

This butterfly is not easily located, but in recent years more and more colonies have been discovered, usually in association with its larval host-plant, the large sour-plum. The pupae are greyish brown and angular and are disguised to match the background of the twigs and branches to which they are attached; they are also found on grass-stems at the base of the host-plant. Like the previous species, the larvae eat out troughs in the leaves and lie in them; they are very difficult to detect.

Saffrons are on the wing in spring and summer, generally flying in thick bush habitats, somewhat more slowly than other *Iolaus* species. They occur from Zululand around Lake Sibaya northwards to the Transvaal Lowveld and the western and northern Transvaal north of Pretoria. The species is fairly common in Mozambique.

Larval host-plant: *Ximenia caffra* (large sour-plum).

Iolaus sidus Trimen, 1864   LYCAENIDAE

red-line sapphire/rooistreepsaffier   **no. 107: p. 83**
Wingspan: ♂ 25-28; 30-33 mm

The red-line sapphire is not unlike the sapphire (species 105), especially in the case of the female. The male is a metallic pale blue in colour above, with almost half the forewing taken up by a large triangular black patch covering the apical area. The hindwing is also blue, with a brown patch on the costa near the base and a narrow black line along the outer margin bounded by a fringe of white cilia; the wing fold along the inner margin is grey-brown and there are two indistinct eye-spots near the anal angle. The female is larger than the male, her upperside is a lighter blue, and she has a black apical area extending along both the outer margin and costa of the forewing as a broad band; the hindwing also has a broad brown band along the costa, extending down the outer margin and culminating in two reddish eye-spots near the anal angle.

Both sexes have two long fine hair-tails on each hindwing and a third much smaller tail half-way along the outer margin. The undersides of both sexes are whitish with an orange fringe of cilia on the outer margin of the forewing and a narrow red bar extending half-way across the wing from the costa towards the inner angle. There are two red stripes on each hindwing forming a 'V' with its 'arms' on the costa and its point close to the two red-and-black eye-spots near the anal angle.

The species occurs in coastal bush and inland thornveld from around Great Fish Point in the eastern Cape to Transkei, Natal and Zululand, and further north to Swaziland, Mozambique and Nelspruit in the Transvaal. It is not uncommon, but the East London area in particular is favoured by collectors.

It tends to occur in localized colonies where its larval host-plants are in abundance and it is easily netted when settled low down or when feeding. In the main, however, it is usually a high- and fast-flying insect, the males often engaging in 'hilltopping' (see page 18). Its pupae and larvae may readily be found on its food-plants – various species of mistletoe. Like others of the genus, the larva of the red-line sapphire leaves tell-tale markings on the leaves on which it is feeding. Its pupae are often found on the surface of these leaves, or in the axils of the leaves and stems of the food-plant. Adults may be found on the wing throughout the year.

Larval host-plants: *Englerina woodfordioides*; *Moquiniella rubra*; *Tieghemia quinquenervia*; *Tapinanthus oleifolius*; doubtless also other species of mistletoe of the family Loranthaceae.

Iolaus mimosae mimosae Trimen, 1874   LYCAENIDAE

mimosa sapphire/doringboomsaffier   **no. 108: p. 84**
Wingspan: ♂ 24-27; ♀ 25-28 mm

One of our soft and gentle-looking butterflies, the mimosa sapphire is a light powder-blue in colour, the female being a slightly lighter blue than the male and a little larger in size. Both sexes have an extensive black-brown apical area which extends almost half-way across the forewing and continues along the costa and outer margin as a broad band. The uppersides of the hindwings of both sexes are also light blue, with grey-brown wing folds along the inner margin. Both sexes have three indistinct eye-spots and two hair-tails on each hindwing near the anal angle, used as in *Cyclyrius pirithous* (page 178) to deceive predators. The underwings in both sexes are a light grey-brown with two narrow dark red-brown stripes traversing both wings parallel to the outer margins; there are also two small eye-spots, one rather indistinct, on each hindwing near the hair-tails.

It is a frustrating insect to net, as it plays endlessly within the branches of the trees upon which its food-plant grows semiparasitically – usually thorny acacias ('mimosa') but often the alien syringa or Persian lilac. It may occasionally fly out but will immediately dart into another tree close by. I have found that when its mistletoe larval host-plant is in bloom, the females are busy laying; here the eggs and larvae can be found easily and, if taken together with a small clump of the mistletoe (but see page 248), can easily be bred through to the adult form. The mistletoe, unfortunately, does not last well if the container is poorly ventilated; extra material, however, can be kept wrapped in the 'crisper' compartment of a refrigerator. Regrettably, the larvae of several *Iolaus* species tend to be cannibalistic, a trait I have found to be particularly pronounced in the mimosa sapphire. When breeding this species it is therefore advisable to keep only one larva per container.

The species is on the wing in the summer months and is found from the Transvaal, south through Swaziland, Zululand and Natal to East London and the eastern Karoo as far west and as far inland as Graaff-Reinet. Suitable habitats, however, are few and far between and are determined by the presence of the mistletoe host-plant for the larvae to feed on.

Larval host-plants: Mistletoes of the family Loranthaceae, including *Moquiniella rubra.*

Iolaus aphnaeoides Trimen, 1873 LYCAENIDAE

yellow-banded sapphire/geelstreepsaffier **no. 109: p. 85**
Wingspan: ♂ 24-27; ♀ 27-31 mm

The yellow-banded sapphire is a rare and local butterfly confined to the eastern Cape and Transkei from Grahamstown and the Amatola Mountains to Port St. Johns. Earlier records from Natal have now been assigned to *I. diametra natalica.* It is associated with woodland habitats.

This attractive small 'blue' is heavily marked with black. The basal half of the male's forewing is metallic light blue but the rest of the wing is black, extending as a marginal band along both costa and outer margin. The hindwing is also blue but has a broad black band extending from the costa along the outer margin and there is a narrow black band bisecting the wing from mid-costa to the anal angle. The female is slightly larger than the male and the blue on her forewing shades briefly to white as it approaches the black band on the outer margin. She also possesses a black band which bisects her hindwing; the area to the basal side of this band is blue, but the area to the outer marginal side is white. Both sexes possess two hair-tails on each hindwing and a third tail-like projection half-way up the outer margin; there are also ocellus-like spots at the anal angles of both upperside and underside. As with related lycaenids these features are intended to deceive predators (see page 246, bottom).

The undersides are similar in both sexes and unmistakable, being white with four distinctive orange bands on each wing, spaced across the wing at equal intervals from the outer margin. There is a row of black dots bordering the band on the outer margin. The undersides of species 110, *I. diametra natalica,* are very similar but the two species can be readily distinguished as explained in the text for *Iolaus diametra* below.

From available records the yellow-banded sapphire appears to be on the wing only in the summer months.

Larval host-plants: Mistletoe species of the family Loranthaceae, formerly assigned to the genus *Loranthus* but now known as *Tapinanthus prunifolius* and *Actinanthella wyliei.*

Iolaus diametra natalica Vári, 1976 LYCAENIDAE

Natal yellow-banded sapphire/Natal-geelstreepsaffier **no. 110: p. 84**
Wingspan: ♂ 25-28; ♀ 25-30 mm

The Natal yellow-banded sapphire is very similar to the yellow-banded sapphire *I. aphnaeoides* and until only a few years ago was thought to be the same species. The differences between the two are very slight – the black on the upperside of the Natal yellow-banded sapphire spreads a little more towards the bases of the wings and there is a little more white in the forewing of the female. Noticeable too, is the striping on the underside which is orange-yellow compared with the richer orange of the yellow-banded sapphire. More detailed differences are also evident: for example, on the underside anal angle of the hindwing of the yellow-banded sapphire there is a single, short, fine black line which runs for a little way from the anal angle eye-spot parallel to the inner margin; in the case of the Natal yellow-banded sapphire this is a double line. This is clearly shown in photograph **110b** (page 84) and photograph **109** (page 85).

It occurs from mid-Natal northwards through Zululand in coastal bush, and also in woodland as far inland as Weenen. It may be found flying in all months of the year but is more abundant in the summer.

Larval host-plant: *Actinanthella wyliei* (family Loranthaceae).

187

Iolaus alienus alienus (Trimen, 1898)   LYCAENIDAE

brown-line sapphire/bruinstreepsaffier   **no. 111: p. 84**

Wingspan: ♂ 30-35; ♀ 32-38 mm

The brown-line sapphire is one of the larger members of its genus. It has characteristically elongated metallic-blue forewings with a larger black apical area extending as a broad
black band along both costa and outer margin. The hindwings are similarly banded in black along the
outer margin and costa, and in grey-brown along the wing folds of the inner margins. The females are
larger than the males, are paler blue and have a broken blue line in the brown band along the outer
margin of the hindwing. Both sexes have two antenna-like tails on the hindwing, the upper short and
hair-like, the lower one (at the anal angle) slightly more substantial than is usual in this genus. There is
a single eye-spot associated with these tails on the upperside of the hindwing (the female's eye-spot
being the more elaborate), and two on the underside. These eye-spots and the false 'antennae' are
used as in *Cyclyrius pirithous* (page 178) to deceive predators.

The undersides of the brown-line sapphire are different from those of all other *Iolaus* in South Africa
and are grey with a light-brown border on the outer margins; even when fresh, the undersides of this
species appear 'worn'. Apart from the two eye-spots near the tails, there is another near the hindwing
costa, one on the forewing costa and one on the forewing inner margin.

This butterfly is generally only netted in the late afternoon. It appears to fly only after 2 p.m. and
males may then be found on small koppies and hilltops where they settle frequently on the twigs and
branches of trees. Females are scarce and more frequently encountered on the lower slopes of hill-
ocks; they are not often caught.

Brown-line sapphires are on the wing from August to November (although there is a record for
May) and are found from northern Zululand to Pretoria and the eastern Transvaal.

Larval host-plants: Mistletoes of the family Loranthaceae.

Iolaus aemulus aemulus Trimen, 1895   LYCAENIDAE

short-barred sapphire/wegkruipertjie   **no. 112: p. 85**

Wingspan: ♂ 23-25; ♀ 25-27 mm

As in the brown-line sapphire, the male and female short-barred sapphire are almost alike, with a metallic-blue background colour and with the apical half of the forewing black-
brown. The females, however, are whitish-blue rather than blue towards the outer margins. There are
three dark spots on the uppersides of each hindwing on the outer margin near the anal angle, associated with the two antenna-like hair-tails characteristic of the sapphires (see *Cyclyrius pirithous*, page
178, and also photograph **112b** on page 85). Its undersides are pure white with a red line along the
outer margin of both wings, inside of which is a row of small black dots; on the forewing there are two
red bars projecting at right angles from the costa on the forewing and extending half-way across the
wing towards the inner margin. On the hindwing a red bar from the mid-costa meets another from the
inner margin near the anal angle in a V-shape. Although the underwing pattern of this species is similar
to that of *I. diametra natalica* and *I. aphnaeoides* the bars are much narrower.

The short-barred sapphire is found only in the coastal bush from East London to Durban. It used to
be fairly common but with the destruction of much of its habitat it has become scarce in recent years.
Nevertheless with careful searching it can be found, usually in association with trees carrying the larval
food-plant.

It breeds on mistletoes of the family Loranthaceae, the red-flowered *Tieghemia quinquenervia* having been identified with certainty. The best time to look for larvae and pupae on the trunks of the host
trees is once the flowers fall, perhaps around June and July. The pupae are small and extremely difficult to find, each one adapting itself perfectly to the colours of its environment. The adults usually
emerge in the middle of November, depending on the conditions in which the captive pupae are kept.
The species is usually on the wing from November and December through to March.

Larval host-plant: *Tieghemia quinquenervia.*

Aphnaeus hutchinsonii Trimen, 1887

Hutchinson's highflier/silwerrokkie
Wingspan: ♂ 27-35; ♀ 35-40 mm

LYCAENIDAE

no. 113: p. 85

Strikingly beautiful both on its upper- and undersides, Hutchinson's highflier is a bright metallic-blue above but with a large black apical patch extending across more than half of the forewing and a broad black edge to the costa and outer margin of the hindwing. The black apical area carries several small white spots. There are two tails on each hindwing, the lower tail at the anal angle being much longer than the short stubby tail on the outer margin just above. The undersides are extraordinarily attractive, being olive-brown with a number of large silver spots, each edged in black and dark red; there is a small eye-spot on the anal angle of the hindwing.

Hutchinson's highflier is found from the Estcourt district of Natal to Zululand, Swaziland and to the bushveld areas of the Transvaal. It is fond of flying and playing above the trees on the tops of small koppies and is not easy to capture unless the collector is equipped with extensions to his net. It is on the wing from early September to early November. The females are very scarce.

The life-cycle of this species is not as yet fully recorded. The larval food-plants probably include various species of acacia, the larvae reportedly boring into and living within the soft pith in the twigs and smaller branches. Recently it has been reported that the larvae associate with ant colonies, a habit shared by many other lycaenids.

Larval host-plants: *Acacia* spp. including *Acacia robusta* (splendid thorn; brack thorn).

Spindasis natalensis (Westwood, 1852)

Natal barred blue/Natal-streepvlerkie
Wingspan: ♂ 25-29; ♀ 28-32 mm

LYCAENIDAE

no. 114: p. 86

The 'barred blues' of the genus *Spindasis* acquire their name from the bars in the apical area of the forewing and sometimes the hindwing. The Natal barred blue has a blue background colour above with broad brown-black margins to the costa and outer margins of both fore- and hindwings. The apical half of the forewing is orange with two broad black bars, the bar nearer the apex traversing only half-way across the orange suffusion. Although the sexes are similar, the female is larger and darker than the male and has a whitish suffusion to the blue zones. Both sexes possess two hair-like tails on each hindwing and the hindwings are lobed at the anal angle. The undersides of both sexes are light yellow and are crossed by several broad, dark, reddish-brown bars each of which has a diffusely margined gold stripe up its middle; when viewed under a hand lens, this stripe looks like gold leaf reflecting in bright sunlight. There is a prominent eye-spot on the underside of each hindwing at the anal angle. *Spindasis natalensis* form *obscura* occurs as a variant of this species in the Natal and eastern Cape portions of its range; in this form the orange apical patch is obscured by a suffusion of black scales to a greater or lesser degree.

Like other lycaenids with hair-tails, the Natal barred blue tends to sit and rest with its head down and its tails up. The hindwings are then slowly and alternately rubbed over each other, the eye-spots and tails resembling a moving 'head' and 'antennae'. This defensive ploy diverts the attention of potential predators away from the true head of the insect. In photograph **114b** (page 86), however, the specimen is sitting with its head upwards. (See also page 246).

Its flight is extremely rapid and it darts from one position to the next, seldom giving the collector a chance to net it. When feeding on flowers, however, its defences seem to drop altogether and it may be easily captured. A word of warning: the rapid fluttering of its wings in the net can reduce them to shreds in a few moments – particularly the fragile tails; remove them as soon as possible.

The larvae live in hollowed-out tubes formed by ants eating out the pith inside a stalk of the host-plant, and later emerge to pupate on the bark of the host-plant. There is a very clear association with ants in this species, the ants obtaining a honey-like exudate from glands on the larva's back. In captivity it is recommended that this constant flow of fluid is soaked up regularly with blotting paper as it provides a fertile breeding-ground for disease if ants are not present to remove it.

The Natal barred blue is on the wing all year round and occurs along the east coast from Port Alfred in the eastern Cape north-eastwards to Natal, and from there to the Orange Free State and the Transvaal. It prefers woodland or coastal forest habitats and, unlike *S. mozambica*, the males engage in 'hilltopping' on high ground or above tall trees in the heat of the day (see page 18).

Larval host-plants: *Canthium inerme* (turkey-berry); *Mundulea* spp.; *Clerodendrum glabrum* (the resin-leaf).

Spindasis mozambica (Bertolini, 1850)   LYCAENIDAE

Mozambique barred blue/Mosambiek-streepvlerkie   **no. 115: p. 86**
Wingspan: ♂ 22-25; ♀ 25-28 mm

To the casual observer, the Mozambique barred blue and the Natal barred blue could be one and the same species. Indeed, for a description of the upperside of *S. mozambica* the reader is referred to the account for *S. natalensis* (page 189). The undersides, however, provide the key to the separation of the two species. The background colour of the underside of *natalensis* is pale yellow; in *mozambica* it is a richer golden-yellow. Each band on the underside of *natalensis* is reddish-brown with a gold-suffused midline band within it; in the case of *mozambica* the bands are orange-yellow with black edging on the outsides and sometimes a very narrow golden line along the midline.

The females are larger than the males and the outer margins of their wings are slightly rounded, not straight as in the males. Both sexes have two hair-tails to each hindwing.

Although similar in appearance to the Natal barred blue, the Mozambique barred blue in fact has different habitat requirements, preferring grassy slopes or more open bush. The males do not apparently 'hilltop' (see page 18) as a rule although *natalensis* males do. They are also slower on the wing than *natalensis* and are easily netted. They often sit high on the longer grass stems, from which vantage-points they engage in territorial battles with other butterflies.

This species is absent from the Cape and occurs in grassland environments in Natal and Zululand and in certain bushveld areas in the eastern and northern Transvaal. It is on the wing during the summer months.

Larval host-plant: *Sphenostylis angustifolia* (wild sweetpea).

Spindasis ella (Hewitson, 1865)   LYCAENIDAE

Ella's barred blue/Ella-streepvlerkie   **no. 116: p. 86**
Wingspan: ♂ 21-24; 25-30 mm

Ella's barred blue is smaller than the previous two species but is much the same in appearance. The black markings on the upper surface of the forewings, however, are less intense and could be described as brownish-black. Nevertheless the easiest way to distinguish this species from its relatives is to look at the black bands in the orange area of the forewing: instead of having more or less straight or gently curving edges, they have noticeably kinked and irregular edges. The undersides of the wings are similar to those of *natalensis* but slightly darker. Like other *Spindasis* species Ella's barred blue has two hair-tails on each hindwing and an eye-spot on the underside next to the anal angle. (The defensive function of these features is described under *S. natalensis* on page 189; see also photograph **116b** on page 86).

It is a fast-flying and alert species and spends much of the day flitting about the tree-tops, alighting on a selected twig and returning to the same spot after short flights. It is fond of 'playing' about the tops of small koppies and appears to enjoy chasing other butterflies.

It occurs in bushveld, thornveld and savanna habitats from around Kuruman in the north-east Cape through the northern and western parts of the Orange Free State to the Transvaal, Swaziland and the northern half of Natal. It is on the wing mainly in the summer months but there is certainly a winter emergence in the warmer areas of northern Natal.

Larval host-plant: Ant-attended larvae have been reported in galls found on acacia trees; the lepidopterist C. Dickson suggests that they emerge at night to feed on the acacia leaves.

Chloroselas pseudozeritis pseudozeritis (Trimen, 1873)   LYCAENIDAE

brilliant gem/skitterjuweeltjie   **no. 117: p. 87**
Wingspan: ♂ 20-24; ♀ 20-24 mm

The male brilliant gem is a small butterfly with a brilliant steel-blue colouration, tinted with a pink-blue sheen on the hindwing. The blue, however, is a 'structural' colour and can only be seen if observed at the correct angle (see page 8, top). In photograph **117** (page 87), for example, the brilliant gem belies its name and appears almost uniform brown in colour. The female has a more rounded forewing outer margin and is grey-brown with a fine dusting of blue near the base of both wings. The undersides of both sexes are copper-brown, spotted all over with silvery dots ringed in black. There are two small hair-tails on each hindwing and an eye-spot at the anal angle on both upperside and underside; these are used as in other lycaenids to deceive potential predators (see page 246).

Many of the known localities of this butterfly in South Africa seem to have been destroyed, either by sugar-cane or pineapple plantations. It has never been common but has been found from time to time in small localized colonies. I believe, however, that many colonies still await discovery by collectors, particularly in the vast open lands of Zululand on the eastern side of the Ubombo Mountains and especially in the drier thorn-tree areas. Pennington recorded occasionally seeing numbers of brilliant gems circling around the tops of two or three adjacent trees.

It is on the wing from September to March and ranges from the Bathurst district of the eastern Cape northwards to Natal and Zululand and thence through the bushveld of the Transvaal to Zimbabwe.

The brilliant gem occurs extralimitally north to Kenya; the subspecies occurring in South Africa is *C. pseudozeritis pseudozeritis.*

Larval host-plant: Not yet recorded for the nominate subspecies *pseudozeritis* in South Africa, but in Kenya the larvae of the subspecies *tytleri* were found associating with ants on the tropical African *Acacia seyal* (formerly *A. stenocarpa*).

Desmolycaena mazoensis (Trimen, 1898) LYCAENIDAE

purple gem/persjuweeltjie **no. 118: p. 87**
Wingspan: ♂ 20-24; ♀ 22-25 mm

The purple gem is another species which I believe is more widespread than is commonly thought. It is a small butterfly and is possibly overlooked or mistaken for one of the more common butterflies of the genus *Anthene*, the undersides of which are much the same.

The male is deep blue above but there is a strong purple sheen to the greater part of the wings which can be seen when the light strikes it at a certain angle; photograph **118** (page 87) was taken from above and consequently the male appears to be almost uniform brown. The costa and apex of the forewing and the costal and inner margins of the hindwing lack the iridescent purple and are plain brown. The female is grey-brown with a faint sheen of pink and blue in the base of the wings. The undersides in both sexes are cream-coloured and speckled with black-and-silver spots, with a chequered effect around the outer margins. There is a hair-tail at the anal angle of each hindwing.

The species occurs from northern Zululand through Swaziland to the Transvaal Lowveld, appearing to prefer thornveld savanna. It is on the wing from September to April, but is perhaps more abundant in November. On occasion males engage in 'hilltopping' (see page 18).

Larval host-plants: Various *Acacia* spp.; the larvae possibly feed on the young flower-buds.

Axiocerses tjoane (Wallengren, 1857) LYCAENIDAE

common scarlet/ralierooivlerkie **no. 119: p. 87**
Wingspan: ♂ 22-27; ♀ 26-30 mm

The common scarlet is a common but often localized species which has until recently been known as *Axiocerses bambana.*

The sexes are markedly dissimilar, the male being bright red with the apical half of the forewing black-brown, as also the inner angle and the costal margin; blackish markings intrude into the red from the mid-costa and the basal portions of both wings are suffused with black scales. The outer margin of the hindwing is narrowly bordered in blackish-brown and the anal angle is lobed and has a narrow pointed tail. The female on the other hand is predominantly orange with a broad dark-brown band along the outer margin of the forewing and a narrower band along the costa. Both wings are spotted with blackish dots, the outer dots on each wing tending to be marshalled into rows parallel to the outer margin. The undersides of both sexes are similar, the forewings being orange and the hindwings deep copper, both wings being dotted with black-edged golden spots which are larger on the forewing.

Common scarlets often fly together in large numbers, usually around small thorny bushes, where they feed and play together with other butterflies. When settled they rub the hindwings slowly together, leaning the body alternately to left and right; this behaviour is intended to deceive predators (see page 246, bottom). They are very alert and fast on the wing, but can be easily netted when feeding.

They are on the wing in all months of the year and occur from Port Elizabeth north-eastwards through Transkei to Natal and Zululand, Swaziland and the bushveld of the Transvaal.

Larval host-plants: *Acacia* spp.

Axiocerses amanga (Westwood, 1881)   LYCAENIDAE

bush scarlet/bosrooivlerkie   **no. 120: p. 88**
Wingspan: ♂ 25-28; ♀ 27-30 mm

The males of the bush scarlet and common scarlet are similar, but the wings of the former are more angular and the red colouration is slightly tinted with orange. The male bush scarlet also has less extensive black-brown markings on the apical half of the wing and no black or brown blotches on the red area near the forewing costa. The hindwing is red with dark brown at the base and a narrow fringe of dark brown along the costal and outer margins. The wing-veins are outlined in blackish-brown to a greater or lesser extent. The female resembles the male but is more orange and the black zone around the apex is less extensive. Both sexes have a slightly lobed anal angle to the hindwing and a short tail. The underside of the hindwing is a deep copper; the forewing is more orange and carries several black-edged silver spots basally. A good distinguishing feature is the short white blaze along the basal edge of the forewing costa on the underside; this shows clearly on photograph **120a** (page 88). It is broader than the similar blaze of *A. tjoane*.

The bush scarlet is seldom found in large colonies. It is fast on the wing and very wary when approached, but it is, however, often attracted to flowers on small bushes where it can easily be netted. As in other butterfly species, the males are fond of sitting on the twigs of bushes from which vantage-points they chase off any butterflies which intrude into their air-space.

This species is found in Natal and Zululand northwards to the Transvaal; it prefers open thornveld country and may be found on the wing in all the months of the year, although it is scarcer in the winter.

Larval host-plants: *Ximenia americana* (small sour-plum); *Ximenia caffra* (large sour-plum).

Leptomyrina hirundo (Wallengren, 1857)   LYCAENIDAE

tailed black-eye/langstertswartogie   **no. 121: p. 88**
Wingspan: ♂ 18-21; ♀ 18-26 mm

Although the tailed black-eye's colouration is not particularly spectacular, this small butterfly is in fact easily recognizable both at rest and on the wing. The male's uppersides are almost uniformly dark grey, but for a single white-edged black spot in the inner angle of the forewing and a series of around five similar spots on the outer margin of the hindwing, increasing in size towards the anal angle. The female is slightly larger and more grey-brown in colour. Both sexes have a single exceptionally long and twisted hair-tail on each hindwing at the anal angle. The undersides of both sexes are whitish with a number of narrow golden-brown curving bars; towards the outer margins these bars coalesce to form two parallel broken lines. There is a black spot in the inner angle of the forewing and two black spots near the hair-tail on the anal angle of the hindwing.

The tailed black-eye is slow in flight and, as it flies about its succulent food-plants, the white undersides seem to flash, giving the impression of a small slow fire-fly.

It breeds on several species of succulents and where these are found in suitable localities, this butterfly usually abounds. Small white eggs are laid on the undersides of the leaves and the minute larvae, when they emerge, burrow into the leaf and spend their lives feeding between the upper and lower surfaces of the fat and succulent leaf. When one leaf is 'empty', the larvae merely burrow into the next, only emerging ultimately to pupate on the underside or in a concealed place close by; sometimes they pupate within the shrivelled leaf. Ants are usually in attendance on the larvae to obtain 'nectar' from the dorsal glands. The eggs and larvae are easy to find and virtually any common garden succulent will be accepted as food. Perfect specimens of the tailed black-eye are a wonderful sight with their delicate scales looking as soft as velvet.

It is a coastal species, preferring the open thorn country where it flies in the shade of trees close to the ground, usually not far from its larval food-plants. It occurs from around Uitenhage and Cookhouse in the eastern Cape, north-eastwards through Natal and Swaziland to the eastern Transvaal; it is rather rare and local in the latter province. The tailed black-eye can be seen on the wing all year round but more so in the hotter months.

Larval host-plants: Succulent plants of the family Crassulaceae including some *Kalanchoe* spp., *Cotyledon* spp. and *Crassula* spp.

Gonatomyrina lara (Linnaeus, 1764)   LYCAENIDAE

Cape black-eye/Kaapse swartogie   **no. 122: p. 89**
Wingspan: ♂ 20-28; ♀ 22-30 mm

The Cape black-eye is a species almost entirely restricted to the Cape Province, from Port Nolloth on the Atlantic seaboard near the mouth of the Orange River south to Cape Town and eastwards to East London; it also occurs in the mountains of Lesotho and in the inland districts of the Cape. The sexes are similar, both being a rich brown colour above, with a prominent white-edged black eye-spot in the inner angle of the forewing and a smaller, fainter spot immediately above it. On the hindwing there are three white-edged black eye-spots on the outer margin up to the anal angle. The ciliate fringes along the outer margins of both wings of both sexes are sometimes chequered in white and brown. The undersides are cryptically mottled and speckled in grey and brown and there are three white-edged black eye-spots on the outer margin of the forewing increasing in size up to the inner angle. There are no eye-spots on the underside of the hindwing. The hindwings are lobed at the anal angle but there is no tail.

This species is on the wing mostly during the summer months, but can be seen in all months of the year when conditions are suitable.

The eggs are laid on several species of *Cotyledon* and other succulents of the family Crassulaceae; one can be confident that where these various food-plants are found, so too will the butterfly be discovered. Seldom flying higher than a metre above the ground, it is easily netted. A common habit of the Cape black-eye is for it to sun itself with wings outspread. It is often found in gardens.

This species was formerly known as *Leptomyrina lara*.

Larval host-plants: Succulents of the family Crassulaceae, including *Kalanchoe lugardii* (in tropical Africa) and *Cotyledon* spp.

Gonatomyrina gorgias gorgias (Stoll, 1790)   LYCAENIDAE

common black-eye/gewone swartogie   **no. 123: p. 89**
Wingspan: ♂ 20-28; ♀ 22-30 mm

Transkei and Natal gardeners who find their succulent cotyledons being eaten will probably discover the culprits to be the larvae of the common black-eye, *Gonatomyrina gorgias*. It is well worth the sacrifice of a few leaves, however, to have this elegant insect as a regular visitor to one's garden. This small butterfly closely resembles the Cape black-eye both on the upper and lower sides, but is larger and has a pearl-like sheen to the uppersides, particularly in the male. The female common black-eye has more rounded outer margins to her wings than the male, which has distinctly angular, straight-sided wing margins.

Although widespread, the common black-eye is seldom found in great numbers although one or two seem to inhabit every garden with suitable host-plants, laying their eggs on the fleshy leaves of cotyledons in particular. I have even observed a female laying eggs on a small fleshy plant growing in a window-box on the eighth floor of a block of flats in a built-up residential area. It is in fact rather easily bred from eggs. The leaves should be removed from the plant together with the eggs and placed flat in a sealed container; when the larvae hatch they will burrow into a leaf and live between the upper and lower surfaces. Make sure fresh leaves are always readily available. When the larvae are ready to pupate, they will often do so within the leaf itself although they may also leave the leaf and attach themselves to the sides of the container.

In the Transvaal, butterflies formerly assigned to *G. gorgias* have been re-assigned to the very similar *G. henningi*. As all three *Gonatomyrina* species look so much alike, an identification may perhaps be best made on a geographical basis, *G. lara* occurring from the west to the east Cape, *G. gorgias* from Transkei to Natal and *G. henningi* in the Transvaal and northern Cape. The common black-eye may be found on the wing in all months of the year but is commoner in summer. The map shows the combined distribution ranges of *G. gorgias* and *G. henningi*.

This species was formerly known as *Leptomyrina gorgias*.

Larval host-plants: Many and varied, but in the main various species of *Cotyledon* and *Kalanchoe* in the well-known succulent family Crassulaceae.

Capys alphaeus (Cramer, 1777)   LYCAENIDAE

protea scarlet; orange-banded protea/suikerbossie   **no. 124: p. 90**
Wingspan: ♂ 32-36; ♀ 40-45 mm

Two subspecies of the protea scarlet are presently recognized. The nominate race, *C. alphaeus alphaeus*, occurs in the western Cape from the Citrusdal area south to Cape Town and east to Port Elizabeth, following the fynbos vegetation zone associated with the winter rainfall climate of the western Cape; it is the race portrayed on page 90. The subspecies *extentus* occurs in the summer rainfall regions from the Amatola Mountains of the eastern Cape through Transkei to inland Natal and thence to the eastern and central Transvaal.

It is a distinctive, large and robust species, brown-black in colour and with a large orange-red patch in the middle of each wing; on both fore- and hindwings these patches meet the inner margin. The fringe of cilia around the outer margin of each wing is distinctively chequered in black and white. The undersides are cryptically patterned in greys and browns with an orange patch in the centre of each forewing and an irregular band of white-edged coalesced dark spots across the centre of the hindwing. The female is usually larger than the male and has more rounded wings.

Subspecies *extentus* is in part distinguished from subspecies *alphaeus* by the greater amount of red on the wings; the red is also paler and more orange in hue.

Although this butterfly seems to prefer hilltops where it lays its eggs in young protea buds, it will also frequent flat veld as long as proteas are found there. Larvae and pupae can be found in the protea-heads, where the tell-tale hole excavated by the larvae provides an excellent clue to its presence inside; the larva pupates inside the protea-head and the adult eventually emerges from the exit-hole prepared by the larva. When this species is bred in captivity, the protea-heads should be kept in breeding cages with plenty of ventilation, and checked daily for newly emerged adults.

The protea scarlet is normally on the wing from September to March, but can be observed throughout the year in the Cape Peninsula when conditions permit.

Larval host-plants: *Protea cynaroides* (king protea); *P. repens* (real sugarbush); *P. nitida* (wagontree); *P. roupelliae* (silver sugarbush); other *Protea* species.

Capys penningtoni Riley, 1932   LYCAENIDAE

Pennington's protea/Pennington-suikerbossie   **no. 125: p. 90**
Wingspan: ♂ 32-35; ♀ 38-40 mm

Pennington's protea provides a good example of a restricted and local species. It was discovered in 1929 amongst the hills and koppies west and south-west of Pietermaritzburg and is believed to be entirely confined to this limited area of the Natal Midlands.

It is a dull-orange butterfly with a narrow dark-brown border on the forewing costa, broadening at the apex and along the outer margin. There is a narrow dark-brown border on the outer margin of the hindwing. The basal areas of the wings are suffused with brown. The sexes are alike although the female is larger than the male. Although it is not dealt with separately in this field guide, it is perhaps worth noting that the male of the related species *C. disjunctus* closely resembles Pennington's protea; the female *disjunctus*, however, is grey-brown and quite unlike the male. *Capys disjunctus* occurs from the Transkei through Natal to the Transvaal (including Johannesburg). The undersides of Pennington's protea resemble those of the previous species, the protea scarlet, but are darker and the orange of the forewing is barely developed (compare photographs **125e** and lower **124**, page 90). The cilia along the outer margins of the wings are chequered in black and white.

Larvae and pupae may be found in the same way as those of the protea scarlet and perfect adult specimens can be obtained by gathering the protea buds in which they are feeding – but with due consideration for the law of the land (see page 249, top) – and breeding them out in captivity. Like other members of this genus, the males will 'play' on koppies and hilltops during the hotter parts of the day. Females are scarce, or at least rarely encountered, and are usually found on the lower slopes either on or around the larval food-plant. For a number of years it was feared that this species might have become extinct but fortunately it was recently rediscovered in other localities in the Natal Midlands and many fine specimens have been obtained, chiefly by rearing the larvae.

The species is on the wing from September to March.

Larval host-plant: The buds of *Protea caffra* (common sugarbush).

194

Phasis thero (Linnaeus, 1764)   LYCAENIDAE

foxtrot copper; silver-arrowhead copper/jakkalsdrafkopervlerkie
Wingspan: ♂ 35-40; ♀ 42-48 mm   **no. 126: p. 91**

The foxtrot copper was one of the first butterflies to be discovered in the Cape. Several different 'varieties' of what were thought to be this species were subsequently recorded and two of these have in recent years been raised to species rank. The foxtrot copper is now recognized as consisting of two subspecies: the nominate subspecies *thero* (photographs page 91) occurs in the south-west Cape, the Peninsula and along the southern Cape coastal areas to Grahamstown in the eastern Cape; subspecies *cedarbergae* was named from the Cedarberg Mountains near Citrusdal.

The sexes of this very attractive and rather variable large lycaenid are similar, both being brown above with seven or eight large orange spots scattered over the forewing. The hindwing uppersides have two faint black spots at the anal angle and may have a row of small orange marks along the anal end of the outer margin. Both fore- and hindwings have slightly scalloped outer margins and there are two short pointed tails to each hindwing. The undersides are grey-brown with a large orange area in the basal part of the forewing and a characteristic and prominent silver hook-shaped bar in the centre of the hindwing; the forewing has several black spots with silver-dotted centres and the hindwing has scattered black-edged silver bracket-shaped markings in addition to the hooked bar.

Its flight is typical of the genus, notably fast and undulating, particularly, for example, when it is observed flying around the taller bushes among the sand-dunes in the western Cape coastal areas. When it settles on a twig it must be approached carefully, as it is alert and can readily escape the net.

It has been recorded on the wing from August to December with a second brood in March and April; odd individuals have also been recorded in January and February. The larvae are ant-attended as in many other lycaenid species and live in tunnels in the stems of the food-plant; they also pupate in the hollowed-out stems.

Larval host-plants: *Rhus* spp. (wild currants); *Melianthus major* (honey-flower).

Tylopaedia sardonyx (Trimen, 1868)   LYCAENIDAE

king copper/koningkopervlerkie   **no. 127: p. 91**
Wingspan: ♂ 35-40; ♀ 40-45 mm

This large and striking copper occurs throughout the arid Karoo of the Cape Province and extends into the southern Orange Free State; it is absent from the coastal areas of the Cape. Two subspecies are recognized: *T. sardonyx sardonyx* occurs over the greater part of the species' range but is replaced by *T. sardonyx peringueyi* in Namaqualand. The photographs on page 91 are of the subspecies *sardonyx*.

The male is orange above with a broad black band along the outer margin, widening at the apex and the inner angle. Another irregularly edged black band crosses the forewing from the costa to the inner angle and there is a small black patch at mid-costa. The scalloped outer margin of the hindwing is bordered narrowly with black and there is a large triangular black patch at the junction of the costa and outer margin whose point extends more or less into the middle of the wing. There is a short pointed tail at the anal angle. The female tends to be a duller orange than the male and her black markings may be reduced in extent. The underside of the forewing in both sexes is orange-brown with a series of black-bordered silver spots in a line parallel to the costa and grouped subapically, or sometimes, as in photograph **127b** (page 91), forming a short line parallel to the apical portion of the outer margin. The hindwing underside of the subspecies *peringueyi* is uniform copper-brown, but in subspecies *sardonyx* (photograph **127b**) there are usually two short white streaks at right angles to the costa and one long white streak in mid-hindwing parallel to the outer margin.

King coppers are found singly along gullies or near rocky outcrops, more commonly those which are west-facing. They can fly very rapidly but may be captured when they settle to feed on such flowers as mesembryanthemums. Sometimes small colonies are found inhabiting a particular locality, where they may be encountered year after year. Females are not found as easily as the males, but both sexes indulge in 'hilltopping' on koppies during the hotter parts of the day (see page 18).

The king copper is on the wing from August to March, but is more abundant in the earlier months from September to November.

Larval host-plant: Unknown.

Argyraspodes argyraspis (Trimen, 1873)　　　　　　　　LYCAENIDAE

large silver-spotted copper/silwerkolkopervlerkie　　　**no. 128: p. 91**
Wingspan: ♂ 30-35; ♀ 35-40 mm

　　　　This large and striking lycaenid is predominantly orange above with broad dark-brown outer margins widening on the forewing at the apex, and on the hindwing at the curve where the costa and outer margin meet. The outer margins have a ciliate fringe chequered boldly in dark brown and white. The females are larger than the males, but otherwise the sexes are similar. There are two short tails to each hindwing. The undersides of this species are unmistakable with bright silvery spots and blotches scattered over both fore- and hindwings, but larger and more numerous on the latter. The background colour of the hindwing underside is dark brown, while that of the forewing is orange and brown like the upperside forewing except that the orange shades to yellow near the inner margin. The male's wings are angular, the female's rounded.

　　　　An alert and fast flier, this butterfly tends to keep just one step ahead of the collector, settling frequently on the ground or on low vegetation. When settled it slowly rubs its hindwings together, a mannerism it shares with many other lycaenids – but somewhat inexplicably as it has no eye-spots to deceive predators and its tails are short and stubby.

　　　　The large silver-spotted copper is found all over the Karoo, Namaqualand and the southern Orange Free State. Koppies and mountain-tops are favourite haunts during the hotter parts of the day. Later in the afternoon they may be found patrolling along the lower slopes of ridges and hills, where they are easier to net.

　　　　They are on the wing from August to April, depending upon the prevailing weather conditions in its arid habitat.

Larval host-plant: Unknown.

Anthene definita definita (Butler, 1899)　　　　　　　LYCAENIDAE

common hairtail/donkerkortstertjie　　　　　　　　　　**no. 129: p. 93**
Wingspan: ♂ 25-28; ♀ 25-28 mm

　　　　There are 21 species of hairtail of the genus *Anthene* in southern Africa. A characteristic of the genus is the presence on each hindwing of either two or three short tails made up of tufts of fine hair, hence the common name. They are small butterflies and the males are usually uniform brown or blue above. The common hairtail is typical of the group, the male being dark purple above with a narrow darker margin to both wings. It does not have a prominent coloured spot at the upper-side anal angle as does *Anthene amarah* (photograph **131a**, page 92), but in some specimens two black spots may be visible (photograph **129a**, page 93). The female is quite different above, with a silvery-blue suffusion to the basal halves of the wings, shading to whitish in the outer half. There is a squarish brown spot in mid-wing near the forewing costa and a row of similar brown spots parallel to the broad brown band along the outer margin; the hindwing is similarly patterned but the outer margin carries a row of faint whitish oval marks and near the anal angle a black spot bordered on its inner edge with orange. Both sexes have three hair-tail tufts on each hindwing and, while the male's outer margins are straight-edged, the female's are rounded. The male's undersides are grey-brown with a series of darker bars edged with off-white parallel to the outer margins; the female is similar but with the background shading to off-white on the outer half of the wings. Both sexes have two dark spots near the anal angle, the larger one being noticeably orange-edged on its inside margin.

　　　　The common hairtail ranges widely from the south-western Cape eastwards along the coastal districts to Natal and Zululand, and north to most of the Transvaal. It flies from ground level to the tops of the tallest trees and is often found in large numbers darting swiftly about and playing along the slopes of hills, particularly where there is water or damp ground. It may be found on the wing in all months of the year when conditions permit.

Larval host-plants: Many and varied, which probably accounts for the species' widespread distribution range. *Acacia* spp. (including several alien Australian species); *Albizia* spp.; *Schotia* spp.; *Kalanchoe* spp.

Anthene lemnos lemnos (Hewitson, 1878)　　　　　　LYCAENIDAE

large hairtail/grootkortstertjie　　　　　　　　　　**no. 130: p. 92**
Wingspan: ♂ 26-30; ♀ 26-30 mm

The large hairtail closely resembles the common hairtail but is slightly larger. The males are again a uniform dark purple above with very narrow black margins, while the females differ from the common hairtail in having no row of brown spots on the forewing; they also have less blue and more white on the hindwing. The undersides of the two species are similar, but the large hairtail has a row of three white-edged dark spots in the basal area of the hindwing and a further spot half-way along the hindwing costa; although these spots are grey-brown in the male and only slightly darker than the background colour, in the female they are conspicuously dark brown. There are three hair-tail tufts on each hindwing. The male's wings have straight-edged outer margins; the female's are more rounded.

Anthene lemnos is a shade-loving, rapid-flying species. Its flight, however, is not sustained for long and it can be netted fairly easily. The males often frolic and chase each other in the tree-tops.

It has a restricted distribution in South Africa, being found only in the coastal bush of Natal and Zululand (and north into Mozambique). It may be found flying in all months of the year but is more abundant in the warmer months.

Larval host-plant: *Erythrococca berberidea*.

Anthene amarah amarah (Guérin-Méneville, 1849)　　　　LYCAENIDAE

black-striped hairtail/swartstreepkortstertjie　　　　　**no. 131: p. 92**
Wingspan: ♂ 20-24; ♀ 22-25 mm

The male of the black-striped hairtail is light brown above with a beautiful golden sheen; the outer margins have a very narrow dark-brown border, fringed on the outside with delicate white cilia. Parallel to the hindwing outer margin is a row of faint whitish circular marks ending near the anal angle in a black spot which has an orange border on its basal angle. There are only two hair-tufts on each hindwing at the anal angle (compare with *A. definita* and *A. lemnos* which have three). The female is similar to the male but is marginally larger, has a rounder outer margin to her forewing and is mid-brown above rather than light brown. The undersides of both sexes are yellowish-brown with a series of whitish and light-brown bars arranged approximately in lines parallel to the outer margin. The underside of the hindwing, however, also carries several white-edged black spots basally and along the costa, as well as two black spots near the anal angle, bordered on the inside with orange. The key identifying feature of this species, however, is the triangular black wedge on the underside of the forewing, extending from a point at the base of the wing to almost half-way along the inner margin; this may be seen, although partly obscured, in photograph **131b** (page 92).

Dozens of specimens are often found flying together, feeding from the flowers of acacia trees. The males are territorial and chase off any intruders with rapid flight, returning to carefully selected perches on twigs high up in the trees. The females, however, seem more sedate and fly slowly about in the grass, resting and feeding from flowers below the trees.

The black-striped hairtail is on the wing all year round, although more plentifully in the warmer months. It is widespread in South Africa and is found from Swellendam in the southern Cape, eastwards and north-eastwards through Natal and Zululand to the Transvaal bushveld.

With careful searching, the larvae can be found among the open flower-buds on various species of acacia. They are often attended by ants which 'milk' their honey-glands.

Larval host-plants: Various species of acacia, including *Acacia karroo* (sweet thorn).

Anthene butleri livida (Trimen, 1881)　　　　　　LYCAENIDAE

pale hairtail/vaalkortstertjie　　　　　　　　　　**no. 132: p. 93**
Wingspan: ♂ 24-27; ♀ 23-27 mm

The pale hairtail is probably the most common member of its genus — which has 21 representatives in southern Africa. It is found throughout the eastern half of South Africa and is absent only from the north-western Cape, Namaqualand, Bushmanland and the south-western Cape.

The males are mid-brown tinged with grey above and have a silver-blue suffusion extending outwards from the base of the hindwings. The females are larger than the males, have more rounded wings and have a stronger suffusion of blue. When fresh, the wings of both sexes reflect a light sheen.

Like *Anthene amarah amarah* both males and females have a single black eye-spot on the outer margin of the upperside of the hindwing near the anal angle, bordered on its inside edge with orange. An indistinct series of light-edged spots, bolder in the female than the male, extends in diminishing size along the outer margin from the eye-spot. There are two small orange-bordered black eye-spots at and near the anal angle where there are also two inconspicuous short hair-tufts. In general, the undersides are pale brown mottled with darker and lighter brown streaks running parallel to the outer margins; there is a small but distinct dark spot on the costa of the hindwing near the base.

Wherever lycaenid butterflies 'frolic' and gather together, males of the pale hairtail will almost certainly also be there as active participants, particularly on hilltops and in mountainous areas but also around trees in savanna country.

The eggs, larvae and pupae can usually be found readily in town gardens or in the wild, associated with succulent plants of the genus *Cotyledon*.

The eggs are small and white and are mostly laid at random on the undersides of the thick fleshy leaves into which the larvae 'plough' or burrow. They usually pupate on the undersides of the leaves, or very occasionally on the plant stems, often low down on the plant.

Larval host-plants: *Kalanchoe crenata*; *Cotyledon* spp.

Cacyreus lingeus (Stoll, 1782)
bush blue/bosbloutjie
Wingspan: ♂ 25-28; ♀ 25-28 mm

LYCAENIDAE

no. 133: p. 94

The male bush blue is a uniform dull blue above, slightly darker basally, and has a largely white but partly brown ciliate fringe to the outer margins of the wings. The female is brownish with a suffusion of violet-blue basally and a series of whitish markings on both wings near the outer margins; she also has a white patch with a dark cross-bar at the apical end of the forewing cell. Near the anal angle of the hindwing there is a light-edged black spot, lacking in the male; both sexes have a single hair-tail at the anal angle. The undersides of both sexes are cryptically patterned with irregular brown patches on a white background; these are more diffuse on the hindwing. There is a dark spot associated with the hair-tail and a less conspicuous spot in the anal angle.

Its flight is irregular and usually slow and it may often be seen hovering or zigzagging over small plants and shrubs. Damp, muddy patches attract it, and it feeds directly on the moisture in the soil. It is found in the wetter forests and wooded areas along the coastal zone of South Africa from the southwest Cape to Natal and parts of the Transvaal.

It may be found on the wing at any time of the year, but is less plentiful in the winter months.

Larval host-plants: Flowers and seeds of *Coleus* spp. and other garden plants of the genera *Salvia*, *Calamintha*, *Lavandula*, and *Mentha* (all in the family Labiatae).

Cacyreus marshalli Butler, 1897
geranium bronze; geranium blue/malvabloutjie
Wingspan: ♂ 18-21; ♀ 18-22 mm

LYCAENIDAE

no. 134: p. 94

Gardeners who cultivate geraniums and pelargoniums will be familiar with the aptly named geranium bronze, as the larvae of this little lycaenid feed on the buds, flowers and seeds of a wide range of wild and cultivated species of these plants. A careful search around the damaged tips of geranium shoots will often yield larvae, although it should be emphasized that the damage they cause is minimal and more than outweighed by the pleasure of having the butterflies in one's garden.

The alternative common name 'geranium blue' is misleading as this is one of the 'blues' that has not a vestige of that colour on its wings. Both sexes are a dull darkish brown above with the fringe of cilia along the outer margins of both wings chequered in white and brown; both also possess a single white-bordered black eye-spot near the anal angle of the hindwing and a single small white-tipped brown hair-tail at the anal angle. The undersides of both sexes resemble those of *C. lingeus* (species 133) but the forewing appears more brown with thin white bars. There is a dark eye-spot at the base of the hair-tail and a less conspicuous spot at the anal angle. The female is slightly larger than the male and has rounded rather than straight outer margins to her forewings.

The geranium bronze has a weak and lazy flapping flight and seldom flies higher than a metre or so above the ground. It settles frequently on flowers and may remain near the same flower-bed in a garden for days on end. It usually flies alone.

This butterfly is widespread through South Africa, and is absent only from Namaqualand, Bushmanland, the Karoo and the western half of the northern Cape. It is found on the wing in most months of the year, but more so in the summer.

Larval host-plants: *Geranium* spp.; *Pelargonium* spp.

Tuxentius melaena (Trimen, 1887) LYCAENIDAE

black-pie/bontbloutjie **no. 135: p. 95**
Wingspan: ♂ 18-20; ♀ 22-24 mm

This curious and attractive black-and-white butterfly has two recognized subspecies in South Africa. The nominate race *T. melaena melaena* occurs from the eastern Cape northeastwards through Transkei and most of Natal and Zululand to the northern and western Transvaal; subspecies *griqua* occurs in the eastern half of the northern Cape, in the area sometimes still called Griqualand West. The photographs on page 95 are of the nominate race.

The sexes are similar but the females are slightly larger than the males. The forewing is black above with three or four squarish patches of white in the central area; the hindwing has a more extensive and continuous white area in the centre of the wing, irregularly edged and open to the inner margin. Along the black outer margin of the hindwing is a barely discernible row of darker black spots, the largest of which is situated next to the single hair-tail. The undersides of both sexes are white with several irregular blackish bands and spots, larger on the forewing than the hindwing. There is a row of smaller black dots on each outer margin, white-centred on the hindwing, and a prominent dark eyespot associated with the hair-tail.

Owing to its striking appearance, the black-pie is conspicuous on the wing and easily recognized. However, it is very alert and easily disturbed from where it may be resting, flying up in wider and wider circles, until it makes off for safer grounds. It may be found on the wing in any month of the year, especially in the warmer parts of its range.

Until recently, this species was known as *Castalius melaena*.

Larval host-plant: *Ziziphus mucronata* (buffalo-thorn).

Tarucus sybaris sybaris (Hopffer, 1855) LYCAENIDAE

dotted blue/spikkelbloutjie **no. 136: p. 95**
Wingspan: ♂ 23-26; ♀ 23-26 mm

To see the dotted blue feeding on a flower, wings closed, is an event to set any collector's heart beating a little faster. The undersides of both male and female are exquisite – creamy white with a narrow black border to the forewing costa and to the outer margins of both wings, and with an evenly spaced series of black spots over both fore- and hindwings. The outer margins are fringed with white cilia. On the upperside the sexes differ. The male is violet-blue with dark-brown outer margins and a dark-brown spot at the end of the cell slightly below mid-costa; this is a variable characteristic, however, and there can be more spots as shown in photograph **136a** on page 95. The female is dark brown above with a blue sheen basally, and a white central area to the forewing, blotched with dark brown. Both sexes have a dark hair-tail tipped with white at the anal angle of each hindwing. *Tarucus sybaris* is the only one of the three *Tarucus* species to possess hair-tails.

Slow in flight, the dotted blue tends to fly low, feeding regularly on small flowers. Although it can be found flying all through the year in warmer areas, its peak flying period is from September to April. This is the best time to search for it. Look on and about its larval food-plant, the buffalo-thorn, but beware when swinging your net, for this low-growing plant possesses vicious thorns which can rip the material of an expensive net very easily.

While not a common butterfly, the dotted blue is relatively widespread in South Africa, occurring from the eastern Cape to eastern Natal and north and west to the Transvaal and parts of the Orange Free State and north-eastern Cape.

Larval host-plants: *Ziziphus mucronata* (buffalo-thorn); other *Ziziphus* spp.

Tarucus thespis (Linnaeus, 1764)   LYCAENIDAE

macchia blue; vivid blue/fynbosbloutjie; bossiesveldbloutjie   **no. 137: p. 96**
Wingspan: ♂ 24-27; ♀ 24-27 mm

The macchia blue is so called because it is associated with the fynbos of the south-western Cape, a vegetation type closely allied to the *macchia* of Mediterranean Europe. The macchia blue's distribution, however, extends north beyond the fynbos boundaries into southern Namaqualand, and east to the Amatola Mountains of the eastern Cape.

The uppersides of the male are a uniform rich sky-blue; this is attractively set off by a chequered black-and-white ciliate fringe to the outer margins of both fore- and hindwings. It cannot be confused with *T. sybaris* as it has no hair-tails on the hindwings. Although the female's uppersides are almost identical to those of the female *T. sybaris* (species 136), she is slightly more blue, lacks hair-tails and has a conspicuously chequered brown-and-white ciliate fringe to the outer margins of both fore- and hindwings. The undersides of both sexes are similar and are cream-coloured and mottled with a scattering of squarish or oblong dark-brown blotches.

It is a low- and slow-flying butterfly, keeping to the bush of both hillslopes and valleys. It has been recorded in all months of the year, but is more commonly seen in the summer.

Larval host-plants: *Saxifraga* spp. (cultivated saxifrages in gardens); *Phylica imberbis.*

Lampides boeticus (Linnaeus, 1767)   LYCAENIDAE

lucerne blue; long-tailed blue/lusernbloutjie   **no. 138: p. 96**
Wingspan: ♂ 28-32; ♀ 25-32 mm

This very common butterfly is widely distributed throughout the world, from Africa to Europe, Asia and Australasia. It shares with *Vanessa cardui* (page 173) the claim to being the most widespread of all butterfly species. Its larvae feed on a wide variety of leguminous plants (family Fabaceae, formerly Leguminosae) including the widely grown fodder crop lucerne – hence its name. The adults also feed from lucerne flowers. Its larvae can occasionally reach pest proportions on commercial bean and pea crops.

The male is violet-blue in colour above, with a narrow brown border to the outer margins of the wings; this is itself bordered on the outside edge of the wing by a whitish ciliate fringe. There are two small black spots near the anal angle of the hindwing, which subtend a white-tipped dark hair-tail. These features are used as in other lycaenids to deceive potential predators into attacking the wrong end of the butterfly (see photographs **138a** and **138b** on page 96 and the text on *Cyclyrius pirithous* on page 178). The female is slightly larger than the male and although her forewing is still largely blue, it is lighter in hue and the grey-brown outer margin is broader than the male's. Her hindwing is brown with a blue flush basally and there is a row of faint white-edged brownish 'ocelli' on the outer margin which culminates in two white-rimmed black spots at the hair-tail. There is a row of diffuse white marks parallel to and inside the row of 'ocelli'. The forewing undersides of both sexes are grey-brown with an irregular series of yellowish-brown bars and whitish streaks roughly parallel to the outer margin; the hindwing has a similar pattern but there is also a broad whitish bar across the wing parallel to the outer margin. The two black ocelli at the hair-tail are margined with white on the outside and with orange on the inside.

This species is consistently patterned throughout its wide geographical range, but there is often variation in size even within one locality; smaller specimens may on occasion be mistaken for other species of 'blue'.

The lucerne blue is found throughout South Africa, from coast to mountain-top. Its males engage in 'hilltopping' and it flies in all months of the year. The larvae are attended by ants.

Larval host-plants: These are many and varied but chiefly include flowers, pods and seeds of such indigenous and alien leguminous plants as *Ulex, Colutea, Lathyrus* and lucerne.

Harpendyreus noquasa (Trimen, 1887)   LYCAENIDAE

marsh blue/moerasbloutjie   **no. 139: p. 97**
Wingspan: ♂ 18-20; ♀ 18-20 mm

The marsh blue is a localized species apparently confined to the inland regions of Transkei and Natal with outlying populations on the Transvaal Highveld around Breyten and near Mbabane in Swaziland.

The males are violet-blue above with a narrow brown border to the outer margin of the forewing which widens to cover the apical area. All three margins of the hindwing are narrowly bordered in brown. The female is dark brown above with a light dusting of blue basally. Both sexes have a small black spot on the upperside of the hindwing near the anal angle and both are tail-less. The undersides are fawn-coloured with several wavy-edged bands of darker brown fringed with lighter brown. There is a single black spot near the anal angle of the hindwing.

This species prefers damp localities and males and females will often be found playing along the edges of rivers and dams and in or about small gullies. It is usually found only in small numbers. Its flight is zigzagging and slow and its habit of keeping close to the ground makes it rather difficult to net.

Photograph **139c** on page 97 shows the upperside of a bilateral gynandromorph (see page 251 under 'Gynandromorph'), the left half displaying male colouration, the right half female colouration. The flight period of the marsh blue extends from September to April.

Larval host-plant: *Alchemilla capensis.*

Eicochrysops messapus (Godart, 1823)   LYCAENIDAE

Cape blue (subsp. *messapus*)/Kaapse bloutjie   **no. 140: p. 97**
cupreous blue (subsp. *mahallakoaena*)/koperbloutjie
Wingspan: ♂ 18-20; ♀ 16-19 mm

This lovely small butterfly has two recognized subspecies in South Africa. The nominate race *messapus* occurs from Cape Town to the eastern Cape and north to Lesotho and the Orange Free State, while the subspecies which occurs in the bushveld areas of Natal, Zululand and the Transvaal revels in the beautifully sonorous name *Eicochrysops messapus mahallakoaena*. This subspecies is the subject of photographs **140a, b,** and **c** on page 97.

The two subspecies differ markedly. The male of the Cape blue is blue above with a narrow black border to the outer margins and a small black eye-spot ringed with orange near the anal angle of the hindwing. In the cupreous blue, the blue colouration has an attractive orange-red blush which spreads outwards from the base of the wings and covers most of the forewing and, to a lesser extent, the hindwing. In the sunlight such a male resembles an opal, with the blue and golden-red scales sparkling on the wings. The females of both are a dull-brown colour above and also carry the black-and-orange eye-spot on the hindwing; in *mahallakoaena*, however, as shown in photograph **140c**, the orange area of the eye-spot may be several times larger than the black. The undersides are light brown with flecks of lighter and darker brown and several dark spots; on the forewing these spots form a row parallel to the outer margin. Subspecies *mahallakoaena* has more whitish-brown undersides than *messapus* and its black-and-orange spot on the underside anal angle is more prominent.

The cupreous blue in the Transvaal and Natal prefers the warmer parts of the bushveld and has a decided preference for localities where thorn-trees abound. There it will fly slowly through the long grass, particularly in wet or damp marshy spots. In the Cape it occurs in low fynbos vegetation. Specimens can be found abundantly in the warmer months, but also during the winter on occasion.

Larval host-plants: *Thesium* spp.

Eicochrysops hippocrates (Fabricius, 1793)   LYCAENIDAE

white-tipped blue/witpuntbloutjie   **no. 141: p. 98**
Wingspan: ♂ 22-24; ♀ 23-25 mm

The male of the white-tipped blue is dark brown above with a small, inconspicuous, black-and-orange spot at the anal angle of the hindwing, immediately above the single hair-tail. It has a white ciliate fringe to the outer margins of the wings. It may be readily distinguished from all other little brown butterflies, however, by its having a white tip to the apex of the forewing, the white shading gradually into the brown of the rest of the wing. The female is also brown but has a dusting of silvery-blue on the wings. She too has a small black-and-orange eye-spot at the anal angle of the hindwing, but in addition there is a short row of less conspicuous black-and-white spots along the outer margin. The undersides of both sexes are creamy white, speckled sparsely with brown and black dots and streaks. There is a black-and-orange eye-spot at the base of the hair-tail, used as in other lycaenids (see *Cyclyrius pirithous*, page 178) to deceive predators.

The white-tipped blue has a rapid but irregular flight. It favours stream- and river-bank vegetation where it flies about, settling frequently on small bushes and shrubs and feeding from small flowers. It is a somewhat localized little butterfly and only one or two are ever in sight at the same time. By patrolling along watercourses, however, collectors should usually be able to net several specimens.

It occurs from the Port St. Johns area of Transkei north along the coast of Natal and Zululand and thence inland to the south-eastern Transvaal and north to the Soutpansberg. It is normally on the wing between August and May.

Larval host-plants: *Polygonum* spp.; *Rumex* spp. (sorrels; docks).

Cupidopsis cissus (Godart, 1824)   LYCAENIDAE

meadow blue/vleibloutjie   **no. 142: p. 98**
Wingspan: ♂ 25-30; ♀ 25-32 mm

        The meadow blue is a common inhabitant of grassland habitats in the eastern half of South Africa. The male is a rich violet-blue above with a narrow brown border to the wing margins. There are two orange-and-black spots near the anal angle of the hindwing, the smaller one at the anal angle itself sometimes being only orange. The female is a lighter blue above, with a broad brown apex and with brown suffusing into the blue from the margins. The three or four small orange spots or patches at the anal angle of the hindwing are fused, but the largest has a black spot on its outer side. This species is tail-less. Male and female undersides are similar and are greyish-brown with a black-and-orange spot at the hindwing anal angle with smaller orange marks nearby. There are several white-edged dark-brown or black spots on both wings; these are larger on the forewing where most of them are marshalled into a row parallel to the outer margin.

This species is found throughout South Africa except for the Karoo, the western Cape and Nama-qualand. It occurs from the coast inland to the slopes of the highest mountains. It flies slowly, keeping quite close to the ground and it is easily netted as it patrols about flowers in the grass. It is more abundant in the higher rainfall areas and is on the wing from September to April or May.

Larval host-plants: *Eriosema* spp.; *Vigna* spp. (Both genera are in the family Fabaceae).

Freyeria trochylus (Freyer, 1845)   LYCAENIDAE

grass jewel/grasjuweeltjie   **no. 143: p. 99**
Wingspan: ♂ 13-16; ♀ 16-18 mm

        Considered to be the third-smallest butterfly in South Africa, the grass jewel is often overlooked as it flies slowly low down in long grass environments. The males and females are similar, both being dark chocolate-brown above with an oblong patch of three fused orange spots containing three black dots. The female is slightly larger than the male. The undersides are pale brown with parallel series of brown and black spots, each of which is surrounded by a ring of silver-gold scales. On the outer margin of the hindwing near the anal angle there are three juxtaposed orange spots with black centres. It is a tail-less species.

The grass jewel seems just as much at home in the bushveld amongst thorn-trees as on grassy mountain slopes. It normally flies singly but small colonies will be found occasionally in the lush grass in the vicinity of marshy areas. When disturbed it circles slowly and often returns to its original position. It is easily netted. The distribution range of the species covers the eastern half of South Africa, excluding the south-western Cape, the Karoo, Namaqualand and the north-west Cape.

It is on the wing all year round but is less common during the cold winter months and at the height of summer.

Larval host-plants: *Indigofera cryptantha*; *Heliotropium* spp.

Azanus jesous jesous (Guérin-Méneville, 1849)   LYCAENIDAE

topaz blue/hemelsbloutjie   **no. 144: p. 99**
Wingspan: ♂ 22-25; ♀ 22-25 mm

When fresh, the upperside of the male topaz blue is a deep violet-blue with a reflected pink blush. Its wing margins are narrowly dark brown to black but with a white ciliate fringe along the outer margins of both fore- and hindwings which contrasts attractively with the blue. The female's upperside is dull brown with a whitish area in the middle of the forewing which contains a comma-shaped brown spot at the apical end of the cell. In some specimens there may be a slight flush of blue near the base of the wings. Along the hindwing outer margin are several barely discernible black spots, the second from the anal angle being the most visible. The undersides of both sexes are light brown with an orange-brown stripe along the basal half of the costa, an outer marginal row of dark-brown or black spots on both wings, a narrow dark-brown border to the outer margins of both wings, and a series of brown bars and dark spots over the remainder of the wings.

On hot days with the sweet-scented acacia trees in bloom, dozens of these little butterflies can usually be spotted milling about the tree-tops chasing each other, or settling on the flowers to sip nectar. They also congregate to suck moisture from muddy or damp patches in the road or in the veld with other butterfly species. They fly swiftly and irregularly and are difficult to net on the wing. Care must of course be exercised while trying to net them on their thorny *Acacia* perches.

The species is most abundant from September through the warmer months to May, and occurs throughout South Africa with the exception of the western Karoo, Namaqualand and the extreme north-west Cape.

Larval host-plants: The flowers, buds and young leaves of various *Acacia* spp.; *Entada spicata* (Jack's beanstalk).

Oraidium barberae (Trimen, 1868)   LYCAENIDAE

dwarf blue; Barber's blue/dwergbloutjie   **no. 145: p. 100**
Wingspan: ♂ 8-11; ♀ 11-14 mm

The dwarf blue is reputed to be the smallest butterfly in the world, and is certainly the smallest in South Africa. The males may measure as little as eight millimetres from wing-tip to wing-tip although they are usually larger than this; the females are larger than the males.

The sexes are similar, both having dark-brown uppersides with a white-and-brown chequered ciliate fringe to the outer margins of both wings. The undersides are mid-brown and freckled all over with lighter and darker streaks. Their most distinctive feature however, is the row of four tiny eye-spots along each hindwing outer margin, each spot surrounded by golden scales.

The dwarf blue flies slowly and its diminutive size makes detection difficult unless one is specially searching for it. An open net placed unobtrusively in its flight path is not considered an obstacle and it will normally fly inside quietly, settle down in the folds of the net and sun itself lazily. In order to obtain perfect specimens for a collection it is advisable not to squeeze the thorax of this little butterfly in the field but rather to place it in a tiny vial for storage in a cool dark spot during the day; it can then be dealt with at night using a proper killing-jar to ensure that the specimen is not damaged in any way.

Localities frequented by this butterfly may yield specimens from one year to the next, but on occasion it vanishes inexplicably for two or three years before suddenly reappearing. Sandy patches with short grass seem to be its preferred habitat and it seldom ventures further than a couple of metres in any direction before returning to its original patch.

In the warmer regions it flies throughout the year and it has been recorded from the Cape Province (except for the extreme south-west Cape, the eastern Cape coastal districts and the north-west parts of Gordonia), Natal and Zululand, the Orange Free State and the Transvaal.

Larval host-plant: *Exomis microphylla* ('brakbossie'; 'hondepisbossie').

Zizula hylax hylax (Fabricius, 1775)

Gaika blue/Gaika-bloutjie
Wingspan: ♂ 15-17; ♀ 15-19 mm

LYCAENIDAE

no. 146: p. 100

The Gaika blue is another of the tiny blues so often overlooked because of their diminutive size. Some collectors unreasonably disregard these little butterflies on account of their rather drab and uninteresting colours, but to the true connoisseur of butterflies with an eye for detail they are quite fascinating. The male Gaika blue is variable in size but usually very small. It is a dull blue in colour above with a narrow border of brown to the wing margins, broadened at the apex of the forewing; there is a narrow whitish ciliate fringe to the outer margins of both wings. The females are slightly larger and are completely dull brown above although when fresh they have a white, sometimes slightly chequered, ciliate fringe to the outer margins. The undersides of both wings of both sexes are a whitish light brown with a narrow brown border to the outer margins, paralleled by a row of brown spots and then a scalloped brown line. This in turn is paralleled on both wings by a row of oval dark-brown spots (larger on the forewing) with a few dark spots scattered over the remainder of the wings. There are no eye-spots and no tails.

This species is a weak flier and it flutters feebly over low vegetation, tending to remain close to the ground near open grassy places, feeding from flowers and occasionally sucking moisture from damp muddy spots.

It has been recorded from most of South Africa with the exception of the Great Karoo, Namaqualand and the north-west Cape north of Upington. In the warmer parts of its range it can be found on the wing throughout the year but in colder areas it will be found only in the warmer months from September onwards, when the spring brood starts emerging.

Larval host-plants: *Phaulopsis imbricata*; *Ruellia* spp.; *Justicia* spp.

Lycaena clarki Dickson, 1971

Clark's sorrel copper/Clark-kleinkopervlerkie
Wingspan: ♂ 22-25; ♀ 25-30 mm

LYCAENIDAE

no. 147: p. 101

In general, butterflies of the family Lycaenidae are known as the 'blues' and the 'coppers'. Clark's sorrel copper is one of the latter. The male is a rich metallic-copper above with a narrow border of brown to the outer margins of both wings which broadens fractionally over the forewing apex and which has a slightly scalloped inner edge on the hindwing. In sunlight a magnificent pink blush is reflected from the wings, extending outwards from the base and stopping abruptly near the wing margins. There are several black spots on the forewing near the outer margin and apex and one prominent one at the apical end of the cell; there may be another, smaller spot inside the cell. There are no black spots on the hindwing upperside, a feature that distinguishes the male from the female. The female resembles the male but is slightly larger, always has several well-developed black spots on her hindwing upperside and lacks the upperside bloom of pinkish-violet so characteristic of the male.

The undersides of the male and female are similar, the forewing being light orange with a light-brown outer margin and spotted with light-edged blackish spots, and the hindwing being grey-brown with a large number of smaller dark dots encircled with grey.

The closely related species *L. orus* occurs in the south-west Cape; although its uppersides are virtually the same as those of *L. clarki*, it may be distinguished from the latter by the light edging to the dark spots on the underside of its hindwing being more diffuse, less clearly circular, and more white.

Clark's sorrel copper is attracted to water and swampy localities and here it congregates in large colonies. It is nevertheless also found inland in grassland areas where water is lacking, its range extending from the south-west Karoo to the eastern Cape, the Orange Free State, the southern Transvaal north to Johannesburg, and the Natal Midlands. It probably flies in all months of the year but is certainly on the wing between August and April. It tends to fly slowly near the ground, settling on rocks, soil or low plants.

Larval host-plants: *Rumex* spp. (sorrels and docks) including *R. lanceolatus* (common dock).

Aloeides thyra (Linnaeus, 1764)   LYCAENIDAE

mountain copper; red copper/bergkopervlerkie   **no. 148: p. 101**
Wingspan: ♂ 24-26; ♀ 28-30 mm

The genus *Aloeides*, with 45 recognized species in southern Africa, constitutes a daunting complex of closely allied butterflies with an extensive range throughout the subcontinent. The mountain copper, *A. thyra*, was described originally in 1764 and, because of the difficulty in separating closely related forms, until recently included several butterflies now believed to be distinct species. As presently understood, *A. thyra* is distributed from Lambert's Bay and Clanwilliam in the south-western Cape, eastwards to Swellendam and perhaps Stilbaai.

Although in the mountain copper the sexes are similar, there are useful distinguishing features: the female is larger than the male; her forewing has a markedly rounded outer margin compared with the virtually straight margin of the male; and her hindwing appears fuller and is proportionately longer than that of the male.

The uppersides are orange with a broad black band along the outer margin of the forewing, widening over the apex and continuing along the costa. On the hindwing there is a somewhat narrower uneven-edged black border to the outer margin, widening to form a large black patch where it joins the costa. The wing veins are conspicuously dusted with black scales and the outer margins of both wings have a black-and-white chequered ciliate fringe. The hindwing underside is brown with irregular small grey patches which tend to coalesce in mid-wing. The forewing underside has dark-brown margins and an orange central area with black spots which are silver-centred near the costa; the outer spots are arranged in a line parallel to the outer margin.

The larvae of the mountain copper associate with ants, at least in their later stages; they shelter by day in ants' nests, emerging at night to feed on the host-plants, journeying to and from the plant in company with the ants. The adult has a short, swift but erratic flight and is usually on the wing between August and April. It occurs from sea-level to mountain-top.

Larval host-plants: *Aspalathus* spp., including *A. laricifolia, A. acuminata* and *A. cymbiformis* (family Fabaceae).

Aloeides pallida (Riley, 1938)   LYCAENIDAE

giant mountain copper/reusebergkopervlerkie   **no. 149: p. 101**
Wingspan: ♂ 30-35; ♀ 35-40 mm

Aloeides pallida has three recognized subspecies. The nominate race, *pallida*, is a Karoo butterfly, having been recorded over the area from the southern Orange Free State to Willowmore and Port Elizabeth in the eastern Cape and to Matjiesfontein in the south-west Karoo; the subspecies *littoralis* occurs along the coast from Hermanus to Stilbaai and Knysna; and the subspecies *grandis* – the largest butterfly in the genus *Aloeides* – is found in the Cape mountains from Franschhoek east to Garcia's Pass at Riversdale. The subspecies in photograph **149** (page 101) is *Aloeides pallida grandis*.

Like *Aloeides thyra*, the giant mountain copper is orange above with broad black margins to the forewing costa and outer margin (widening over the apex), and to the hindwing outer margin (widening at its junction with the hindwing costa). The wing-veins are outlined in black to a greater (subspecies *littoralis*) or lesser (subspecies *pallida*) extent, and the black borders to the outer margins have a slightly uneven inside edge. There is a more or less visible black-and-white chequered ciliate fringe to the outer margins of the wings. The female is larger than the male.

The forewing underside is orange shading to brown on the margins and carries several black dots which are silver-centred nearer the costa, and arranged in a row near the outer margin. The hindwing underside is brown, lighter in subspecies *pallida*, darker in subspecies *grandis*, with a dark-edged grey-brown mottling over the whole wing but arranged in a row near the outer margin.

The giant mountain copper is on the wing between the months of September and January, with some late-summer specimens been recorded as late as April. It takes short, quick flights, settling frequently on the ground or on low plants with wings folded.

Larval host-plants: *Aspalathus* spp.

Aloeides simplex (Trimen, 1893)   LYCAENIDAE

Kalahari copper/Kalahari-kopervlerkie   **no. 150: p. 101**
Wingspan: ♂ 27-30; ♀ 32-35 mm

    The Kalahari copper was formerly known also as the Namaqualand copper until it was realized that the *'simplex'* butterflies in Namaqualand were actually assignable to two other distinct species; these were formally described in 1977 as *Aloeides bamptoni* and *A. nollothi*. *Aloeides simplex*, as now understood, is distributed throughout the northern Cape north of the Orange River through to Botswana and South West Africa/Namibia.

    This butterfly is almost entirely orange above in both sexes but has a narrow black border to the outer margins of both wings, widening slightly at the forewing apex. It is the most orange species of its genus. The ciliate fringe to the outer margins is chequered in black and white. The forewing underside is orange shading to brown on the costa and outer margin, widely at the apex, while the hindwing underside is sandy-brown, grey-brown or chestnut-brown depending on the specimen. As with the previous *Aloeides* species dealt with here, the black spots near the forewing underside outer margin are arranged in a line and those near the costa are silver-centred. Dark-edged greyish spots and blotches are evenly distributed over the hindwing underside, and those near the outer margin coalesce to form a continuous line parallel to the margin.

    The female is larger than the male and has a rounded outer margin to its forewing, compared with a straight outer margin edge in the male.

    The flight period of the Kalahari copper is from August to April.

Larval host-plants: Unknown, but probably similar to those used by other species in this genus.

Aloeides penningtoni Tite & Dickson, 1968   LYCAENIDAE

Pennington's copper/Pennington-kopervlerkie   **no. 151: p. 102**
Wingspan: ♂ 25-30; ♀ 27-32 mm

    The butterfly formerly known as *Aloeides natalensis* has been studied in detail by Henning and synonymized (1987) with *Aloeides penningtoni*.

    It is a variable butterfly in its markings and colours and is not easy to distinguish from other similar members of the genus. In fact to reach a decision on the identification of this and other *Aloeides* species, you must know where the butterfly was collected and you should preferably have access to series of specimens from different localities to compare with your own material.

    Pennington's copper is typical of the genus, being orange above with a broad black border to the forewing outer margin broadening over the apical area and tapering off along the costa. There is a slightly narrower black border to the outer margin of the hindwing, broadening at the junction of the outer margin and the costa. Its colouration above is similar to that of *A. pallida* but with less width to the black borders. The undersides when fresh are particularly beautiful: the forewing is orange, broadly bordered with a dark mauve or purplish colour, the whole dotted with black spots silver-centred towards the costa and those towards the edge arranged in a row parallel to the outer margin. The hindwing underside is entirely dark mauve to purple, mottled with the grey patches typical of most other *Aloeides* species.

    This localized but fairly well-distributed butterfly is commonly found on the mountainous and hilly areas of Natal south to Port St. Johns and East London and the area around Grahamstown in the eastern Cape; it seems to prefer open grassy slopes. It is on the wing during the warmer months from August to the advent of winter, but it is likely to occur sparingly also in the winter months.

Larval host-plant: Unknown. The larvae, however, are known to associate with ants.

Aloeides barklyi (Trimen, 1874)   LYCAENIDAE

Barkly's copper/Barkly-kopervlerkie   **no. 152: p. 102**
Wingspan: ♂ 30-33; ♀ 32-35 mm

    Barkly's copper is one of the few members of the genus *Aloeides* which is distinctive enough in appearance to be both identified and sexed from a distance while it is on the wing. Where other *Aloeides* species have uppersides coloured in various combinations of orange with brown, dark brown or black, the upper surface of Barkly's copper is a spectacular silvery-grey. The male is entirely silvery-grey above except for the outer margins of both wings which carry a narrow border of brown; on the forewing this expands at the apex to form a small, almost rectangular brown patch which extends lengthwise a little way along the costa. There is a brown-and-silver chequered ciliate fringe to the outer margins of both wings. The female's upperside resembles that of the male but the brown border on her forewing outer margin is broader and the remainder of the apical half of the forewing is orange. There is a dusting of brown scales at the junction of the hindwing costa and outer margin. When Barkly's copper is in flight, it is very conspicuous with the regular on-and-off flashing of the silver sheen in the sun.

The undersides are quite typical of the genus, however, with orange forewings and brown hindwings. The forewing has a narrow brown border to the outer margin, paralleled by a row of black spots; the remainder of the wing has several black spots, those nearest to the costa being silver-centred. The hindwing is evenly spotted with small, dark-edged grey-brown blotches, the outermost ones forming a row parallel to the outer margin.

This attractive butterfly occurs in the inland districts of Namaqualand, from Springbok, Garies, Kamieskroon and Clanwilliam eastwards into the western Karoo. It favours rough hillsides and displays a preference for koppies. Its flight period extends from August to October and probably later.
Larval host-plant: Unknown at present.

Aloeides taikosama (Wallengren, 1857) LYCAENIDAE

African copper/Afrika-kopervlerkie **no. 153: p. 102**
Wingspan: ♂ 23-27; ♀ 27-33 mm

Most members of the genus *Aloeides* have uppersides patterned in orange and black, or orange and dark brown. The African copper, however, is largely brown above, particularly in the case of the male. His uppersides are a dull grey-brown with a faint and narrow greyish-orange bar extending a short distance into the forewing from the costa just below the apex; there is also a faint, narrow, greyish-orange scalloped border parallel to the outer margin of the hindwing. The ciliate fringe to the outer margins of both wings is chequered in brown and white. The female is larger than the male, has more rounded outer margins to her forewings, and has broader and clearer orange markings replacing the grey-orange markings of the male on both fore- and hindwings. The undersides are typical of the genus – see, for example, the description of *A. pallida* (page 205).

The African copper is widely distributed throughout the Natal Midlands northwards through Swaziland to almost the whole of the Transvaal.

It is on the wing in the warmer months of the year but little is known of its life-history as yet.
Larval host-plant: Unknown.

Aloeides pierus (Cramer, 1779) LYCAENIDAE

streaked copper; dull copper/Kaapse kopervlerkie **no. 154: p. 103**
Wingspan: ♂ 25-30; ♀ 25-30 mm

The streaked copper is extremely variable in the extent of its brown colouration; males, however, usually have bright orange fore- and hindwings with broad black-brown borders to the costa and outer margin of both wings. The forewings are more strongly marked with black than the hindwings and some individuals lack orange on the forewings altogether. The wing veins are outlined in black and there is a black-and-white chequered ciliate fringe to the outer margins of both wings. The female is similar to the male but her dark markings are generally brownish-black rather than black. The undersides of both sexes are also extremely variable in background colour but in general are typical of the genus *Aloeides* (see description, for example, of *A. pallida* on page 205).

This species is on the wing from October to the end of April, depending on the climatic conditions. It tends not to fly far when disturbed, often returning to its original post. It favours sitting on open sandy patches of ground, where several males and females can often be observed together. Like *A. taikosama*, it has a wide distribution range for the genus, extending from the western Cape in a broad easterly swathe from the coast to the Karoo as far east as Queenstown, and with records also from Lesotho and Kimberley.
Larval host-plants: *Aspalathus* spp. (family Fabaceae – formerly Leguminosae).

Chrysoritis chrysantas (Trimen, 1868)   LYCAENIDAE

Karoo copper/Karoo-kopervlerkie   **no. 155: p. 103**
Wingspan: ♂ 22-25; ♀ 27-30 mm

The Karoo copper is a most attractive and distinctive butterfly. The sexes are similar and their uppersides are a shimmering orange-red colour overall, with a few small black spots scattered in the apical half of the forewing. There is a black border to the outer margins of both wings, widening at the forewing apex, and there is a very narrow dark border to the forewing costa. Along the outer margins of both wings is a distinct black-and-white chequered ciliate fringe. The forewing underside is orange with scattered black spots, those nearer the costa being suffused with gold; the outer margin carries a light-brown border containing darker spots. The hindwing underside tends to be a deep reddish-brown and carries scattered, diffuse-edged, darker and lighter spots or blotches.

The species is found only in the Great Karoo, Little Karoo and in the inland districts of Namaqualand. Its flight period is from September to March and it favours flat terrain or gentle slopes. Once disturbed from its resting-place, it seldom returns, and its fast and irregular flight may lead the would-be collector a merry dance.

Larval host-plant: Unknown.

Poecilmitis pyramus Pennington, 1953   LYCAENIDAE

Swartberg copper/Swartbergkopervlerkie   **no. 156: p. 103**
Wingspan: ♂ 28-30; ♀ 30-32 mm

The Swartberg copper is typical of the genus *Poecilmitis*, a complicated group of closely similar 'copper' butterflies with some 48 species in southern Africa. The male Swartberg copper is orange above, dotted with black spots, and the basal area of both wings is a lustrous blue suffused with a pinkish blush. The edges of the forewing are bordered in black, narrowly on the costa and broadly on the outer margin and on the outer half of the inner margin. The edge of the outer margin is dotted with white, giving a chequered effect. The orange area of the hindwing is also spotted with black, but the black border to the outer margin is narrow, chequered with white, and fades away before the anal angle. The female resembles the male but is larger, and lacks the blue colouration, having dark-brown bases to the wings. The undersides of both sexes are similar, with light orange forewings spotted with black and cryptically marked hindwings streaked with yellow, orange, brown and dark-brown from the base.

It is a strong flier and may travel some distance after being disturbed, settling on rocks or on the ground. Its flight period is from October to January.

Larval host-plant: Unknown.

Poecilmitis lycegenes (Trimen, 1874)   LYCAENIDAE

Natal copper/Natal-kopervlerkie   **no. 157: p. 104**
Wingspan: ♂ 20-25; ♀ 22-27 mm

Male and female Natal coppers are similar in appearance although, as is commonly the case with lycaenids, the female is larger than the male and has a more rounded edge to the outer margin of the forewing. This butterfly is a bright copper-red in colour above with a slight metallic sheen. The outer margin of the forewing has a narrow black border, widening over the apex and tapering off along the costa. There are a few small black spots scattered over the apical half of the forewing. The hindwing inner and outer margins also have black borders, the inner edge of the border to the outer margin having a wavy outline. The forewing underside is orange with several black spots, those near the outer margin forming a row parallel to the edge of the wing. The hindwing underside has a matt orange-brown background colour and is faintly and irregularly banded with dots.

The Natal copper appears to be strictly confined to the Natal Midlands, the Utrecht district of northwest Natal and the neighbouring parts of the Transvaal and Orange Free State (including Harrismith). It favours grassy upland areas and is especially attracted to rocky outcrops where its larval food-plants grow. The hills and koppies in the Balgowan, Rietvlei and Estcourt areas are regarded by collectors as prime localities for this species.

The larvae are attended by ants and, at the end of the larval stage, pupate within ants' nests or

208

under rocks close by and near the food-plants. The utmost restraint must be exercised in searching for pupae among the rocks or in ants' nests, and in fact this practice should be avoided. If it is necessary to do so, however, carefully lift rocks to look for the small black pupae, and then replace the rock in exactly the same position.

The flight period of the Natal copper is from September to March.

Larval host-plants: *Myrsine africana* (Cape myrtle); *Diospyros austro-africana.*

Poecilmitis thysbe (Linnaeus, 1764)   LYCAENIDAE

Thysbe copper/pragkopervlerkie   **no. 158: p. 104**
Wingspan: ♂ 23-27; ♀ 26-30 mm

To the South African butterfly pioneer Roland Trimen last century, the Thysbe copper 'perhaps excels in beauty all other South African Lycaenidae'. This sparkling red and silver-blue butterfly is a 'must' for any collection. The male is orange-red above with a black border to the outer margin of the forewing, this black border itself being chequered lightly on its outside edge with orange. The outer margin of the hindwing is dotted with black. The outstanding feature of this butterfly, however, is the lustrous suffusion of blue-pink which spreads out over slightly more than the basal half of each wing. This reflects like mother-of-pearl in sunlight. There are a few black spots scattered over the orange outer halves of both wings. The female is larger than the male and has rounded, not straight, outer margins to her forewings. Her upperside markings are similar to the male's but the blue-pink areas on the wings are less extensive, covering less than half of each wing. The forewing underside is light orange with a light-brown outer margin and several evenly spaced black spots; the hindwing underside is variously streaked outwards from the base in various shades of brown, silver and yellow, the browns dominating. The anal angle projects 'tail'-like from the rounded hindwing outline.

The Thysbe copper is found in the coastal areas of the south-western and southern Cape east to Port Elizabeth, from coastal sand-dunes to the slopes of mountains such as those at Piketberg and Citrusdal. It rests on the ground or on flowering bushes. Its flight period is from August until April.

Larval host-plants: *Aspalathus* spp.; *Zygophyllum flexuosum* ('spekbroodbossie'); *Z. sessilifolium*; *Z. morgsana* ('skilpadbossie'); *Chrysanthemoides monilifera* (brother-berry); *Lebeckia plukenetiana.*

Poecilmitis natalensis Van Son, 1966   LYCAENIDAE

coast copper/kuskopervlerkie   **no. 159: p. 104**
Wingspan: ♂ 22-26; ♀ 24-28 mm

The coast copper, *Poecilmitis natalensis*, was only described in 1966, having previously been confused with *P. chrysaor*, the burnished copper, which occurs in the Cape, Orange Free State and Lesotho. The coast copper's distribution range extends from Coffee Bay and other localities in coastal Transkei north through the coastal areas of Natal to northern Zululand (Umkomaas, Umhlanga Rocks, Stanger, Pietermaritzburg, Howick and Greytown).

The males and females are similar although the female has more rounded outer margins to both fore- and hindwings. Both sexes are a metallic copper-red above with narrow black borders to the outer margins of the forewings, widening slightly at the apex; there is also a narrower black border to the hindwings, fringed on the outside with orange-red, the black ending in a short tail at the anal angle. Both fore- and hindwings have an irregular band of squarish black dots roughly parallel to the outer margins and a single black bar in the discal cell of each wing. This serves to distinguish the coast copper from the burnished copper, which has the forewing discal-cell bar but lacks the one in the hindwing. The forewing underside is orange and carries several dark-edged gold dots; the hindwing underside is orange-brown overall, flecked lightly with transversely elongated dark-edged lighter spots.

This lovely butterfly is not particularly common but is widespread along the Natal coast and inland towards the thornveld areas. It darts swiftly about the veld, settling on flowers and low shrubs and may be found on the wing during the summer months.

Larval host-plants: *Chrysanthemoides monilifera* (brother-berry); *Cotyledon orbiculata* (pig's ears).

Poecilmitis nigricans (Aurivillius, 1924)   LYCAENIDAE

blue jewel copper/bloujuweelkopervlerkie   **no. 160: p. 105**
Wingspan: ♂ 25-29; ♀ 28-32 mm

As stated above in the text on *Poecilmitis thysbe*, Roland Trimen regarded that species as perhaps the most beautiful of all lycaenids. Had *P. nigricans* been described when Trimen made that statement, there can be little doubt he would have chosen it over *thysbe* as the fairest of all, for the blue jewel copper is indeed one of the most exquisite of butterflies.

The apical third of the male forewing, bounded by a line from mid-costa to the inner angle, is black, bordered on the outer margin by a black-and-white chequered ciliate fringe. The rest of the forewing is suffused with silver-blue, lighter towards the costa. The male's hindwing is also silver-blue basally, shading to deep blue and finally to a dark-brown border on the front half of the outer margin and a brown-veined orange border on the posterior half. Overall the butterfly has an opal-like glow. The females are colourful but less striking: the basal third of each wing is grey-white, the remainder being orange spotted with black and bordered along the outer margins with a black band edged with a black-and-white ciliate fringe. The anal angle of the hindwing projects beyond the curve of the hindwing as a short tail. The undersides resemble those of *P. pyramus* (page 208).

The blue jewel copper is essentially a montane species although it has been recorded from low-lying country near Mamre north of Cape Town. It occurs from Mamre and the Cape Peninsula east along the mountains to Hermanus, Riviersonderend and to the Swartberg massif in the southern Cape. Two subspecies are recognized: the nominate race *nigricans* occupies the species' western range while the eastern race has been named *zwartbergae* for the Swartberg Mountains where it is found. Photographs **160a** and **160b** on page 105 are of subspecies *nigricans*.

This butterfly is a fast and evasive flier and, when disturbed, may not return to its original station. It is on the wing between September and April.

Note: *The blue jewel copper is protected by the Nature and Environmental Conservation Ordinance 1974 (Ordinance 19 of 1974) (Cape) and collecting is allowed only under permit from the Cape Department of Nature and Environmental Conservation in Cape Town.*

Larval host-plants: *Zygophyllum* spp. including *Zygophyllum fulvum* ('spekbossie'); *Osteospermum polygaloides.*

Poecilmitis uranus Pennington, 1962   LYCAENIDAE

Montagu copper/Montagu-kopervlerkie   **no. 161: p. 105**
Wingspan: ♂ 26-30; ♀ 26-30 mm

The Montagu copper is very similar to the blue jewel copper, and arguably quite as lovely. It may be distinguished from the blue jewel copper, however, by the fact that the black apical area to the male's forewing is much narrower. Clearly this leaves more space for the extraordinary shades of blue which radiate out from the base, deepening towards the outer margins. The blue colouration basally is lightly covered in white, especially towards the costal edge of the forewing and the whole bluish area is suffused with an opal-like glow. Sometimes two or three tiny orange spots are enclosed in the black apical area. The male's hindwing upperside resembles that of the blue jewel copper. The female by comparison is drab: she is orange above with several large black spots on each wing, a broad black outer-marginal border edged (as in the male) with a black-and-white chequered ciliate fringe, and with the basal third of both wings coloured pearl-grey. The undersides resemble those of *P. nigricans* (above) and *P. pyramus* (page 208).

This species is confined to the south-west Cape mountains from around Ceres and Franschhoek east to Montagu; it is absent, however, from the Cape Peninsula. It tends to occur at higher altitudes than the blue jewel copper and is a fast flier, favouring rocky ridges on mountain slopes. It often settles on low rocks or on the ground. The flight period is from November to March or April.

Larval host-plants: *Zygophyllum* spp.; *Aspalathus spinosa* (dancing-thorn).

Lepidochrysops variabilis Cottrell, 1965   LYCAENIDAE

Cottrell's brown blue/Cottrell-bruinbloutjie   **no. 162: p. 105**
Wingspan: ♂ 27-30; ♀ 27-30 mm

The males and females of this species are similar, being uniform mid-brown above with distinctly brown-and-white chequered ciliate fringes to the outer margins of both fore- and hindwings. In certain parts of its range, notably the Natal Midlands, there may be a light suffusion of blue around the bases of the wings. The undersides of this species are extremely variable – hence the species name *variabilis* – and are difficult to describe briefly. Essentially, however, they are light brown with darker brown spots and patches and usually an irregular-edged whitish band on the hindwing. Females tend to be less marked on the forewing underside than the males. An 'average' underside is portrayed in photograph **162b** (page 105) – in so far as one can select an average specimen in this species.

It is an alert, fast-flying butterfly and not easily netted. However it seldom flies far from its grassy hillslopes or from the rocky koppies where the males congregate around midday. The females are usually found on the lower slopes where they are joined by the males in the cooler hours of the day.

Cottrell's brown blue is a widespread species, found sparingly in the Cape Peninsula but more abundantly in the mountains of the south-western Cape from Citrusdal eastwards to Grahamstown, Transkei, Lesotho, the Natal Midlands and north to the eastern Transvaal mountains.

After the second moult, the larvae of this species leave their food-plants and enter the nest of their host-ant, *Camponotus niveosetosus*, where they remain until their final instar and pupation. There they feed on ant pupae, safe from the veld-fires which so frequently sweep their montane habitats. The flight period is mainly from November to December but there are earlier and later records.

Larval host-plants: *Selago* spp. including *S. corymbosa* ('bitterblombos'); *Becium* spp.

Lepidochrysops ignota (Trimen, 1887)   LYCAENIDAE

Zulu blue/Zoeloebloutjie   **no. 163: p. 106**
Wingspan: ♂ 25-28; ♀ 25-28 mm

The Zulu blue is one of the 'blues' which have no blue colouration at all. The males and females are similar and are uniformly dark brown above with a light ciliate fringe to the outer margins of both wings and an inconspicuous and indistinct black eye-spot at the anal angle of the hindwing. The undersides are a uniform light brown with broken bands of inconspicuous lighter markings especially on the hindwing and along the outer margin of the forewing. The forewing also carries a series of light-edged dark-brown to black spots in a row parallel to the outer margin with a single spot at the end of the cell. There are two or three dark spots in the basal area of the hindwing and a dark eye-spot at the anal angle.

This species flies slowly and unconcernedly about the grass and is relatively easy to net. If disturbed, however, it can summon up an amazing turn of speed to elude capture.

It is found in the Natal Midlands from Estcourt northwards to Ladysmith, and thence into the Transvaal north to the Lydenburg district and along the Wolkberg to Haenertsburg. It has also been recorded from the Pretoria area.

The flight period of the Zulu blue is from September to November.

Larval host-plants: *Becium* spp.

Lepidochrysops tantalus (Trimen, 1887)   LYCAENIDAE

king blue/koningbloutjie   **no. 164: p. 106**
Wingspan: ♂ 31-34; ♀ 30-35 mm

The king blue is one of the more delicate of our blue butterflies. The male is entirely blue-brown above with a small dark bar or spot at the apical end of the forewing cell. The females vary in the extent of the blue on their brown upperside forewings, but it spreads out from the basal area of the wings at least as far as an inconspicuous row of half a dozen dark-brown dots which parallels the outer margin not far from the margin itself. The blue is more metallic in appearance than that of the male. The female also has a dark spot at the apical end of the forewing cell. The hindwing upperside of the female is brown, sometimes with a faint submarginal line of blue dots. The undersides of both sexes are light brown with two darker-brown irregular-edged bands across the wings parallel to the

211

outer margins. There is an inconspicuous dark dot near the anal angle of each hindwing, with other black dots in the basal area of the hindwing and a short dark bar at the apical end of the forewing cell.

This species is on the wing from the latter part of September through to November. It favours grassy hillslopes from the Mbashe (Bashee) River in Transkei through to the Natal Midlands and north to the mountainous parts of the eastern Transvaal.

Larval host-plant: *Becium obovatum.*

Lepidochrysops ortygia (Trimen, 1887)   LYCAENIDAE

koppie blue/koppiebloutjie   **no. 165: p. 106**

Wingspan: ♂ 33-38; ♀ 37-42 mm

The koppie blue was named in 1887 and for some time included a complex of closely related species now regarded as distinct. As presently understood it is distributed from the hillslopes and koppies of the Krugersdorp and nearby districts in the Transvaal Highveld, southwards through the eastern Orange Free State and Lesotho to the eastern Karoo, and thence south to Bedford and Somerset East. It is replaced in other regions by several other similar species including, for example, *L. swartbergensis* in the Swartberg of the southern Cape and *L. wykehami* of the Namaqualand hills.

The male is a shiny violaceous blue above with a basal brown border to the outer margins of both wings, the margins themselves bearing a brown-and-white chequered ciliate fringe. There is a short brown bar across the apical area of the forewing cell and a dark eye-spot near the anal angle of the hindwings. On the female's upperside the blue is less extensive, radiating somewhat streakily over the basal half but reappearing as a light scalloped line parallel to the outer margin of the hindwing. Otherwise her upperside is brown, with a dark-brown bar at the end of the forewing cell and an indistinct row of darker spots parallel to the outer margin of the forewing. Like the male she has a chequered brown-and-white ciliate fringe to the outer margins of both wings and an eye-spot at the anal angle; the eye-spot is however noticeably larger than that of the male and is orange on its inside edge.

The undersides of the wings are alike in both sexes, being light brown with a small eye-spot at the anal angle of the hindwing. Both wings have a row of inward-pointing white chevrons near their outer margins and the forewing has a row of white-edged dark-brown spots, each touching the next, from the costa to the inner margin. A similar spot is placed at the end of the forewing cell. The base of the hindwing carries five or six white-edged black spots, and there are several whitish rings in mid-wing.

The peak flight period is during November and December but the koppie blue may be found from October to February.

Larval host-plants: *Selago* spp.; possibly *Becium* spp.

Lepidochrysops plebeia plebeia (Butler, 1898)   LYCAENIDAE

twin-spot blue/dubbelkolbloutjie   **no. 166: p. 106**

Wingspan: ♂ 31-35; ♀ 35-40 mm

Although the female twin-spot blue is conspicuously blue above, the male has no blue colouration at all. He is brown above with a white ciliate fringe to his outer margins, a small faint dark-brown bar at the apical end of the forewing cell, and a black-and-orange spot at the anal angle of the hindwing. There is also a short hair-tail at the anal angle. The male is slightly diaphanous and the underside markings show through to the upper surface of the wings. The female is an almost metallic-blue colour above, this radiating out from the base of the wings to the broad brown borders along the outer margin and costa of both fore- and hindwing. There is a prominent darker-brown bar at the end of the forewing cell and other brown spots in mid-hindwing and along the outer margin of the hindwing. The prominent black-and-orange spot at the anal angle is larger than the male's. The wing veins are clearly outlined in brown. The undersides of both sexes are pale brown with white-edged mid-brown spots arranged approximately in rows parallel to the outer margins. There are usually six white-edged black spots in the basal part of the hindwing; *L. patricia* has five (see opposite page, top).

The twin-spot blue is a widespread species favouring open woodland and grassland habitats. It occurs from the Mbashe (Bashee) River in Transkei north-eastwards to Natal and Zululand and thence to the Transvaal, north-west Orange Free State and the extreme north-east Cape. Its flight period is from September to April. It is often found in large numbers in local colonies.

The specific name of the twin-spot blue has previously been incorrectly rendered as '*plebeja*'.

Larval host-plant: *Lantana rugosa* (bird's brandy).

Lepidochrysops patricia (Trimen, 1887)   LYCAENIDAE

Patricia blue/Patricia-bloutjie   **no. 167: p. 107**
Wingspan: ♂ 35-38; ♀ 35-40 mm

The male Patricia blue uppersides are a deep, rich metallic-blue with narrow brown borders to all wing margins except the forewing inner margin. There is a short dark-brown bar at the apical end of the forewing cell, and a black eye-spot with an orange mark on its inward edge situated near the anal angle of the hindwing. There is a short hair-tail beside the eye-spot. The female uppersides are similar to those of *L. plebeia plebeia* (species 166) but have more brown proportionate to blue while the wing veins are less prominently marked. The undersides of both sexes are similar to those of *L. plebeia plebeia* but there are only five light-edged black spots in the basal area of the hindwing, not six as is usually the case with *plebeia*; in addition, the hindwing markings of *L. patricia* are somewhat less clearly defined, the whitish marks in particular being less bold.

This butterfly can be found in a variety of environments from open grassland to bushveld or the fringes of forests in grassveld; it is often found on hillslopes. It may be found year after year at the same localities. The males engage in 'hilltopping' on sunny days (see page 18) and have a fast and erratic flight.

It occurs from the southern Cape (Little Brak River and Oudtshoorn) eastwards to most of Natal and northwards and inland through the eastern Cape to the Orange Free State, the eastern parts of the northern Cape, and the Transvaal. It is on the wing from September to March, but is more common in November and December; there are also records for the winter months.

The larvae feed on *Lantana* species in the first two stages of their development. Later, however, they live in ants' nests, eating ant larvae and pupae. They pupate in the ants' nests.

Larval host-plants: *Lantana* spp. in the early stages. They readily feed on the introduced species *L. camara* which is now a proclaimed noxious weed in South Africa.

Lepidochrysops letsea (Trimen, 1870)   LYCAENIDAE

Free State blue/Vrystaat-bloutjie   **no. 168: p. 107**
Wingspan: ♂ 30-35; ♀ 30-35 mm

The Free State blue is another 'blue' which has no blue colouration whatsoever. The sexes of this small brown butterfly are similar although the female is larger than the male and slightly lighter in colour. Both have brown uppersides fringed on the outer margins with white cilia and with a characteristic black eye-spot near the anal angle of the hindwing; this spot is ringed with orange, heavily so on its inward edge. The undersides of both sexes are a lighter brown with series of whitish streaks parallel to the outer margins, and on the hindwing extending into the middle of the wing. There are four contiguous, prominent, white-edged black spots in a row just below the apex of the forewing and a similarly coloured short bar at the end of the cell. On the hindwing there are another five or six such spots scattered over the basal half of the wing. There is also a black-and-orange eye-spot at the anal angle of the hindwing.

This is a grassveld species and it characteristically flies low over the veld, frequently feeding on flowers. It flies slowly and it is easily netted.

The flight period is from October to February and it is found from Steynsburg in the north-east Cape northwards through the Orange Free State and western Lesotho to the southern Transvaal.

Larval host-plant: *Hemizygia pretoriae* (family Labiatae).

Pinacopteryx eriphia eriphia (Godart, 1819)   PIERIDAE

zebra white/kwagga   **no. 169: p. 107**
Wingspan: ♂ 40-55; ♀ 40-55 mm

Male and female zebra whites are similar in appearance with a dark-brown to black background colour above, marked boldly with yellow. The forewing has two broad yellow bands which curve over the wing from the base of the costa and inner margin respectively to stop short of one another below the apex. There is a row of four prominent yellow spots which lie parallel to the outer margin. The hindwing also has a series of (smaller) yellow spots around its outer margin, and two broad yellow bands, one from inner margin to mid-costa and the other from the middle of the inner margin across the wing but stopping short of the marginal spots. The females are larger than the males and their markings are slightly less well-defined, making them look a little worn even when they are fresh. The upperside markings are mirrored on the undersides but the black or dark-brown background colour is replaced by light or mid-brown. There are seasonal differences in this species, the dry-season form having its undersides speckled in brown or pink. Photograph **169b** (page 107), however, is of the wet-season form.

The zebra white tends to fly low but although it appears to be a weak flier when flitting through the bush of the thornveld, when it is disturbed it can show a remarkable turn of speed.

It is widespread through South Africa, being absent only from the Cape Peninsula, coastal Namaqualand, north-west Gordonia district and the mountainous parts of Lesotho.

Larval host-plants: *Boscia oleoides* (bastard shepherd's tree); *Maerua cafra* (bush-cherry).

Colias electo electo (Linnaeus, 1763)   PIERIDAE
African clouded yellow; lucerne butterfly/lusernvlinder; lusernskoenlapper
Wingspan: ♂ 35-40; ♀ 35-40 mm   **no. 170: p. 109**

The male of the African clouded yellow is orange-yellow above with a broad black border to the outer margin of both wings, widening in the apical area of the forewing. There is a black spot just below the middle of the forewing costa at the apical end of the cell, and the inner margins of the hindwings are tinted yellow. The female is somewhat similar to the male but with less distinct markings; there is a brown suffusion over most of the hindwing and the basal half of the forewing, and there are several yellow flecks in the black apical area of the forewing. A second female form occurs not uncommonly in which the yellow of the upperside is replaced by whitish grey. Photograph **170d** (page 109) portrays this form, *aurivillius*. The undersides of both sexes are golden or greenish yellow with a row of black spots parallel to the outer margin of the forewing, a black spot at the end of the forewing cell, and a prominent black-edged white spot in the centre of the hindwing.

The African clouded yellow is also justifiably called the lucerne butterfly; when in flower, fields of lucerne attract swarms of them to feed from the flowers and lay their eggs. The larvae are often referred to as 'lucerne caterpillars', and can on occasion reach pest proportions.

Farmers faced with a lucerne-caterpillar plague counter the problem by gathering lucerne and several hundred larvae. These are placed in a sealed container calculated to cause overcrowded conditions; the highly humid environment permits bacteria and fungal diseases to flourish, causing the death of the caterpillars. The container is then emptied of its contents which are crushed into a pulpy mass and strained. The resulting liquid is diluted with water and sprayed over the lucerne-fields to spread the disease to the larvae infesting the crop.

This account should serve as a warning to would-be breeders of butterflies. It is most important to keep containers clean and sterilized as butterfly diseases are extremely contagious.

The African clouded yellow is found throughout the southern African subcontinent and may be seen on the wing all year round when conditions are suitable.

Larval host-plants: *Medicago sativa* (lucerne); *Trifolium* spp. (clover); *Vicia* spp. (vetches); many other legumes, including *Robinia pseudo-acacia* (locust-tree or false acacia) and a wide range of other plants.

Catopsilia florella (Fabricius, 1775)   PIERIDAE
African migrant; African vagrant/Afrikaanse swerwer   **no. 171: p. 108**
Wingspan: ♂ 55-60; ♀ 55-65 mm

As its common name suggests, the African migrant (or African vagrant) is a butterfly which periodically undertakes large-scale migrations. One recorded in April 1966 advanced on a 650-kilometre front through Transkei and Natal and must have consisted of many hundreds of thousands of individuals. The species is widespread through the whole of South Africa and appears to be equally at home on mountain slopes, in thornveld and in deserts. It is occasionally seen flying along beaches and out to sea.

The upperside of the male is rich-cream with a greenish tinge and with a small black spot or streak at the apical end of the forewing cell. There is usually only the merest hint of brown outlining the edge of the wing near the forewing apex. Three female forms are recognized: form *pyrene* is similar to the male above but with a clearly visible narrow brown edge to the forewing costa and apex and half a dozen brown dots along the rim of the forewing outer margin; the rare form *hyblaea* is cream dusted with yellow scales and has the same, but lighter, brown markings as form *pyrene*; the common form (photograph **171c**, page 108) is sulphur-yellow with a chestnut edge to the forewing costa and apex and a series of dots along the outer margin of the forewing, large enough to give a chequered effect. There are fainter dots along the outer margin of the hindwing. The undersides of the male are light yellow dusted with light-brown scales, and those of the female orange-yellow. Both are finely mottled, the female strongly so, and both have a light-centred brown spot in mid-forewing. The male (photograph **171b**) has a single small spot in hindwing while the female usually has a cluster of one to three brown-edged cream spots in the middle of the hindwing.

Colour in this species is, however, very variable and the best way to separate the sexes is to look for the hair-pencil or scent-pencil possessed only by the male. This tuft of white hair is situated at the base of the upperside of the hindwing.

This fast-flying species can be found on the wing in any month of the year. Its eggs are laid singly, are long and tapered and are easily seen on the undersides of the leaves of its larval food-plant. It is easily bred in captivity.

Larval host-plants: *Cassia* spp. and presumably several other plants, judging by this butterfly's widespread distribution.

Eurema hecabe solifera (Butler, 1875)　　　　　　　　　　　PIERIDAE

common grass-yellow; Lowveld yellow/Laeveldgeletjie　　　**no. 172: p. 109**
Wingspan: ♂ 35-40; ♀ 35-40 mm

Until recently the common grass-yellow was known as *Eurema hecabe senegalensis*. However, a taxonomic revision has determined that *E. senegalensis* is a valid species in its own right and that South African common grass-yellows should now be known as *E. hecabe solifera*. The Zimbabwean form *brenda* of what used to be called *E. hecabe senegalensis* has been removed from *E. hecabe* and allocated to *E. senegalensis*.

The common grass-yellow is a variable butterfly exhibiting seasonal dimorphism. In the main, both sexes are bright yellow above (the females slightly duller with a dusting of grey scales) with broad black borders to the outer margins of both wings, broadening over the apical area of the forewing and narrowing again to a point half-way along the costa. The inner edge of the black apex where it meets the yellow is irregular and wavy, not evenly curved as in *E. brigitta* or *E. desjardinsii*; this is a useful diagnostic feature. Wet-season forms have broader black margins than dry-season forms. Photograph **172a** (page 109), for example, is of a male specimen collected in the dry season; the black on the hindwing outer margin is reduced to a row of small dots. The wet-season form would have a continuous black band along this margin and a wider area of black on the forewing. The undersides of both sexes are yellow with a scattering of small brown patches and dark-edged light spots – the latter in the basal half of the wings. In the dry-season forms, there is a dark-brown subapical patch on the forewing underside, perhaps fading as it approaches the outer margin as in form *bisinuata* (photograph **172b**).

It occurs from the Mbashe (Bashee) River area of Transkei north-eastwards to the coastal half of Natal and thence to the eastern and northern Transvaal. It frequents open country as well as bushveld and savanna and is rarely seen in the denser forests.

The common grass-yellow is a weak flier and easily netted. It seldom flies higher than a metre or two above the ground.

Larval host-plants: *Acacia* spp.; *Hypericum aethiopicum* (St. John's wort); *Cassia mimosoides* ('boesmanstee').

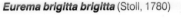

Eurema brigitta brigitta (Stoll, 1780)　　　　　　　　　　　PIERIDAE

broad-bordered grass-yellow/grasveldgeletjie　　　　　　　**no. 173: p. 110**
Wingspan: ♂ 30-35; ♀ 30-35 mm

The broad-bordered grass-yellow is another of our small and bright-yellow pierids. Both male and female are a rich yellow above with a black border from the base of the forewing costa, widening at the apex and narrowing again down to the inner angle of the forewing. It continues along the outer margin of the hindwing. The inside contour of the black in the apical area is rounded, like *E. desjardinsii*, but unlike *E. hecabe solifera* where the inside contour is noticeably irregular. The width of the black border varies with the season, being wider in summer – as in form *zoe* illustrated in photographs **173b** and **173c** on page 110. The female's yellow upper surface in the summer is often dusted with black (photograph **173c**). The undersides of both sexes are yellowish with several faint darker streaks on the hindwing; the dry-season form *brigitta*, however, has the yellow suffused with a pink sheen especially in the apical area of the forewings. Note that the outer margin of the hindwing is rounded – unlike that of the next species, *E. desjardinsii*, which has an angled outer margin.

Eurema brigitta occurs through most of South Africa with the exception of the drier western Karoo, the south-western Cape and Namaqualand. It flies slowly close to the ground, frequently settling on twigs and flowers. It rests under small bushes, often hanging by one leg only; in this position the slightest breeze makes it flutter like a leaf. This precarious resting posture may possibly be a means of deceiving potential predators which may mistake it for a dry yellowing leaf. It may be found on the wing in any month of the year.

Larval host-plants: *Hypericum aethiopicum* (St. John's wort); *Cassia mimosoides* ('boesmanstee').

Eurema desjardinsii marshalli (Butler, 1897)   PIERIDAE

angled grass-yellow/reënbosgeletjie   **no. 174: p. 110**
Wingspan: ♂ 35-38; ♀ 35-40 mm

The upperside of *Eurema desjardinsii marshalli* closely resembles that of *E. hecabe solifera* and *E. brigitta brigitta* but may be distinguished from the former by its rounded inside contour to the black apical area of the forewing, and from both species by its distinctly angled hindwing outer margin. This can be clearly seen in photographs **174a** and **174b** on page 110. As with the other 'yellows', the wet-season form has broader black margins on both wings (photograph **174a**); in the dry-season form the black borders are much narrower, particularly on the hindwings where they may be reduced to a row of spots on the outer margins. The undersides are yellow in both sexes, lightly flecked with brown in the wet-season form, and more heavily marked in the dry-season form.

The angled grass-yellow occurs along the eastern coastal zone of South Africa from around Plettenberg Bay in the southern Cape, east through Transkei and north through Natal to Swaziland, the eastern Transvaal escarpment and the Soutpansberg. It keeps away from the drier thornveld areas and prefers habitats around the edges of woodland and rain-forest; it is often seen flying in open grassland, presumably in search of new breeding-grounds.

It is a low- and slow-flying butterfly, and is on the wing all year round in the warmer regions.

Larval host-plant: *Cassia mimosoides* ('boesmanstee').

Eronia cleodora cleodora Hübner, 1823   PIERIDAE

vine-leaf vagrant/druiweblaarswerwer   **no. 175: pp. 110-111**
Wingspan: ♂ 45-60; ♀ 50-60 mm

The male and female vine-leaf vagrants are similar in colour pattern. They are white above with a broad uneven-edged black border to the scalloped outer margin of the hindwing, and a similar band on the forewing outer margin widening over the apical area to a point almost half-way along the costa. There are two white spots in the black apex, the one nearer the costa being the smaller. The female's hindwing upperside is slightly tinged with light yellow; this is perhaps the easiest way to distinguish the sexes. The hindwing underside is yellow with a wide brown band along the outer margin, a brown blotch half-way along the costa, and a row of irregular brown blotches across the middle of the wing which joins the outer marginal band. The basal two-thirds of the forewing are white, while the apical third is brown shading to dark brown or black on its inner edge and carries a large V-shaped yellow blotch on the costal side of the apex (photograph **175a**, page 110).

The vine-leaf vagrant is common in the eastern coastal belt north-eastwards from Port Elizabeth to Natal and Zululand and in the inland areas of the eastern Transvaal and the Soutpansberg. It is predominantly a woodland butterfly and is very fast on the wing; periodically, however, it pauses to feed on flowers where it can be easily netted. It may be found flying in all months of the year.

Larval host-plant: *Capparis fascicularis* var. *zeyheri* ('wag-'n-bietjie').

Eronia leda (Boisduval, 1847)   PIERIDAE

autumn-leaf vagrant; orange-and-lemon/herfsblaarswerwer   **no. 176: p. 111**
Wingspan: ♂ 50-55; ♀ 45-55 mm

The autumn-leaf vagrant is one of the most eye-catching of the pierids. It exhibits seasonal sexual dimorphism in that the male and female have similar uppersides in the dry season but differ in the wet season. In the dry-season (winter) form, both sexes are a bright sunflower-yellow above with the apical half of the forewings bright orange, slightly browner round the tip of the apex; the female, however, can be distinguished from the male as she has a short row of four or five brown spots in the orange apical zone parallel to the outer margin. (Photographs **176b** and **176d** on page 111 show dry-season female and male respectively.) In the wet-season (summer) form the male remains almost the same, the only slight change being the darkening of the border around the apical orange tip; the apical area of the female is brown, not orange, and usually reduced in size. The apical brown spots are present as a distinguishing feature of the females in both seasonal forms.

The undersides of both sexes are yellow, mottled finely on the hindwing, with brown flecks, particularly so in the dry season. However the male's forewing has flecks only in the apical area while the female's forewing (photograph **176c** – a wet-season specimen) has an orange-brown flush to the apical area, speckled with brown and with two or three small, dark-edged silver spots. The female's hindwing underside, in addition to the male's brown mottling, is dotted with brown-edged silver spots of various sizes and has a triangle of orange-brown pointing into the wing from half-way along the outer margin; this triangle includes the largest of the silver spots.

The autumn-leaf vagrant's flight is extremely fast making it difficult to net. It flies on long straight courses, seldom stopping during its flight. The following strategy is suggested for the capture of this species: peer intently into the distance, select your proposed victim which will be easily recognized by its bright colour, anticipate its course, intercept it *en route* and strike quickly because once missed and disturbed, it is unlikely to offer you a second chance. The best time to seek it is late afternoon when most butterflies slow down and feed from flowers. Females appear to be scarcer than the males. The autumn-leaf vagrant inhabits the same areas as *E. cleodora* (species 175) but only from as far south as Port St. Johns, and in lesser numbers. It is more widespread than *E. cleodora* in the northern Transvaal. Favoured habitats are coastal bush, thorn bush and savanna woodland.

It is on the wing all year round, but more so in the summer months.
Larval host-plant: *Capparis tomentosa* ('katdoring').

Nepheronia argia varia (Trimen, 1864)   PIERIDAE

large vagrant/grootswerwer   **no. 177: p. 112**
Wingspan: ♂ 50-65; ♀ 60-70 mm

The large vagrant is the largest 'white' to be found in South Africa. It is easily recognizable by its large size and by its distinctive mode of flying. The male is white above, often with a slight tinge of blue and has a black apical area on his forewing; this tapers off smoothly on the costa but either smoothly or brokenly on the outer margin. (Unlike the female, the male never has an orange-red patch at the base of the forewing). There are no markings on his hindwing upperside. The females, on the other hand, are extremely variable and several different forms have been named. The form *aurora* shown in photograph **177b** (page 112) has white forewing uppersides, white hindwing uppersides and a fairly prominent orange-red patch at the base of the forewing; the dark apical patch is much reduced and brownish compared with the male and the outer margins of both wings carry dark-brown spots or blotches at the ends of the veins, giving a chequered effect. Another form, *giara*, is similar but has light orange-yellow hindwing upper surfaces and lacks the orange-red forewing bases. Still another, form *varia* (shown in photograph **177d**), has yellow hindwings, white forewings, orange-red forewing bases and dark-brown apical and marginal markings, reduced in extent in the apical area compared with the male.

The male's forewing underside is white with yellow shading at the apex and with a brown patch on the costal side of the apex; the hindwing is light yellow with a small brown patch close to the midpoint of the outer margin. The female's undersides, however, are more variable. The common form *varia* is portrayed in photograph **177c**; it has rich-yellow hindwings, yellow-edged white forewings, brownish apical and marginal markings, and a large orange-red patch at the base of each forewing. The male never has the red patch on the forewing base either above or below; the female may – depending on the form.

217

The large vagrant is a forest butterfly and seldom leaves the shelter of the bush. It is found from Port Elizabeth in the eastern Cape east and north-east through the coastal forests of Transkei, Natal and Zululand to Mozambique and the eastern Transvaal.

It is on the wing all year round, but more plentiful in the summer months; it has been recorded, however, that the biggest brood in Pondoland is in April and May.

Larval host-plant: *Cassipourea ruwensorensis* (from tropical Africa).

Nepheronia buquetii buquetii (Boisduval, 1836)   PIERIDAE

Buquet's vagrant/Buquet-swerwer   **no. 178: p. 112**
Wingspan: ♂ 45-50; ♀ 45-50 mm

The male Buquet's vagrant is white above with a narrow black border to the forewing costa, widening over the apex and narrowing again down the outer margin to the inner angle. As this black margin can be greatly reduced in some specimens, Buquet's vagrant could be confused with the African migrant (*Catopsilia florella*, species 171), especially when on the wing. Both sexes may be distinguished at close quarters from *C. florella*, however, by the prominent dark-edged ocellus at the end of the cell in the middle of the underside of the hindwing – the remainder of the undersides being white but with a sparse and faint dusting of brownish scales. The female is similar to the male but her forewing markings are a lighter brown. This species is sometimes known affectionately by collectors as the 'green-eyed monster' as its eyes and proboscis are tinged with green; unfortunately, however, the green fades shortly after a specimen has been set and stored in a cabinet.

Buquet's vagrant is strictly a coastal species along the eastern seaboard from Knysna to Natal, from where it penetrates inland into Zululand, the Transvaal Lowveld and the northern Transvaal. It is also found further inland in certain areas, usually along rivers. This butterfly is an inhabitant of woodland and bushveld environments and is on the wing all year round when conditions permit.

Larval host-plant: *Azima tetracantha* (bee-sting bush).

Nepheronia thalassina sinalata (Suffert, 1904)   PIERIDAE

Cambridge vagrant/blouswerwerwitjie   **no. 179: p. 113**
Wingspan: ♂ 50-55; ♀ 55-60 mm

The male of the Cambridge vagrant is a pale sky-blue colour above ('Cambridge blue') with a narrow black border to the forewing costa which broadens considerably over the apex and narrows again down the outer margin to the inner angle. (The blue colour in pinned specimens unfortunately, however, fades with the passage of time.) The inside edge of the black border is uneven-edged. The hindwings are unmarked. The females are white to pale yellow above, slightly deeper in colour basally, and have the forewing markings as in the male but sometimes dark brown rather than black and with two small diffuse white patches in the dark-brown apical area. The female's hindwing upperside has a series of blackish spots on the outer margin at the ends of the wing veins. The female form *sinalata* has the same colouration but with a mid-yellow hindwing; this is the form portrayed in photograph **179b** (page 113). The undersides of both sexes are plain white but with a silky blue-silver sheen.

In South Africa the Cambridge vagrant occurs mainly in the forests in the Soutpansberg and in the Transvaal Drakensberg. It is common in Malta Forest at Tzaneen, and it has also been recorded in the Lydenburg district and on occasion in northern Zululand.

This extremely attractive but shy butterfly remains close to the edge of forests and thick bush from where it ventures into the open for short distances to feed and sun itself.

It is easily netted, but if disturbed, tends to fly straight into the undergrowth and out of sight. It is on the wing all year round, but is more scarce in the winter months.

Larval host-plant: *Hippocratea africana*.

Colotis amata calais (Cramer, 1775)   PIERIDAE

topaz arab/geelarabier   **no. 180: p. 113**
Wingspan: ♂ 32-35; ♀ 32-35 mm

The topaz arab is rather similar in appearance to the female lucerne butterfly *Colias electo* (page 214). The male uppersides are pinkish-yellow with a black apical half to the forewing carrying two rows of pinkish-yellow spots. There is a small black patch at mid-costa and another extending into the wing from a large pinkish-yellow spot at the inner angle. The hindwing has a broad black costal border and outer marginal border, the latter with very small pinkish-yellow spots on the margin edge and a row of larger spots submarginally. The female is similar to the male but has a pinkish-yellow basal area shading outwards to yellow. The undersides of both sexes are a paler yellow with a black patch at the forewing cell and two more near the inner angle of the forewing. In the dry season the undersides may be tinged with pink.

This small pierid flies close to the ground, somewhat slowly and erratically; it stops occasionally to feed on flowers, when it may be caught easily. It favours bushveld and savanna woodland.

It may be encountered on the wing in any month of the year and is found from northern Zululand through Swaziland to the eastern Transvaal, the Soutpansberg, and the far north-western Transvaal.

This butterfly was formerly known as *Colotis calais*.
Larval host-plant: *Salvadora persica*.

Colotis doubledayi angolanus (Talbot, 1929)   PIERIDAE

Doubleday's orange/Doubleday-arabier   **no. 181: p. 113**
Wingspan: ♂ 33-35; ♀ 35-37 mm

Doubleday's orange closely resembles the veined orange (species 182). The sexes are similar. The uppersides are butter-yellow with a prominent black spot or bar at the end of the forewing cell, wing veins heavily outlined in black, and a broad black outer margin to both wings which is chequered on the forewing with narrow yellow spots and on the hindwing with rounded yellow spots. There is a wavy broad black band across the forewing approximately parallel to the outer margin and a similar but much fainter band on the hindwing (sometimes almost non-existent as in photograph **181a** on page 113). This hindwing band is usually well developed in *C. vesta argillaceus* (photograph **182b**). The undersides of Doubleday's orange are orange-yellow with a black spot at the end of the forewing cell (visible in photograph **181b**) and three or four other more- or less-developed black smudges in the outer half of the forewing. Both the fore- and hindwings carry faintly visible rows of yellow spots.

This species is usually seen patrolling two to three metres above the ground and flying up and down the dirt roads in its arid habitat. It flies fairly rapidly and seldom stops to rest or feed. Large numbers have been reported on the wing from September to October and also in April and May, but they are possibly on the wing at other times of the year in reduced numbers.

In South Africa it is found only in the stony valleys and along the dirt roads near Vioolsdrif on the Orange River in Namaqualand. It extends northwards through South West Africa/Namibia.
Larval host-plant: *Maerua schinzii* (ringwood tree).

Colotis vesta (Reiche, 1849)   PIERIDAE

veined orange/bontarabier   **no. 182: p. 114**
Wingspan: ♂ 35-40; ♀ 35-40 mm

Two subspecies of the veined orange are recognized in South Africa: *Colotis vesta argillaceus* occurs in northern Natal, Swaziland and the eastern Transvaal while subspecies *mutans* is found in the western Transvaal, Botswana, Zimbabwe and South West Africa/Namibia. The photographs on page 114 are of subspecies *argillaceus*.

Although the veined orange resembles the previous species closely, there are distinguishing features. On its hindwing upperside the veined orange has a well-developed irregular-edged black band from mid-costa towards, but not reaching, the anal angle; this band is poorly developed or non-existent in *C. doubledayi*. In addition, the basal third of the upperside of each wing is whitish, not yellow. The undersides have the same orange-yellow background colour as *C. doubledayi* but the black spot in the forewing cell is usually larger and the other black marks coalesce in *C. vesta* into a dark-brown zigzag band mirroring the one on the upperside of the forewing; on the hindwing, the upperside black markings are mirrored below in brown, including the wing veins. The female resembles the male closely but is larger and sometimes a much lighter shade of yellow as in photograph **182b**.

There is some difference between wet- and dry-season forms of this species, the latter forms having a pinkish-buff tinge to the undersides.

It flies lazily fairly close to the ground, feeding from flowers and it is very easy to net if not disturbed beforehand.

Colotis vesta prefers thorn and bush country and is found from around Durban northwards to Zululand and Swaziland and thence to the Transvaal bushveld. It is fairly localized in its distribution but colonies usually cover large areas and are well-populated. It is found on the wing in all months of the year, but is more abundant in the warmer months.

Larval host-plant: *Maerua angolensis* (bead-bean).

Colotis celimene amina (Hewitson, 1866) PIERIDAE

lilac-tip/boomwagter **no. 183: p. 114**
Wingspan: ♂ 35-40; ♀ 35-40 mm

The lilac-tip is a particularly attractive 'white'. The males are white above with the apical half of the forewing from mid-costa to the inner angle coloured lilac, bordered in black and with the wing veins in the lilac area broadly outlined in black. An irregular black line runs across the middle of the lilac area. The hindwing outer margin is broadly bordered in black with a row of small white spots along the margin; there are also similar but smaller white spots on the tips of the lilac bars where they meet the outer margin at the apex. The female's upperside is patterned as in the male except that the apical half of the forewing is entirely black, but for three or four smudges of white in the middle of the black area and several tiny white dots along the edge of the outer margin. The undersides of both sexes are similar, the forewing being yellow at the base, white in mid-wing and yellow streaked with brown in the apical area; there is a large reddish bar at the apical end of the forewing cell. The hindwing is yellow with the veins outlined in buff.

The female of the subspecies *pholoe*, which occurs in South West Africa/Namibia and Botswana, retains much of the lilac colouration of the male in its forewing apical area.

The male lilac-tip has the unusual habit of occasionally hovering like a small hummingbird two to three metres above the ground close to a tree; it will hold its position there for several minutes before darting to a different locality to recommence hovering once more. Driving in the bushveld of the northern Transvaal, one may often see these hovering males at regular intervals along the road, one per tree. This phenomenon has been observed by many a collector and it is a pity that the more rarely encountered females are not as obvious in their habits.

This species is widespread over the greater part of the northern and western Transvaal but is absent from the Lowveld and the southern parts of the province. There is also a localized population in mid-Natal in the Bushmans and Mvoti river valleys and on the Mgeni River at Nagle Dam.

It may be found on the wing in all months of the year, but more abundantly in the summer.

Larval host-plants: *Capparis* spp. (caper-bushes); *Boscia* spp. (shepherd's trees).

Colotis erone (Angas, 1849) PIERIDAE

coast purple-tip/Natal-perspuntjie **no. 184: p. 115**
Wingspan: ♂ 40-45; ♀ 45-50 mm

The coast purple-tip is another 'white' with unusually coloured wing-tips. It exhibits both seasonal and sexual dimorphism. The wet-season male is white above but has the apical third of his forewing, from mid-costa to a point not far from the inner angle, patterned in purple and black. In the main block of purple markings there are usually only three discrete and substantial cells of purple, perhaps tailing off on the costal side with one or two narrow purple streaks. There may be an outer row of two or three very small grey spots nearer the apex. A very small black dot appears at the end of the forewing discal cell, and the veins of both wings are outlined in black; on the hindwings the black vein endings on the outer margin expand to form small black 'deltas'. In the dry-season male all black areas are reduced and the black discal spot, the black veins and the black 'deltas' may all be lacking.

In South Africa *C. erone* can easily be confused with *C. ione* (species 185) and *C. regina* (species 186), both of whose males have similar purple tips. *Colotis regina*, however, is separable on size alone: its male wing-tip to wing-tip stretched span is around 60 mm, to around 45 mm for *C. erone* and 50 mm for *C. ione*. It also has at least five discrete cells of purple in the main block, the cell nearest the costa usually being transversely divided into two, and the purple cells 'fill' the black apical area almost completely – unlike *C. erone*. *Colotis ione*, which can be the same size as *C. erone*, usually has at least four (sometimes five) discrete and substantial purple cells which, like those of *C. regina*, but unlike the three cells of *C. erone*, tend to fill the black apical area comprehensively.

The females are very variable in colour, not only seasonally. None have purple tips. Form *natalensis* (photograph **184b**, page 115) is a wet-season form which resembles the male but is black and white above with no purple, the black extending broadly to the inner angle and in a broad band round the outer margin of the hindwing. She has a small dot at the end of the forewing discal cell and a large black spot half-way along the forewing inner margin, opposite another black spot on the mid-costa of the hindwing. There are three white spots in the apical area as well as a fourth very small one near the costa. The dry-season forms have reduced black markings. Form *jobina* (photograph **184a**) is one such; it is similar to form *natalensis* but the black on the hindwing, for example, is reduced to a series of diffuse spots. The female form *erone* (photograph **184c**) is another wet-season form and resembles form *natalensis* except that it has a large orange-red patch in the black apex, with an included row of black spots. Dry-season females have reduced black markings. The undersides vary by sex, season and form but the forewings are usually white with yellow apical areas with or without dark markings; the hindwings are usually yellowish overall with a greater or lesser incidence of black or brown spots, bands or mottling.

The coast purple-tip is a woodland species, occurring from around Port St. Johns in Transkei north along the Natal coast to Mozambique. The males tend to fly on a straight fast course along open pathways and roads at about knee-height. The females are often found resting and sunning themselves in such situations, perhaps waiting for males. Even at the speed that males fly, they will interrupt their flight to inspect any white object in sight. Even small pieces of paper are enough to attract their attention, and these can often be used as decoys for netting them.

They are on the wing all year round but are more common in the summer months.

Larval host-plant: *Maerua racemulosa* (forest bush-cherry).

Colotis ione (Godart, 1819)   PIERIDAE

purple-tip/perspuntjie   **no. 185: pp. 116-117**
Wingspan: ♂ 45-50; ♀ 45-50 mm

The male purple-tip is very similar to the males of the coast purple-tip (*C. erone*) and the queen purple tip (*C. regina*). For a description of the male upperside and how to separate it from its two allies, the reader is referred to the section on *C. erone* (species 184).

The hindwing upperside veins are outlined in black in both wet-season and dry-season forms of *C. ione*, but more strongly in the former. In the wet season too, each vein meets the outer margin of the hindwing in a small 'delta' of black (photograph **185d**, page 116). The wet-season forms always have a small black spot at the end of the forewing cell, but this may be lacking in dry-season forms.

The females are notably polymorphic, that is they exist in a variety of forms (see pages 19 and 252). Females of the dry-season form *jalone* are off-white above with the apical halves of their forewings entirely orange-red. Female form *leda* has similar orange-red apices but its wings have a primrose-yellow ground-colour. The female form *xanthosana* is a wet-season form and has a yellow ground-colour, strong black borders to all margins and a red patch with black dots in the apical area (photograph **185g**). The female form *pepita* is another wet-season form (photographs **185e** and **185h**), similar to *xanthosana* but with a row of small white or yellow patches in the apical area and no red patch.

The undersides are too varied to describe in detail here, but the range is indicated by photograph **185c** (wet-season form *ione*, male), photograph **185f** (wet-season form *ione*, female) and photograph **185e** (wet-season female form *pepita*.)

The purple-tip shares its southern range with the coast purple-tip, that is from the Transkei coastal areas northwards along the Natal coast. It spreads out through the thorn- and bushveld areas of Zululand, however, and occurs over most of northern and eastern Transvaal. It is on the wing in all months of the year and although it flies fast, it settles frequently giving the collector an opportunity to catch it.

Larval host-plants: *Maerua racemulosa* (forest bush-cherry); *Maerua rosmarinoides* (needle-leaved bush-cherry).

Colotis regina (Trimen, 1863)   PIERIDAE

queen purple-tip/koninginperspuntjie   **no. 186: p. 118**
Wingspan: ♂ 55-60; ♀ 50-60 mm

The queen purple-tip is the largest of the three purple-tips in South Africa; but size apart, the males bear a confusing resemblance to the males of *C. erone* and *C. ione* and the reader should refer to the text on *C. erone* for hints on how to separate them.

As in *C. ione* the wing veins on the male's upperside are outlined in black in the wet-season form, with a 'delta'-shaped spot of black where the hindwing veins meet the outer margin (photograph **186a**, page 118). In the dry season the black is reduced and the vein markings may disappear altogether. There is a tiny black bar at the apical end of the forewing cell in the male on both upper- and under-side; this is present as a larger spot in the females, which may also have one or two black spots near the forewing upperside inner angle. Unlike the other two purple-tips, the queen purple-tip can have purple markings in the apical area, although there is also a light-yellow form with a black apex containing light-yellow marks. When present, however, the female's purple areas are reduced in size in comparison with the male's, or alternatively broken by black marks or accompanied by white spots.

It is a butterfly of the bushveld and is found from the extreme north-east Cape to most of the Transvaal, and thence through Swaziland to Zululand. Specimens have been taken as far south as Muden and the Valley of a Thousand Hills near Durban.

Like others of its genus, it is fast on the wing and not easily netted unless caught unawares while feeding at flowers. The males search for the females by flying round and round their larval host-plant trees, and collectors are advised to imitate this strategy, but on foot. Hilltops and small koppies are also favourite haunts of this species.

Larval host-plants: *Capparis* spp. (caper-bushes); *Boscia* spp. (shepherd's trees).

Colotis danae annae (Wallengren, 1857)   PIERIDAE

scarlet-tip/skarlakenpuntjie   **no. 187: p. 118**
Wingspan: ♂ 40-50; ♀ 40-50 mm

The male scarlet-tip has, as its name implies, the apical half of the upperside of the forewing coloured scarlet. In the wet-season form (photograph **187a**, page 119) this area is narrowly bordered with black on the costa and outer margin and broadly bordered with black on its inside edge. The basal areas of both wings are grey and the mid-wing areas are white dusted with grey or black scales. There is a broad black border to the hindwing outer margin. As with other *Colotis* species, the dry-season forms have less black colouration, the borders becoming narrower and, in the case of the hindwing outer margin, being reduced to a series of small dots. The basal grey area becomes almost white. The wet-season female (photograph **187b**) has heavier black markings than the male: the grey basal area is black, the black borders are wider (thus reducing the extent of the red in the apex), and there is a row of black spots in mid-hindwing as well as in the red apical area. The female dry-season form has much less black, and the spots in the red apical area and in the fore- and hindwing white mid-wing areas become smaller; the basal areas of the wings also become grey.

Both sexes of the wet-season form have light-brown undersides, with an irregular row of darker-brown spots or blotches across the outer half of both wings – a distinctive feature of the butterfly when it has settled. There is a diffuse orange-yellow band on the forewing below the apex. Towards the margins the wing veins are outlined in dark brown. In the dry-season form this pattern is repeated but the extent of the brown markings is greatly reduced. In both sexes and in both seasonal forms there is a black spot at the end of the discal cell in the forewing; it is, however, reduced in size in the dry-season forms.

The scarlet-tip is a restless and fast-flying butterfly which occurs in savanna and thornveld country from the coastal areas of the eastern Cape through Transkei to the eastern half of Natal and Zululand; it is found also in Swaziland and through the whole of the eastern Transvaal Lowveld and the northern Transvaal. It may be found on the wing in any month of the year.

Larval host-plants: *Maerua angolensis* (bead-bean); *Cadaba natalensis* (Natal worm-bush).

Colotis aurora dissociatus (Butler, 1897)   PIERIDAE

sulphur orange-tip/swaeloranjepuntjie   **no. 188: p. 119**
Wingspan: ♂ 35-40; ♀ 35-40 mm

This butterfly was formerly known as *Colotis eucharis* but this name properly belongs to an Indian species.

The sulphur orange-tip is another butterfly with beautiful contrasting colours. As with other *Colotis* species it is both sexually and seasonally dimorphic. The male wet-season form is portrayed in photograph **188a** (page 119). It is a bright sulphur-yellow in colour above, with the apical half of the forewing coloured orange and bordered narrowly on the costal and outer marginal sides (to the inner angle) in black. This black border broadens very slightly at the apex itself and widens with a dusting of black scales where the orange ends at mid-costa and at the inner angle. The hindwing is also sulphur-yellow but there is a small black spot where each vein meets the outer margin. In the dry-season male the black disappears entirely, and there is only the narrowest edging of brown to the outer edge of the orange apical patch.

The wet-season female (photograph **188b**) shares the orange and yellow markings of the male but is lightly dusted basally with black and has considerably broader black borders. The spots on the hindwing outer margin are much enlarged and virtually coalesce, the veins in the orange apical patch may be outlined in black, there is a black spot at the end of the forewing discal cell and an irregular, much interrupted, wavy line of black spots and patches from the apical area across both fore- and hindwing. In the dry-season female all the black areas are reduced in size with the exception perhaps of the spot on the forewing cell.

The undersides of the wet-season male are entirely yellow with minute black dots at the vein ends on the margins; in the dry season they are finely speckled with brown and pinkish, particularly the hindwing. The wet-season female's undersides are lighter yellow with sparse, fine, black and brown speckling, the forewing black discal spot is prominent and the hindwing has a dark-edged silver spot at the end of the discal cell. In the dry season the underwings are ochre to brown, the hindwing in particular being densely speckled with black and brown through which the smaller silver discal spot shines (photograph **188c**).

The sulphur orange-tip has virtually the same distribution range as the scarlet-tip (species 187) and they are often found flying together. Large numbers may be seen when conditions are suitable.

It is on the wing all year round, but is more abundant in the summer.

Larval host-plant: *Cadaba natalensis* (Natal worm-bush).

Colotis antevippe gavisa (Wallengren, 1857)   PIERIDAE

red-tip/rooipuntjie   **no. 189: p. 120**
Wingspan: ♂ 40-45; ♀ 40-45 mm

The red-tip is one of the most common and widespread of the 'red-tip' group. Like other members of its genus it exhibits sexual and seasonal dimorphism. The wet-season male (photograph **189b**, page 120) is white above with a large red apical patch bordered all round in black, the black continuing narrowly along the costa to the base and more broadly to the inner angle. There is also a broad black border to the outer margin of the hindwing and a diffusely edged black bar which extends from the wing bases along most of the length of the inner margin of the forewing and the costa of the hindwing. At the end of the forewing discal cell is a small (sometimes tiny) black dot. The wet-season female (photograph **189c**) is much more heavily marked with black than the male, the white being reduced on the forewing to a semicircular band and on the hindwing to one large mid-wing patch with associated smaller white markings. The colour of the wet-season female's apex is usually more red than orange and is less extensive than in the male, with proportionately more black.

In the dry season the extent of the black on the wings is much reduced. In the male the red apical patch is scarcely bordered in black, the forewing cell spot may almost vanish, and the edge of the outer margin of the hindwing has only a small streak of black at the end of each vein. The bar along the junction of fore- and hindwing is reduced to black dusting at the wing bases. The dry-season female retains more of her black colouration but white replaces black as the dominant colour.

The undersides of both sexes are yellowish with an orange flush in the forewing apex. In the wet season the wing veins are outlined in black (photograph **189d**) but in the dry season form this black disappears. The dry-season forms, however, are densely speckled with black on the hindwing and on the forewing apical area.

The red-tip is found in coastal bush, open woodland and savanna bushveld habitats from around Great Brak River in the southern Cape eastwards along the coastal districts to Transkei and Natal, and thence northwards to the eastern and northern Transvaal and north-east Cape. It may be found on the wing in any month of the year.

Larval host-plants: *Maerua cafra* (bush-cherry); *Capparis sepiaria* (wild caper-bush); *Boscia oleoides* (bastard shepherd's tree).

Colotis evenina evenina (Wallengren, 1857)

orange-tip/oranjepuntjie
Wingspan: ♂ 40-45; ♀ 35-40 mm

PIERIDAE

no. 190: p. 120

The orange-tip closely resembles the red-tip in appearance but lacks the black spot at the apical end of the forewing cell and has, naturally enough, an orange apical tip, not a red one. Like the red-tip it is strongly sexually and seasonally dimorphic. The male shown in photograph **190a** (page 120) is a male with wet-season colouration, the orange tip being broadly bordered on all sides in black and with bold black spots at the end of each vein on the outer margin of the hindwing. There is a long blackish bar along the costa of the hindwing, and another, perhaps less-developed one along the inner margin of the forewing – both of which are somewhat less prominent than those in the red tip (species 189). In the dry-season male these bars dwindle to diffuse blackish areas at the wing bases, the black borders to the orange tip virtually disappear and there may be no sign of black on the hindwing.

The wet-season female (photograph **190b**) is very similar to the red-tip female, being heavily marked with black. The orange area in the apex is divided into two unequal segments by a curving black bar. Apart from not possessing the black spot at the forewing cell, the orange-tip wet-season female may be distinguished from the red-tip female by the oblique whitish stripe from the black basal area of the hindwing which crosses over into the forewing black basal patch, dividing it into two and making the major (basal) part of it appear to be diverging away from the inner margin. This characteristic is also visible in the dry-season form which shows, like most other *Colotis* species, a great reduction in black pigmentation, although the black curving bar in the orange apex is still prominent.

The orange-tip has a northerly distribution, being found from Namaqualand eastwards into the eastern half of the northern Cape, the Orange Free State and the western, northern and eastern Transvaal; it also occurs in Swaziland and northern Zululand although specimens have been recorded on occasion from the Valley of a Thousand Hills and Muden not far from Durban. It favours dry bushveld habitats and is on the wing all year round, when conditions permit.

Larval host-plants: *Capparis* spp. (caper-bushes).

Colotis pallene (Hopffer, 1855)

bushveld orange-tip;scarce orange-tip/bosveldoranjepuntjie
Wingspan: ♂ 30-35; ♀ 30-35 mm

PIERIDAE

no. 191: p. 121

The bushveld orange-tip is another variable 'red'-tipped species, exhibiting both sexual and seasonal dimorphism – the latter to a marked degree. It bears a close resemblance to other species in this group, the male for example looking like a smaller version of *Colotis antevippe gavisa* (species 189) and the female like *C. evagore antigone* (species 193). Several of the seasonal colour variants have been accorded recognition as named forms.

The male wet-season form is white above with a more red than orange apical third to the forewing, broadly bordered with black. The wing-veins in the red patch are outlined in black. There is a black dot at the end of the forewing discal cell and a diffuse black bar along most of the inner margin from the base. The hindwing costa carries a similar bar and there is a series of contiguous black spots along the outer margin of the hindwing. These black markings are reduced in extent in the dry season. The female wet-season form is considerably blacker above, all black markings being wider than those of the male. The colour in the apical tip of the female's wing is more orange than red, but in summer the orange may sometimes be completely obscured by black as shown in photograph **191b** (page 121); this has been named as female form *absurda*. The outer margins to the female's wings are more rounded than those of the male.

This butterfly has a preference for bushveld areas where it flies slowly and close to the ground, flying in and out of the long grass. It is on the wing in all months of the year, but is scarce in the colder

224

areas in winter. It occurs throughout the northern and eastern areas of the Transvaal and extends south-eastwards to Swaziland and Zululand.
Larval host-plants: *Capparis* spp. (caper-bushes).

Colotis agoye agoye (Wallengren, 1857)   PIERIDAE

speckled sulphur-tip/grasveldgeelpuntjie   **no. 192: p. 121**
Wingspan: ♂ 35-40; ♀35-40 mm

The speckled sulphur-tip is a common butterfly but localized in its occurrence within its distribution range. It occurs from Clanwilliam in Namaqualand across the northern Karoo into the northern Cape and the western parts of the Orange Free State, and thence to the bushveld areas of the northern and eastern Transvaal.

The male is white above with a small orange apical tip to the forewing bordered on the inside edge with a pronounced line of black scales. The wing-veins are outlined finely with black scales and there is a light dusting of black scales over both wings, but particularly the forewing. The female is similar but the apical patch is more orange-grey with a diffuse edge. There may be light markings along the outer edge of the hindwing as in photograph **192b** (page 121). Females tend to have a 'worn' appearance even when fresh.

The undersides of this species are whitish with a hint of yellow in the forewing apex and on the hindwing, and there is a dusting of black scales overall. Dry-season specimens have fewer black scales. There is, however, less seasonal variation in this species than is normal in the genus.

It may be found flying in all months of the year, but is more abundant in summer
Larval host-plants: *Boscia* spp.; *Cadaba* spp.

Colotis evagore antigone (Boisduval, 1836)   PIERIDAE

small orange-tip/kleinoranjepuntjie   **no. 193: p. 121**
Wingspan: ♂ 30-35; ♀30-35 mm

The small orange-tip has a wide African distribution and has many named forms – a situation which has given rise to much confusion and mislabelling. Like others of its genus it is a variable species and is both sexually and seasonally dimorphic. The wet-season male (photograph **193a**, page 121) has a medium-width black border to the forewing costa and outer margin and a broad black margin along the length of the inner margin; the hindwing costa and outer margin are also broadly banded in black. Almost half of the forewing is taken up by the orange-red apical tip and its black border.

It is not easy to distinguish the various 'red-tip' species which share these same male wet-season dress characteristics of black-bordered red apical tip, broad black hindwing outer margin and distinct black 'cross-bars' along the inner margin of the forewing and the costa of the hindwing. The small orange-tip, however, has two useful distinguishing features: firstly, the orange-red tip is not fully enclosed by a black border as the other species are, but is 'open' to the white of the mid-wing on the costal side of its inner border; secondly, there is a black 'notch' into the orange-red tip immediately below the section which is 'open' to the white mid-wing (photograph **193a**).

In the dry season the male, as is usual with the 'red-tips', loses most of his black colouration, the 'cross-bars' disappearing entirely and the black on the hindwings being reduced to small dots on the outer margin. The 'notch' in the orange tip, black-bordered or not, is usually still visible.

The wet-season female resembles the male closely (photograph **193b**), but usually has even more black colouration above. She normally shares the distinguishing characters mentioned above, although in one named summer form, *phlegetonia*, the black in the 'notch' extends along the edge of the orange tip to the costa and confounds both the differentiating criteria mentioned earlier.

The male may or may not (photograph **193a**) have a black dot in the forewing cell; the female always has (photograph **193b**).

The small orange-tip favours open country or bush and avoids the wetter forests. It occurs from the southern Cape eastwards along the coastal zone through Transkei and Natal to Swaziland, most of the Transvaal and the extreme north-east Cape. It may be found on the wing all year round, but more so in the summer months.
Larval host-plants: *Capparis sepiaria* (wild caper-bush); *Cadaba aphylla* (black storm); *Maerua cafra* (bush-cherry).

Colotis eris eris (Klug, 1829)   PIERIDAE

banded gold-tip/goudpuntjie   **no. 194: p. 122**
Wingspan: ♂ 40-45; ♀ 40-45 mm

The banded gold-tip is both sexually and seasonally dimorphic. The wet-season male is white above with a small apical patch of five or six elongated 'cells' of dull gold framed in dull purple, the whole glowing when viewed in bright sunlight. There is a very broad black bar along the inner margin of the forewing, extending up the outer margin and tailing off round its inside edge to the costa. There may or may not be a black dot at the apical end of the forewing discal cell. The hindwing has a broad black band running the length of the costa and a series of small dots round the edge of the outer margin at the vein endings. The female is similar but has a narrower black border to the forewing inner margin and an even more attenuated black margin to the hindwing costa. There are black or brownish spots along the edge of the hindwing outer margin and the black spot at the end of the forewing discal cell is always present. The female's apical patch is similar to the male's, but the purple is replaced by black and the gold 'cells' by smaller white patches. The female is very variable, form *abyssinicus*, for example, having a yellow, not white, background-colour.

The dry-season forms have slightly reduced black markings on the upperside. The undersides of the various seasonal forms are yellowish and whitish in summer and ochraceous and whitish in winter. Nearly all are characterized, however, by a distinctive group of dark spots near the outer margin and near the inner angle. The female always has the black spot at the end of her forewing discal cell.

Whilst on the wing, the banded gold-tip is difficult to net. It flies fast and erratically and remains close to the ground. The males share the habit of the queen purple-tip (page 222) and fly round and round their larval host-plant trees, presumably searching for females.

The species occurs from the Little Karoo and eastern Cape northwards through the Great Karoo to the western Orange Free State and westwards to Namaqualand; it also occurs throughout the bushveld areas of the north-east Cape, Transvaal, Swaziland, Zululand and Natal. It is found on the wing in all months of the year when conditions permit.

Larval host-plant: *Boscia oleoides* (bastard shepherd's tree).

Colotis subfasciatus subfasciatus (Swainson, 1823)   PIERIDAE

lemon traveller/suurlemoensmous; geelsmous   **no. 195: p. 122**
Wingspan: ♂ 45-50; ♀ 45-50 mm

The lemon traveller is, like other of its genus, both sexually and seasonally dimorphic. The wet-season male is lemon-yellow above with a dark apical tip occupying about one-third of the forewing. The apical tip encloses four or five elongated yellow 'cells' and is bordered in grey-black on the costal and outer marginal borders; the inner edge of the tip, however, is closed or virtually closed (photograph **195a**, page 122) by a broad black bar which extends more than half-way across the wing-tip from the costa. There is a small black spot at the apical end of the forewing cell. The female is similar but has an orange tip to the forewing, broadly bordered on its outside edges with brown and on the inside with a brown or black bar analogous to that of the male and thus not fully enclosing the orange (photograph **195b**). It also possesses a black or brown spot at the end of the forewing cell.

In the dry-season forms the dark colouration of the upperside is less pronounced. In the male the grey-black border to the apical tip lightens and the black bar is reduced slightly in length and width; the black bar and discal spot dominate the upperside. The dry-season female's apical patch broadens and becomes more orange with a hint of black or brown on its inner edge. The undersides of both sexes are light whitish-yellow speckled with brown over the hindwing and in the apical tip of the forewing. In the dry season the speckling is more pronounced.

The lemon traveller is believed to be the fastest of our butterflies on the wing, flying low and erratically near the ground. It has the ability to dodge the collector's net and change direction virtually at the same instant and, once missed, it has gone for good. A good time to attempt to net this species is when it is feeding from a flower. It is active in full sunlight, but as soon as the sun is hidden behind a cloud, it immediately settles on open sandy patches of ground to wait for the sun to reappear. Now its defences seem to be down, and with careful stalking specimens can be taken.

Although normally not found in Natal, specimens have been taken on rare occasions. It is resident in the bushveld of most of the Transvaal extending into the eastern half of the northern Cape and the western Orange Free State. It is on the wing in all months of the year but is scarce in winter.

Larval host-plant: *Boscia albitrunca* (shepherd's tree).

Belenois thysa thysa (Hopffer, 1855)   PIERIDAE

false dotted-border/valsvoëlentwitjie   **no. 196: p. 123**
Wingspan: ♂ 50-60; ♀ 50-60 mm

The false dotted-border is yet another sexually and seasonally dimorphic pierid species. The wet-season (summer) male is white above with a narrow black border to the costa, broadening slightly over the apex and continuing down the outer margin to the inner angle as a series of contiguous black triangular spots. The outer margin of the hindwing carries a series of separated large black spots usually paralleled on the inside by a row of black dots. There are also two or three black dots near the inside edge of the black apex to the forewing. The female has wider and more prominent black marginal markings and spots and a light or heavy dusting of black scales over the basal halves of the wings. The attractive pink flush to the forewing base and orange flush to the hind-wing base can be seen to advantage when the black scales are sparse (photograph **196h**, page 123).

The uppersides of the dry-season male are very similar to those of the wet-season male but his black markings are less pronounced, the hindwing inner row of dots sometimes almost disappearing altogether. The female, on the other hand, is apricot above with a pink flush to the forewing base and an orange flush to the hindwing base. Her black markings are reduced in extent somewhat, but are still usually more extensive than the male's wet-season markings.

The male has a yellow hindwing underside and a white forewing underside with a yellow apex, both wings being spotted marginally and submarginally with black along their outer margins. There is a large orange-red patch at the base of the forewing, extending on to the costal border of the hindwing. The female is similar but has a yellow, not white, forewing.

This species is slow on the wing and often descends to feed from flowers, where it can be easily netted. The females are not as commonly encountered as the males.

It occurs in the coastal forests and rain-forests of Transkei from around the Mbashe (Bashee) River north-eastwards to Natal and along the coastal areas of Zululand. It is found on the wing all year round, but is less common in the winter months.

Larval host-plants: *Maerua* spp.; *Capparis* spp.

Belenois zochalia zochalia (Boisduval, 1836)   PIERIDAE

forest white/boswitjie   **no. 197: p. 124**
Wingspan: ♂ 40-50; ♀ 40-50 mm

The forest white is not one of the common 'whites' of South Africa despite its wide distribution. It is sexually and seasonally dimorphic. The upperside of the wet-season male is white with a silver sheen and there is a large black bar at the apical end of the forewing cell, shaped like a dumb-bell and extending to the edge of the costa. It has a black apical tip covering about a quarter of the wing and enclosing a row of small white spots. This black area tails off irregularly to the inner angle. The outer margin of the hindwing has a row of separate black spots. The ground-colour of the female's upperside is variable: it may be white on both wings, or white on the forewing and yellow on the hind-wing, or light yellow on the forewing and ochre-yellow on the hindwing. Her wet-season black mark-ings are similar to, but more extensive than those of the male, the spots on the hindwing, for example, being joined by a zigzag black line on their inside tips, which has the effect of enclosing diamond-shaped white or yellow spots in the outer marginal border (photograph **197d**, page 124). In both sexes the extent of the black markings is diminished slightly in the dry-season forms, but the 'dumb-bell' fore-wing bar remains a prominent feature.

The undersides of both sexes are whitish-yellow or yellow, the basal two-thirds of the male's fore-wing usually tending to white. The base of the female's forewing is flushed with deeper yellow. The hindwing veins and the veins in the apical tip of the forewing are outlined in black or dark brown. The 'dumb-bell' marks are prominent.

The forest white is found in most of the coastal and wooded areas from Great Brak River and Knysna in the southern Cape, eastwards and northwards through Transkei to the wetter forests of Bal-gowan, Pietermaritzburg and Karkloof in Natal. It extends further north through Zululand to the wetter forests of the Transvaal in the Wolkberg and the Soutpansberg, and westwards to Potchefstroom.

It may be found flying throughout the year, but only in small numbers in the winter months, if at all. It is a slow flier and is often found feeding on the nectar of flowers, when it may be easily netted.

Larval host-plants: *Maerua* spp. including *Maerua cafra* (bush-cherry) and *Maerua racemulosa* (forest bush-cherry).

Belenois aurota aurota (Fabricius, 1793)   PIERIDAE

brown-veined white/grasveldwitjie   **no. 198: p. 124**
Wingspan: ♂ 40-45; ♀ 40-45 mm

The brown-veined white is probably the most common of the white butterflies in South Africa and in fact occurs over the greater part of Africa. As is usual in the family Pieridae, the sexes differ in colour pattern. The male is white above with the apical third of the forewing black and a series of black spots at the vein endings along the outer margin of the hindwing. The apical tip encloses several small narrow patches of white and there is a small or large comma-shaped bar at the end of the forewing cell; this may or may not meet the costa. The female is white (photograph **198b**, page 124) or creamy-yellow above with an entirely black apical area and a broad black border to the outer margin of the hindwing, unrelieved by spots. The black bar in the forewing at the end of the discal cell is broader than the male's, joins the costa and continues as a broad bar down the costa to the base; it is in fact pistol-shaped, with the 'butt' at the end of the cell and the 'barrel' pointing down the costa. There is another black spot on the costa of the hindwing and the outer parts of the hindwing veins are outlined in black, with a V-shape formed by the veins at the end of the cell.

The undersides of the male are white with narrow yellow streaks at the base of the hindwing; the veins in the forewing apex and over the whole of the hindwing are broadly outlined in brown. The female is similar but with more yellow, concentrated in the spots along the margins of the wings and on the hindwing costa.

Large migrations of the brown-veined white often take place, sometimes annually in December or January. Countless millions of individuals may be seen flying in a north-easterly direction from the inland parts of Natal; the same phenomenon occurs in the Transvaal. Records from the northern Orange Free State and the Transvaal also note the migratory movement as being in a north-easterly direction. This species occurs in all parts of South Africa and is on the wing in all months of the year.

Larval host-plants: *Boscia oleoides* (bastard shepherd's tree); *Maerua cafra* (bush-cherry).

Belenois creona severina (Stoll, 1781)   PIERIDAE

African common white/Afrikaanse gewone witjie   **no. 199: p. 125**
Wingspan: ♂ 40-45; ♀ 40-45 mm

The African common white is yet another common and widespread species. The male is white above with a broad black apical tip to the forewing extending to the inner angle, and a broad black border to the hindwing. Several small outwardly streaked white spots are enclosed in the black apex and there is a row of large white spots enclosed in the hindwing border. There is a small dot at the end of the forewing discal cell (which can be compared with the large bar of the next species *B. gidica*). The male's forewing underside is white with a yellowish-spotted black apical area and a yellow flush at the base; the hindwing is yellow with a broad yellow-spotted black border to the outer margin and a network of black veins and patches over the rest of the wing.

The female African common white is variable above and may have a whitish, or more usually yellowish ground-colour (photograph **199c**, page 125) with very broad black outer margins to both fore- and hindwings; this may appear slightly greenish in extreme wet-season forms. The black apical tip may contain one or more yellow spots. There is a black spot or bar at the end of the forewing discal cell which can be larger than that shown in **199c** but which is never as well developed as that of *B. gidica* (photograph **200b**, page 126). The female's undersides are bright yellow with brown-black borders mirroring those on the upperside; the hindwing veins are outlined in black.

This butterfly is on the wing all year round and is found on the edges of rain-forests through to the driest savannas. It occurs from around Mossel Bay in the southern Cape eastwards to the wooded areas of the eastern Cape, thence north-eastwards to Transkei, Natal, Swaziland and most of the Transvaal.

Although it is a common butterfly, a series of males and females representing the summer and winter forms makes a beautiful display in any collection.

Larval host-plants: *Boscia oleoides* (bastard shepherd's tree); *Capparis fascicularis* ('wag-'n-bietjie'); *Maerua cafra* (bush-cherry).

Belenois gidica (Godart, 1819)   PIERIDAE

African veined white/Laeveldwitjie   **no. 200: p. 126**
Wingspan: ♂ 40-55; ♀ 40-55 mm

The African veined white is a woodland species, common throughout the eastern parts of South Africa from the Mossel Bay area in the southern Cape eastwards through Transkei to the eastern half of Natal, and thence north to the Transvaal Lowveld and the northern Transvaal.

It is similar to the African common white (species 199) but the size and shape of the black bar on the upperside at the end of the forewing cell distinguish the two species (see below). It also, however, has a slightly different wing shape, the forewings being longer and narrower at the apex; the outer margins too are slightly straighter.

This species is sexually and seasonally dimorphic. The wet-season male (photograph **200c**, page 126) is white above with a row of black spots at the vein endings on the outer margin of the hindwing, and a black apical third to the forewing; within the black apex, however, the inter-vein areas are whitish, heavily dusted with black. There is a large angled black bar at the end of the forewing cell, curving towards the costa. (The male African common white in South Africa only has a dot at the end of the cell.) The overall black colouration is slightly reduced in the dry-season male, but the forewing cell bar remains large.

The wet-season female (photograph **200b**) has a dark-yellow ground-colour above with very broad dark-brown to black outer margins to both wings and a broad black apical third to the forewing. The basal area of the wings is grey-black. (Form *westwoodi* has a white, not yellow, ground-colour, but is less commonly encountered). There is a black spot at the end of the hindwing cell and the bar at the end of her forewing cell is larger than the male's and meets the narrow black costal margin border. The female of *B. creona severina* normally has only a small black spot on its forewing upperside at the end of the cell (photograph **199c**, page 125).

The underside of the male varies from the wet-season form which is whitish with a network of blackish-brown vein markings, to the extreme dry-season form which is patterned in light brown with a white basal area to the forewing and a white stripe across the hindwing from the base to the middle of the outer margin. The female is similar but with yellow replacing white in both forms.

It is a fast flier but often settles on the ground or on flowers. It is on the wing throughout the year.

Larval host-plant: *Capparis sepiaria* (wild caper-bush).

Dixeia charina charina (Boisduval, 1836)   PIERIDAE

African small white/kusstreekwitjie   **no. 201: p. 126**
Wingspan: ♂ 35-40; ♀ 35-40 mm

The African small white is a delicate little species, exhibiting sexual dimorphism and, to a certain extent, seasonal dimorphism.

The male is white above with an attractive sheen to the wings. It has a narrow black (wet season) or dark-brown (dry season) border around the apex of the forewing, the extent of this border varying slightly with the season. The female is also white above but her brown-black markings are more extensive. On the forewing there is a spot at the end of the discal cell, an irregular bar projecting a short distance from the costa subapically, and one or more spots in mid-wing not far from the outer margin. The outer margin has a brown-black border of moderate width made up of fused spots. The hindwing outer margin has a spot at the end of each vein, smaller spots in mid-wing, and one small spot at the end of the discal cell. In the dry season (winter) these markings diminish, the spots on the hindwing disappearing entirely. Photograph **201c** (page 126) shows a specimen intermediate between the two extremes. The undersides of the male and the female are similar, being whitish and often speckled with black, especially on the hindwing in the dry season.

The distribution range of this species is from the coastal districts of the southern Cape around Mossel Bay eastwards through Transkei to the coastal districts of Natal and northern Zululand. It is a woodland species.

African small whites can easily be netted as they play and feed close to the ground. They are found on the wing throughout the year, more abundantly so in the summer months. It is a regrettable fact that some of the favourite haunts of this species are being destroyed at an alarming rate in northern Zululand by the pineapple and sugar-cane industries.

Larval host-plant: *Capparis sepiaria* var. *citrifolia* (wild caper-bush).

Dixeia doxo parva Talbot, 1943   PIERIDAE

black-veined white/swartaarwitjie   **no. 202: p. 127**
Wingspan: ♂ 35-40; ♀ 35-40 mm

The black-veined white, like the previous species, is both sexually and seasonally dimorphic. The male is white above with the veins of both wings lightly outlined in black and with a narrow black tip to the forewing apex, tapering off about half-way down the outer margin. In the dry season the black colour weakens and diminishes in extent, with the veins in particular being less clearly marked (photograph **202a**, page 127). The female has a broader black apical tip, tapering to the inner angle of the forewing, and a spot at the end of the forewing cell. There is also a large spot in the outer half of the forewing. Although the veins of the female's forewing are not clearly outlined in black, those on the hindwing are, at least in the summer. There is a spot at the end of the hindwing discal cell and the outer margin carries a black spot at the end of each vein. In the dry season the black diminishes in extent and in intensity and the discal spots on both wings may vanish. Intermediate forms between the wet-season and dry-season extremes do occur (photograph **202b**).

The underside of the male in the wet season is white with the wing veins lightly outlined in black. As with many other 'whites', however, the dry-season male's hindwing and his forewing apical area are heavily speckled in brown.

This species has a more northerly distribution and was not recorded in South Africa until 1946, when it was found in numbers at Punda Maria. Since then it has been widely recorded from the northern and central parts of Zululand.

It flies slowly and low down in the long grass and under trees, and is easily netted. The black-veined white is found at other localities in Zululand, but these localities, regrettably, seem to be becoming fewer and fewer. Here again butterfly habitat is being destroyed by pineapple and sugar-cane farming.

It may be found on the wing in any month of the year.
Larval host-plants: *Capparis* spp. (caper-bushes).

Dixeia pigea (Boisduval, 1836)   PIERIDAE

ant-heap white/miershoopwitjie   **no. 203: p. 127**
Wingspan: ♂ 40-45; ♀ 40-50 mm

The ant-heap white is one of the more attractive 'whites', especially the female. Like its relatives it exhibits sexual and seasonal dimorphism. The wet-season male is white above with a narrow black border to the apical tip of the forewing, tailing off down the outer margin with smaller dots at the vein endings and not reaching the inner angle. The hindwing may also have small black dots along the outer margin, one to each vein ending. In the dry season the black almost disappears and is reduced to the bare minimum at the apex itself.

The female is a delicately beautiful insect and more variable in colour than the male. In the wet season it may, however, commonly have white forewings and light yellow hindwings shading to white on the inner margin (photograph **203d**, page 127). There will also be a dark-brown narrow border to the apex of the forewing with larger spots than the male along the outer margins of both wings at the vein endings. Like *Dixeia charina charina* there is also a spot in the outer part of the forewing not far from the middle of the outer margin; there is, however, no spot at the end of the forewing discal cell. Extreme wet-season forms may have a submarginal row of small brown spots near the hindwing outer margin. In the dry season, the brown markings dwindle and the yellow on the hindwings may become even lighter. A particularly attractive female form named *rubrobasalis* occurs frequently in the northern parts of the species' range (Swaziland and the Transvaal). It has the female's normal wet-season brown markings but on an apricot-yellow background with a deeper orange at the bases of the wings (photograph **203b**).

The ant-heap white is a common woodland species, often abundant near rivers, found from the coastal areas of Transkei to the eastern half of Natal and Zululand and thence to the eastern Transvaal and the Soutpansberg. It derives its common name, 'ant-heap white', from its association with its larval food-plants – shrubs and trees of the genus *Maerua* – which often grow around termite-mounds, particularly in Zimbabwe.
Larval host-plants: *Capparis tomentosa* (woolly caper-bush); *Maerua* spp.

Dixeia spilleri (Spiller, 1884)   PIERIDAE

Spiller's canary yellow; Spiller's sulphur yellow/Spiller-geletjie   **no. 204: p. 128**
Wingspan: ♂ 35-40; ♀ 35-40 mm

Spiller's canary yellow is a very distinct species and quite unlike our other *Dixeia*
species in colouration. The male has sulphur-yellow wings above, with a slight border of black around
the apical tip of the forewing. His undersides are entirely sulphur-yellow. The female is also usually
yellow above, but with dark-brown borders to the apical tip. As photograph **204c** (page 128) shows,
however, the variation in wing colouration can be considerable. In breeding this species, I have found
all its forms represented in one batch, from white on both wings through to deep yellow-orange forms.

The female's underside is also yellow but carries an extremely faint row of darker spots parallel to,
but well inside, the outer margin of the hindwing; this character is not found in the male and may be
used to distinguish the sexes. In recent years, from about 1980, Spiller's canary yellow has been found
in larger and larger numbers southwards from its usual haunts of Zululand and the eastern Transvaal. I
have even seen them flying in the streets of Durban and as far south as Margate. Population explosions are also seen from time to time and I once encountered this phenomenon with a fellow-collector
on the Hluhluwe-Sordwana road when we found thousands of freshly emerged butterflies flying from
grass level to the tops of the tallest trees. When we returned to the same locality two weeks later, they
were still there in the same numbers and seemed just as fresh.

This fast-flying species may be found on the wing all year round, but in smaller numbers in the winter months. It occurs from the northern and eastern Transvaal southwards through Swaziland to Zululand in northern Natal.

Larval host-plants: *Capparis* spp.

Appias epaphia contracta (Butler, 1888)   PIERIDAE

diverse white/willewitjie   **no. 205: p. 129**
Wingspan: ♂ 40-50; ♀ 40-50 mm

The diverse white is aptly named as it is strongly sexually and seasonally dimorphic. The wet-season male is white above with a very narrow black edge to the forewing costa which
widens out narrowly over the apex then dwindles to dots and disappears just over half-way down the
outer margin. The hindwings are usually unmarked. The wet-season female has a black forewing upperside with two or three white spots near the apex and a broad white bar at the end of the discal cell;
this bar may or may not meet a large white patch which extends into the wing from the outer half of the
inner margin. The hindwing is white with a broad black border to the outer margin and a slight shading
of brown-black at the base (photograph **205d**, page 129).

In the dry season (winter) the female loses much of the black colouration: the border to the outer
margin of the hindwing narrows considerably and the black on the forewing is confined to the apical
third of the wing (still containing the two or three white or cream spots) and to a very narrow black border along the costa (photograph **205a**).

The males are white underneath and the females are white with brown shades replacing the black
of the upperside. Both sexes, however, have a characteristic yellow blaze extending from the base of
the forewing up towards the costa and ending before the end of the discal cell. There is also a yellow
streak along the base of the hindwing costa.

The diverse white is not a common butterfly and is usually encountered flying singly. The males are
more often seen than the females as they tend to fly more in the open. Both sexes are slow on the wing
and can be easily netted unless disturbed beforehand.

The species occurs from the coastal bush of Transkei, Natal and Zululand to the open glades of the
rain-forests in the eastern Transvaal and the Soutpansberg.

Larval host-plants: *Maerua racemulosa* (forest bush-cherry); *Capparis* spp.

Pontia helice helice (Linnaeus, 1764)

PIERIDAE

meadow white; African cabbage white/bontrokkie
Wingspan: ♂ 35-40; ♀ 35-40 mm

no. 206: p. 129

The male meadow white is white above with a characteristic squarish black bar straddling the apical end of the forewing cell but not reaching the middle of the costa. There is a small black patch enclosing two white spots at the tip of the apex and another squarish black patch (containing a single white spot) immediately adjacent to this on the outer margin. There is a dusting of black scales at the bases of the wings as well as at the vein endings on the hindwing outer margin. The female is similarly but more extensively marked with dark brownish-black. The bar around the end of the forewing cell is larger and reaches the costa and there is a large brown-black patch on the inner margin not far from the inner angle. The dark apical patch and the outer marginal patch are larger and touch at two points to enclose a white spot. Along the outer margin of the hindwing is a fused series of dark brown-black patches each containing a large white spot.

The undersides of both sexes are similar. The white forewing carries markings similar to the upperside but the black of the apical patch is replaced by yellow lightly dusted with black scales. The hindwings are white, but with such a broad dusting of black along the veins combined heavily with yellow, that the white colouration is confined to small pockets scattered over the wing.

The meadow white is appropriately named as it occurs in meadows and old fields throughout South Africa, including the Karoo. It prefers open country and grasslands and is often encountered in large numbers. The flight period lasts throughout the year. Although it appears slow on the wing, when approached it shows its recognition of danger by increasing its speed and keeping a few metres ahead of the collector, whether he is advancing at walking pace or at full speed.

This species was previously known as *Pieris helice*.

Larval host-plants: *Heliophila* spp.; *Alyssum* spp.; *Reseda odorata* (alien to South Africa).

Leptosia alcesta inalcesta Bernardi, 1959

PIERIDAE

African wood white/fladderpapiertjie
Wingspan: ♂ 35-40; ♀ 35-40 mm

no. 207: p. 130

The sexes of the African wood white are similar although the female can be larger than the male and her forewings are more rounded. It is white above with a dark brown-black tip over the curve of the forewing apex and a large brown-black spot in the outer half of the forewing opposite the middle of the outer margin. The undersides are white with a light speckling of black over the hindwing and at the base and apex of the forewing. The speckled parts may (photograph **207b**, page 130) or may not (photograph **207c**) be surrounded by yellow markings. The brown-black spot in the outer part of the forewing upperside is repeated on the underside where it is the only prominent feature.

The African wood white has unusual habits for a 'white'. It is a woodland and rain-forest dweller and is easily recognized by its characteristic flight pattern: each stroke of the wings produces lift, whereafter it allows itself to float downwards, saving itself from 'stalling', it seems, only by another flap of the wings. Its progress is slow as it flutters in and out of the undergrowth and it spends much of its time out of the sunlight. It is easily netted, but only when it ventures away from the undergrowth and away from its larval food-plant which possesses thorns which one might think were designed specifically to entangle butterfly nets.

It occurs in the wetter forest areas of South Africa, from the coastal zone of Natal and Zululand through Swaziland to the eastern Transvaal and the Soutpansberg. The flight period extends throughout the year when conditions permit.

Larval host-plant: *Capparis fascicularis* ('wag-'n-bietjie').

Mylothris rueppellii haemus (Trimen, 1879)

PIERIDAE

twin-dotted border/oranjevlerkwitjie
Wingspan: ♂ 50-55; ♀ 50-55 mm

no. 208: p. 131

This lovely delicate-looking butterfly was previously known as *Mylothris poppea*, but as this name is properly applied to a non-South African species, the twin-dotted border is now classified as *M. rueppellii haemus*.

The male is white above with a small black tip to the apex of the forewing and a round black spot at each vein-ending on the outer margin, the spots decreasing in size towards the inner angle. The black spots also occur along the hindwing outer margin, increasing in size from the costal end to the anal angle. There is a large bright-orange patch at the base of the forewing, biased towards the costa, and a yellow-orange flush at the base of the hindwing. The female is similar but the orange colouration is present at both wing-bases (although stronger on the forewing), and it radiates out with steadily diminishing intensity over the whole wing surface.

The undersides are similar to the uppersides but the black forewing apex is replaced by round black dots at the vein endings.

The twin-dotted border occurs in the drier bush and forest areas of South Africa, from the King William's Town area of the eastern Cape north-eastwards through Transkei to Natal and Zululand and thence to most of the Transvaal. Naboomspruit in the Transvaal is a favourite haunt of this butterfly and its collectors. The flight period may extend throughout the year.

The eggs and larvae are easily found on the food-plants, which are mistletoes of the family Loranthaceae. The eggs are bright yellow (photograph **208a**, page 131) and are laid in clusters numbering often over 100 eggs. The larvae are gregarious (**208b**) and remain together to the final stages when they wander off the host-plant to pupate. They are easy to rear in captivity but are prone to disease in humid conditions and develop fungal infections very quickly. The secret of successful rearing is to ensure adequate ventilation.

Larval host-plants: Mistletoes of the family Loranthaceae.

Princeps dardanus cenea (Stoll, 1790)   PAPILIONIDAE

mocker swallowtail/na-aperswaelstert   **no. 209: pp. 132-133**
Wingspan: ♂ 80-90; ♀ 75-85 mm

The family Papilionidae was revised some years ago, necessitating several scientific name changes. Under the new classification, the mocker swallowtail's name has changed from *Papilio dardanus cenea* to *Princeps dardanus cenea*.

Mocker swallowtails provide a classic demonstration of the phenomena of Batesian mimicry (see page 247) and of sexual and seasonal dimorphism (see page 252).

The male mocker swallowtail is a large boldly marked butterfly with the entire outer third of the forewing black from the inner angle to the costa, the black extending down the basal two-thirds of the costal margin as a broad border. A yellow spot is enclosed in the apical angle and the basal two-thirds of the wing are bright yellow. The hindwing is scalloped slightly along the outer margin and there is a long, broad, club-shaped tail on the outer margin not far from the anal angle – a feature lacking in the female. The black markings on the yellow hindwings vary in extent but tend to be more extensive in the wet season. In such forms there is a broad irregular-edged black band crossing the hindwing from the outer section of the costa to the inner margin near the anal angle; there is also a wavy, narrow black band immediately inside the outer margin, paralleling the scalloping and running on to the yellow-tipped tail. In the dry season all hindwing black markings are reduced and broken.

The male's forewing underside is marked in yellow and brown, mirroring the yellow and black pattern of the upperside. On the hindwing underside light brown and darker brown mirror the upperside yellow and black respectively (photograph **209e**, page 132).

It is not possible here to describe all the forms of the female, which are mimics of various species of distasteful danaine butterflies. In general they have the shape of the male except that they lack the hindwing tails. Female form *hippocoonides*, for example, is a mimic of the friar (species 2 – photograph **2**, page 33), female form *trophonius* (photograph **209g**, page 133) resembles form *liboria* of the southern African milkweed butterfly (photograph **1a**, page 33), while the common female form *cenea* (photograph **209h**, page 133) resembles both *Amauris echeria* and the layman, *Amauris albimaculata albimaculata* (photograph **4a**, page 34). One could forgive the uninitiated for thinking that photographs **209g** and **209h** illustrate females of two quite different species.

Despite the existence of this variety of colours and patterns in the female, however, it is also true to say that the basic pattern is approximately the same throughout and that with experience recognition of the various female forms becomes easier.

The mocker swallowtail is essentially a rain-forest butterfly, and is not found in the drier and more open parts of South Africa. It occurs from the Knysna district eastwards along the coastal zone to Port St. Johns, and thence north to Natal and Zululand, Swaziland and the eastern Transvaal montane forests.

The males fly unhurriedly along the edges of forests and are easily recognized. Females prefer to keep within the confines of their woodland habitat and are not seen as frequently as the males. The species is on the wing all year round, but less so in the colder months.

Breeding the mocker swallowtail is an exciting and rewarding experience as one form of female may produce several of the other forms amongst her offspring. The eggs are laid readily by the female and the larvae – if well looked after – will pass through all their stages within a few weeks.

Larval host-plants: Many and varied, but in the main are members of the family Rutaceae, *e.g. Vepris* spp. (white ironwood trees), *Clausena anisata* (horsewood), *Teclea natalensis* (Natal cherry-orange) and *Citrus* spp.

Princeps echerioides echerioides (Trimen, 1868)   PAPILIONIDAE
white-banded swallowtail/witlintswaelstert   **no. 210: p. 134**
Wingspan: ♂ 70-75; ♀ 70-75 mm

The white-banded swallowtail is sexually dimorphic and its female is a Batesian mimic (see page 247) of the unpalatable danaine butterfly *Amauris echeria*, the chief. Although *A. echeria* is not dealt with in this book, it is very similar to *A. albimaculata* (species 4) and readers are invited to compare the female white-banded swallowtail (photograph **210b**, page 134) with photograph **4a** (page 34). Just to confuse the issue, the female form *cenea* of the previous species, *Princeps dardanus cenea*, also mimics *A. echeria* and a further comparison of photograph **210b** is suggested, this time with **209h**.

Although it is a 'swallowtail', tails are not present on the hindwings of this species. The male is black above with a broad cream-white band from the middle of the inner margin of the hindwing across to the costa and from there across the forewing almost to the apex. The band is solid on the hindwing but on the forewing is composed of separate, transversely elongated spots reducing in size towards the apex. There is a row of cream spots along the outer margin of the hindwing. The female is also black, but has a series of white spots near the outer margins of both wings, larger and more centrally situated white patches in the forewing, and a large buff patch on the basal half of the hindwing, separated from the base itself by a triangular black area.

It is slower on the wing than most swallowtails and confines itself to the fringes of the forests, seldom venturing far out into the open. It is attracted to red flowers and if these are present along the edges of its forest habitat, specimens can be taken easily when they are feeding.

It is found in South Africa from the wetter forests of the eastern Cape and the Amatola Mountains to the Transkei, the eastern half of Natal and the forests of the eastern Transvaal and the Soutpansberg.

The females lay well in captivity and the larvae are typical of the genus, being large and humped in the later stages. The pupae are unusually shaped and resemble pieces of dry bark. There are two broods each year, one emerging in September and October and the other in February, its members flying on until April.

This species was formerly known as *Papilio echerioides*.

Larval host-plants: *Clausena anisata* (horsewood); *Vepris lanceolata* (white ironwood); *Zanthoxylum capense* (small knobwood); possibly most *Citrus* species.

Princeps euphranor (Trimen, 1868)   PAPILIONIDAE
forest swallowtail; bush kite/vlieënde piering   **no. 211: p. 134**
Wingspan: ♂ 75-80; ♀ 90-95 mm

The forest swallowtail is the only swallowtail to be confined to South Africa. Unlike *Princeps echerioides* where both males and females are tail-less, both sexes of *P. euphranor* have a prominent tail on the outer margin of each hindwing near the anal angle. It is not as strongly sexually dimorphic as the previous two species and at first glance male and female may appear alike. There are, however, useful distinguishing characteristics which will be discussed below.

The forest swallowtail is black with a yellow band extending from the middle of the inner margin of the hindwing across to mid-costa, and continuing across the forewing from the middle of its inner margin towards the outer part of the costa. On the hindwing this yellow band has a 'blocky' appearance and is made up of several separate segments of yellow, unlike *P. echerioides* where the band is continuously yellow across the hindwing. On the forewing the segments of the yellow band do not diminish towards the apex in as symmetrical a fashion as those of *P. echerioides*. On the outer edge of the middle of the yellow band of the hindwing there is usually a semicircular 'bulge' formed by a group of three small yellow spots; these are in fact clustered round the outside edge of the end of the discal cell and they serve to distinguish both male and female of this species from any other South African swallowtail. There is a small orange spot on the hindwing inner margin near the anal angle. In the male this spot is small and difficult to see; in the female it is conspicuous (photograph **211b**, page 134).

The other difference between male and female is in the spotting along the outer margins. On the male's upperside there is a row of irregular-shaped small yellow spots parallel to the outer margin of the hindwing but absent from the forewing; in the female there is a double row of such spots on the hindwing as well as a clear row parallel to the outer margin of the forewing.

For the collector the male forest swallowtail is a most frustrating butterfly to watch as it sails and glides for most of the day out of reach among the tree-tops, chasing off other butterflies which intrude into its domain. The female is more accessible, preferring to fly lower down in its forest habitat, searching for flowers to feed on and food-plants to lay her eggs on.

This species inhabits the cooler rain-forests from Stutterheim in the eastern Cape north-eastwards to Port St. Johns, Kokstad and inland Natal, and thence to the rain-forests of the Wolkberg and Soutpansberg in the Transvaal. It may be found on the wing from September to April.

It is a curious fact that *P. euphranor* is attracted to red objects, be they flowers or motor-cars. I have netted them as they inspected and 'dive-bombed' my own red car and on another occasion at the same place I used a red towel draped over low bushes to attract them within reach.

This species was formerly known as *Papilio euphranor*.

Larval host-plant: *Cryptocarya woodii* (Cape quince).

Princeps constantinus constantinus (Ward, 1871) PAPILIONIDAE

Constantine's swallowtail/Konstantyn-swaelstert **no. 212: p. 134**
Wingspan: ♂ 75-80; ♀ 80-85 mm

Constantine's swallowtail resembles the forest swallowtail (species 211) very closely. Both male and female have a clubbed tail on each hindwing and both are marked above in black and yellow. The sexes are similar although the female is larger than the male and has more greybrown colour in the basal areas of the uppersides of both wings.

It is distinguished from the forest swallowtail by its possession of a large yellow spot inside the apical end of the forewing discal cell and by its lack of the three spots which in the forest swallowtail curve round the outer edge of the hindwing discal cell. Both sexes of this species have a row of yellow spots parallel to the outer margins of both wings. The hindwing band of yellow is narrower than that of the white-banded swallowtail and is clearly, if barely, segmented; its edges are straighter and more regular than those of the forest swallowtail.

Constantine's swallowtail is a thornveld butterfly and occurs from northern Natal northwards through Swaziland to the western and eastern sides of the Wolkberg and north-westwards to the Soutpansberg. It is a local insect in that it is only found in certain restricted localities and it is on the wing from December to March although also, if conditions permit, throughout the year. It is fast and alert at all times but is not a high-flying butterfly, preferring to fly about two metres or so above the ground. It tends to patrol certain areas where it will often remain for several days. Females are not easily found. They sometimes lay in captivity, but generally are reluctant to do so. However if eggs are obtained they may be bred through to the adult stage with ease.

This species was formerly known as *Papilio constantinus*.

Larval host-plants: *Clausena anisata* (horsewood); *Teclea* spp.; possibly *Citrus* species.

Princeps demodocus demodocus (Esper, 1798) PAPILIONIDAE

citrus swallowtail; Christmas butterfly; orange dog (larva)/
lemoenvlinder; lemoenskoenlapper
Wingspan: ♂ 80-90; ♀ 85-90 mm **no. 213: p. 135**

The citrus swallowtail is the best-known of its family in South Africa and occurs throughout the country, even in the Karoo. The sexes are almost identical and both are tail-less. It is a black butterfly with a yellow band across the hindwing from the middle of the inner margin to midcosta, and a similar but broken band on the forewing from the middle of the inner margin towards the apex; the spots which make up the forewing band are irregular in shape and size. There are three irregular yellow spots inside the apical end of the forewing discal cell and the basal end of the cell is lightly mottled with numerous fine yellow flecks. The outer margins of fore- and hindwings have both a marginal and a submarginal row of yellow spots. There are two large blue, black and orange eye-spots on each hindwing, one on mid-costa and the other on the inner margin not far from the anal angle. The costal spot subtends a half-moon of yellow on its outer edge (male), or a half-moon of yellow with part of it flushed with orange (female – see photograph **213e**, page 135). The outer margin of the hindwing has a scalloped edge.

The undersides resemble the uppersides but the basal end of the forewing cell is longitudinally streaked with yellow, while the yellow spots on the hindwing subtend coloured 'half-eye-spots' into the black area in mid-wing (photograph **213d**).

Although the citrus swallowtail can be found in all months of the year, it is commoner in the warmer months, particularly December, and has thus earned the alternative name 'Christmas butterfly'. Males are often found flying or chasing other butterflies on the tops of small koppies in the heat of the day – a practice known as 'hilltopping' (see page 18).

The larvae ('orange dogs') are sometimes a pest on young citrus trees where they can devour enormous quantities of leaves. They are conspicuous (photograph **213a**) and can readily be collected from any small citrus tree for captive breeding. The larvae of the family Papilionidae possess a curious structure known as an osmeterium (page 251) on the prothorax at the back of the head. This forked, fleshy organ is everted suddenly when the larva is threatened, frightening predators with its bright colour and pungent smell (photograph **213a**).

This species was formerly known as *Papilio demodocus*.

Larval host-plants: Many and varied, mostly *Citrus*-related plants, cultivated and wild; *Clausena anisata* (horsewood); *Toddalia asiatica*; *Zanthoxylum capense* (small knobwood); *Foeniculum vulgare* (fennel); *Vepris lanceolata* (white ironwood).

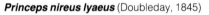

Princeps nireus lyaeus (Doubleday, 1845)   PAPILIONIDAE

green-banded swallowtail; black velvet/groenlintswaelstert   **no. 214: p. 136**
Wingspan: ♂ 75-85; ♀ 75-85 mm

This magnificent and exotic-looking butterfly is another of the tail-less swallow-tails, although there is a noticeable lobe in the hindwing where a tail would normally be situated. The male is jet-black above with an iridescent bluish-green band across the hindwing from the middle of the inner margin of the hindwing (but not touching it) to mid-costa, continuing as a solid band (broken only by black veins) on the forewing towards mid-costa, but ending in a group of two or three spots straddling the apical end of the forewing cell. There are one or two blue spots in the apex and a row of spots near and parallel to the scalloped outer margin of the hindwing.

The female is very similar but the wing spots and bands are a duller, more greenish colour. The female's upper surface is also a less intense shade of black than the male's, with a hint of dark brown in the basal area. Another method of distinguishing the sexes in the green-banded swallowtail as well as other members of the genus *Princeps*, is to look at the tip of the abdomen. The female's abdomen is tapered and terminates in a slight point through which the ovipositor is extruded during egg-laying; the male possesses a pair of 'claspers', each shaped like a half cup, which are used to hold the female while mating.

The undersides, however, provide the best means of distinguishing the sexes in this species. The male is black with a bold cream-white band parallel to the outer margin of the hindwing. The female is mottled in various shades of brown with a dark basal patch in the forewing and one or two cream spots on the hindwing inner margin near the anal angle (photographs **214b** and **d**, page 136). She lacks the cream stripe of the male.

The green-banded swallowtail may be found on the wing throughout the year and occurs from the Mossel Bay area in the southern Cape eastwards along the coastal zone to Transkei, the eastern half of Natal and to the eastern and northern Transvaal. It is a forest and bush species and is a fast and evasive flier. It may, however, be captured at flowers, or at the muddy patches where it drinks, or on fresh animal droppings.

This species was formerly known as *Papilio nireus*.

Larval host-plants: *Clausena anisata* (horsewood); *Calodendrum capense* (Cape chestnut); *Vepris natalensis* (Natal cherry-orange); cultivated citrus.

Princeps ophidicephalus (Oberthür, 1878)   PAPILIONIDAE

emperor swallowtail/koningswaelstert   **no. 215: p. 136**
Wingspan: ♂ 80-110; ♀ 90-120 mm

The emperor swallowtail is the largest South African butterfly, with females of the subspecies _phalusco_ occasionally achieving a stretched wing-tip to wing-tip measurement of some 12 centimetres. Five subspecies (_ayresi_, _entabeni_, _phalusco_, _transvaalensis_ and _zuluensis_) are currently recognized in this country, but for the purposes of this book the differences between them can be considered to be minor. For the record, however, the specimens portrayed on page 136 are of subspecies _zuluensis_ from the Eshowe district in Natal. The sexes are similar and both carry a long tail on each hindwing.

The male is black above with a yellow band from the middle of the hindwing inner margin to the mid-costa, continuing on the forewing to the costa near the apex. The forewing band is made up of clearly separate spots which may or may not touch at their widest points. There is a yellow bar in the forewing cell near its apical end. The outer margins of both wings have a yellow dot between each vein ending and there is also a row of yellow kidney-shaped spots parallel to the outer margins. The long, club-shaped tail is black with a yellow mark on each side of its tip. Both sexes have a large black, blue and orange eye-spot at the middle of the hindwing costa, the spot penetrating half-way into the yellow median band. There is another similar eye-spot on the inner margin, not far from the anal angle. Immediately next to this spot, in the next vein 'compartment', is another, rather elongated quasi-eye-spot; in the male it is blue, black and yellow, while in the female it is blue, black and orange. This is the easiest character to use to distinguish the sexes (see photographs **215a** and **b**, page 136).

The emperor swallowtail is a rain-forest species, occurring from the King William's Town area in the eastern Cape eastwards through the coastal and kloof forests of Transkei to inland Natal, and thence to the rain-forests of the eastern Transvaal and the Soutpansberg. Its flight period is from September to April but it is more abundant in the summer months.

It loves open forest glades and roadways and males may be seen patrolling up and down roads or along the edges of forested areas. It flies fairly low down but it is skilful at avoiding the collector's net and, once disturbed, it is usually too fast to chase.

Waiting along forest roadways is possibly the best way to net it. As it flies past, swing the net and catch it from behind, being careful not to swing too hard as this will result in broken hindwings and tails. In the early morning and late afternoon it feeds from flowers and drinks at wet patches on the ground, where it may be more readily captured.

This species was formerly known as _Papilio ophidicephalus_.

Larval host-plants: _Clausena anisata_ (horsewood); _Zanthoxylum capense_ (small knobwood); _Calodendrum capense_ (Cape chestnut); cultivated _Citrus_ spp.

Graphium morania (Angas, 1849)   PAPILIONIDAE

white lady swordtail/witnooientjie   **no. 216: p. 137**
Wingspan: ♂ 50-55; ♀ 55-60 mm

The white lady swordtail is one of the smaller swallowtails and is another tail-less species. The sexes are similar above and below.

It is black above with a large white area extending into the forewing from the inner margin and another occupying the entire basal half of the hindwing. There is a line of small white spots parallel to the outer margins of both wings, the two or three spots nearest the anal angle of the hindwing being chevron-shaped and pointing into the wing. There is another, shorter row of four white spots on the hindwing between the outer row and the white basal area. The apical and costal areas of the forewing carry several white spots varying in size and shape, two of the largest being in the discal cell.

The undersides are light brown, with white markings corresponding to those on the upperside and with a red-brown blaze on the basal half of the costa which also fills the basal half of the discal cell. This colour also appears to a more limited extent at the base of the hindwing.

The white lady swordtail occurs in woodland habitats from the Natal South Coast around Port Shepstone north through the eastern half of Natal and Zululand to the eastern and northern Transvaal. It is a lone flier and is seldom seen in numbers. It keeps to the edges of woodland and is not easily netted unless caught unawares while feeding on flowers.

The larvae can often be found on the food-plants and are beautifully decorated with bands of yellow and green. I have found that females are rather reluctant to lay in captivity.

This species was formerly known as *Papilio morania*, but a recent revision of the genus *Papilio* has allocated our 'swallowtails' to the genus *Princeps* and our 'swordtails' to the genus *Graphium*.

Larval host-plants: *Uvaria caffra* (small cluster-pear); *Artabotrys brachypetalus* (large hook-berry); *A. monteiroae* (red hook-berry).

Graphium leonidas leonidas (Fabricius, 1793)　　　　　PAPILIONIDAE

veined swordtail/bontswaardstert　　　　　　　　　　　　**217: p. 137**
Wingspan: ♂ 75-80; ♀ 75-80 mm

The veined swordtail, like the previous species, is a tail-less swallowtail. The sexes are similar above and below. It is black above with the forewing carrying several white spots of varying sizes and shapes. The larger spots are situated in mid-wing with the smaller spots forming a row parallel to the outer margin. The hindwing is black with its basal half white (photograph **217a**, page 137) or brownish, and the male has long whitish hairs (hair-pencils – see pages 9 and 251) at the base of the inner margin. There are tiny white spots along the very edge of the outer margin, followed by a row of larger white spots parallel to the outer margin, and finally by a short row of white flecks just outside the white basal area. The undersides are brown with white markings corresponding to those on the uppersides. This species appears to mimic, in colour and posture, unpalatable danaines of the genus *Amauris*, for example *A. ochlea* (species 3). Photographs **217a** (page 137) and **3a** (page 33) invite comparison.

Another form of this species may occasionally be encountered in which the white spots have a green-brown tinge.

This common woodland species is found from the bushveld of the northern and eastern Transvaal south through Swaziland, Zululand and the eastern half of Natal to the King William's Town district of the eastern Cape. It is a wary, alert butterfly which flies off immediately when disturbed and is not easily netted. The best time to attempt to capture it is when it is feeding, *Lantana* flowers being a favourite source of nectar. It is a regular visitor to small koppies during the heat of the day and spends much time playing with and chasing other butterflies. Females are not often encountered and I have found them reluctant to lay eggs in captivity.

Its main flight period is from September to April but it can be seen in the winter months.

This species was formerly known as *Papilio leonidas*.

Larval host-plant: *Monanthotaxis caffra* (dwaba-berry).

Graphium policenes (Cramer, 1775)　　　　　　　　　PAPILIONIDAE

small striped swordtail/Ooskusswaardstert　　　　　　　**no. 218: p. 138**
Wingspan: ♂ 55-60; ♀ 60-65 mm

Some of the butterflies of the genus *Graphium* have exceptionally long tails with white tips and are known as 'swordtails'. *Graphium policenes* is the smallest of the four swordtails occurring in South Africa. The sexes are alike although the male possesses long hair-pencils at the base of the hindwings. It is black above with vivid pale-green markings. On the forewing there is a row of small elongated spots parallel to the outer margin. The middle of the forewing carries a series of around eight large pale-green blotches from the middle of the inner margin, diminishing in size towards the apical area, while the cell contains a series of about five straight transverse bars each ending in a spot outside the cell near the costal margin. The hindwing is similarly marked, with a row of small elongated spots along the outer margin, a series of blotches in mid-wing diminishing in size between mid-costa and the anal angle, and two long bars parallel to the inner margin. There is a red spot on each hindwing on the inner margin a short distance from the anal angle. The tail is long, black and white-tipped. There are three half-moons of grey at the anal angle near the base of the tail.

Graphium policenes may be distinguished from the following species, *G. colonna*, by the latter's more black appearance and lack of mid-hindwing blotches. Two other swordtails not dealt with in this book may be encountered in Natal, namely *G. antheus* and *G. porthaon*; both may be separated from *G. policenes* by the wavy or S-shaped bars in their forewing cells, although *G. porthaon* also has cream-yellow rather than pale-green markings.

The markings on the underside mirror those of the upperside, with browns and white replacing black and green respectively; there is, however, a distinct and more or less continuous red line through the middle of the hindwing from near the base of the costa to the inner margin near the anal angle (photograph **218d**, page 138).

The small striped swordtail occurs in forest and coastal bush from Port St. Johns in Transkei north through coastal Natal and Zululand to the Mozambique border. Its flight period is from September to April. Although it is a common species it usually flies singly, congregating however at damp mud patches to drink. It flies fast and is difficult to catch on the wing without damaging the slender tails. Unfortunately the green colours fade after death. This species was formerly known as *Papilio policenes*.

Larval host-plants: *Uvaria caffra* (small cluster-pear); *Artabotrys monteiroae* (red hook-berry).

Graphium colonna (Ward, 1873)   PAPILIONIDAE

mamba swordtail; black swordtail/mambaswaardstert   **no. 219: p. 138**
Wingspan: ♂ 60-65; ♀ 60-65 mm

The mamba swordtail, like the small striped swordtail, has vivid light-green markings on a black background. The sexes are alike although the male may be readily distinguished from the female by his possession of long white hair-pencils on the inner margin of the hindwing near the base. The tail on the hindwing is long, black, and white-tipped. Although at first sight *G. colonna* and *G. policenes* may appear alike, there are important differences. Both have the row of elongated small spots near the outer margins, but where *G. policenes* has a row of large blotches in mid-hindwing, these are entirely lacking in *G. colonna*. The forewing cell bars are similar, but the one nearest the apical end of the cell in *G. colonna* tends to be wavy, not straight. The mid-forewing blotches of *G. colonna* also differ from those of *G. policenes*, being smaller and more equal in size; they commence not at the inner margin but slightly in from it. There are two red spots on the inner margin of each hindwing near the anal angle. The white tip of the tail is more extensive than that of *G. policenes*.

In South Africa this species is confined to the coastal bush and forest areas of Zululand from about Richards Bay northwards. It is a fairly slow-flying butterfly and can be seen flying lazily along the edges of the forest, perhaps stopping to drink at a muddy patch. At such drinking-spots mamba swordtails make a glorious sight, gently flapping their wings as they walk about seeking moisture. In the darkness of the forest the white-tipped tails are conspicuous and easy to follow.

This species was formerly known as *Papilio colonna*.

It is on the wing between September and May, but can be found in June and July.

Larval host-plant: *Artabotrys monteiroae* (red hook-berry).

Coeliades forestan forestan (Stoll, 1782)   HESPERIIDAE

striped policeman/witbroekkonstabel   **no. 220: p. 139**
Wingspan: ♂ 45-50; ♀ 50-55 mm

This large and attractive skipper is similar to other *Coeliades* species on its uppersides, but is distinctively marked below. The sexes are more or less similar. Its forewing above is uniform brown with a hint of grey; there is a slight suffusion of orange near the inner margin. The hindwing, however, is dark brown in a broad semicircle from the costal margin round the outer margin to the anal angle; the basal area and inner marginal area are light orange and covered with long wing-scales and hairs, while the lobe on the wing at the anal angle is distinctly fringed with bright-orange cilia. The ciliate fringe around the remainder of the outer margin is dark brown.

The underside of the forewing is a lighter brown with a suffusion of grey-white radiating into the wing from the middle section of the inner margin. The hindwing underside is similar to the upperside but has a bold broad white band crossing the wing from mid-costa, parallel to the outer margin. It stops short of the inner margin where there is a single white blotch to mark its end-point. Four other species of *Coeliades* occur in South Africa, all somewhat similar in appearance to *C. forestan*. Only two of them, however, possess a white band on the underside of the hindwing. They can be separated from *C. forestan* by their possession of clear black spots on the white band. *Coeliades anchises* has one black spot on each white area and is known as the 'one-pip policeman'. *Coeliades pisistratus* has two spots and a black blotch on each patch and is known as the 'two-pip policeman'.

Its fast and powerful flight makes the striped policeman hard to net as it zigzags and skips about the undergrowth. It is more frequently seen in the early morning and the late afternoon. The flight period extends throughout the year. It is found from the Port Elizabeth area of the eastern Cape eastwards along the coastal zone through Transkei to the whole of Natal and Zululand, the Orange Free State and the Transvaal.

Larval host-plants: *Combretum bracteosum* (hiccup creeper); *C. apiculatum* (hairy red bushwillow); *Solanum mauritianum** (bug-tree); *Millettia sutherlandii* (bastard umzimbeet); *Robinia pseudo-acacia** (false acacia or locust-tree).
(**both alien species*)

Celaenorrhinus mokeezi (Wallengren, 1857) **p. 139**   HESPERIIDAE

Christmas forester; large sprite/Kersfeesbosjagtertjie   **no. 221: p. 139**
Wingspan: ♂ 35-40; ♀ 38-43 mm

There are two subspecies of the Christmas forester recognized in South Africa. The nominate race, *Celaenorrhinus mokeezi mokeezi*, occurs in the eastern Cape and southern Natal while subspecies *separata* is found in the Zululand and Transvaal parts of the species' range. The subspecies portrayed on page 139 is *mokeezi*.

The males and females of this butterfly are similar in appearance. The uppersides are dark coffee-brown with two wavy-edged, largely hyaline, orange bars on each forewing and an orange spot in the middle of the hindwing. The larger of the two forewing bars starts on mid-costa and traverses the wing almost to the inner angle; the smaller bar traverses half-way across the apical tip from the costa. In the subspecies *separata* there is a row of small orange spots parallel to the outer margin of the hindwing, but these are barely visible or absent in subspecies *mokeezi* (photograph **221a**). The basal areas of the uppersides of the wings are typically covered with fine orange hairs.

The undersides of the wings are almost identical to the uppersides in colour pattern.

The Christmas forester is a forest-living butterfly and is frequently seen sunning itself in open glades and at roadsides in its woodland habitat. It sits with its wings open on top of a leaf and is easily netted; it also, however, has a habit of resting on the undersides of leaves.

It occurs from the Port Elizabeth area of the eastern Cape eastwards along the coast through Transkei to Natal and thence to the forests of the eastern Transvaal and the Soutpansberg.

Its flight period is year-round, but it is scarce in winter.

Larval host-plant: *Isoglossa woodii* (buck-weed).

Tagiades flesus (Fabricius, 1781)   HESPERIIDAE

clouded flat; clouded forester/skaduweedartelaartjie   **no. 222: p. 139**
Wingspan: ♂ 40-45; ♀ 40-45 mm

The clouded flat is easy to spot and identify while on the wing, with the white on its hindwings flashing in the sun. The sexes are similar although the hyaline patches on the female's forewings tend to be larger than the male's. It is dark brown above in the summer form and lighter brown above in the dry-season (winter) form (photograph **222a**, page 139), and is notable for the two groups of hyaline spots on the forewing. One group, or row, of small spots is situated subapically and the other group of larger spots is in mid-wing, extending into the centre of the wing from the costal side. The spots of this group are usually considerably larger in the female than in the male. In the wet-season form particularly, faint black spots may be visible on the hindwing parallel to the outer margin.

The undersides are distinctive, the forewing being similar to its upperside but the hindwing being almost completely white, as is also the underside of the abdomen. The brown is confined to a broad border along the costa and to a broken border on the outer margin near the anal angle. A row of more-or less-visible black spots runs through the white area parallel to the outer margin of the wing, and continues along the costal edge of the white zone.

A related species, *Eagris nottoana*, is rather similar to the clouded flat but the mid-forewing group of hyaline spots straddles the whole wing and not just the costal half.

The clouded flat, like most skippers, is fast on the wing. It settles from time to time, mostly on the underside of a favourite leaf or twig, and here it may be easily netted. The flight period is all year round but it is more abundant in the hotter months. It occurs in rain-forest and coastal bush from Somerset East in the eastern Cape eastwards through Transkei and northwards from coastal Natal to the wetter forests of the eastern Transvaal and the Soutpansberg.

Larval host-plant: *Dioscorea cotinifolia* (wild yam).

Sarangesa motozi (Wallengren, 1857)　　　　　　　　HESPERIIDAE

elfin skipper/motozi-springertjie　　　　　　　　　　**no. 223: p. 139**
Wingspan: ♂ 32-35; ♀32-35 mm

　　　　　　　The sexes of the elfin skipper are similar although the female is slightly larger than the male and the outer margins of her wings are more rounded than the male's. It is dark brown above, slightly mottled in appearance, and has a group of three small squarish hyaline spots near the fore-wing costa just below the apex and several larger hyaline spots in mid-wing. The hindwing is similar but has one round hyaline spot in the middle of the wing – a characteristic which identifies this species immediately. There is a brown-and-white chequered ciliate fringe to the outer margin of both wings.

　　　　　　　The undersides are also dark brown but are somewhat lighter and mottled with small orange patches. These are mostly on the hindwing, particularly near the outer margin, but there are also orange flecks on the forewing around the inner angle.

　　　　　　　This species occurs in savanna woodland or rain-forest from the western, northern and eastern Transvaal southwards through Zululand and Natal to the coastal districts of Transkei and the eastern Cape. It is not a common species but is more abundant in the wetter forests than in the bushveld. It can sustain rapid flight for long periods and normally settles on the ground with its wings open. Although it is most abundant from August to April, it can be found all year round when the climate permits.

Larval host-plant: *Peristrophe hensii.*

Netrobalane canopus (Trimen, 1864)　　　　　　　　HESPERIIDAE

brown-tipped skipper; buff-tipped skipper/bruinpuntspringertjie
Wingspan: ♂ 30-35; ♀ 35-40 mm　　　　　　　　　　**no. 224: p. 140**

　　　　　　　The brown-tipped skipper is an unmistakable species with its oddly shaped angular wings and clear hyaline wing-patches. The sexes are similar.

　　　　　　　The forewing upperside has a dark-brown basal area and a dark-brown apical area occupying about one-third of the wing. The entire mid-wing area is transparent with irregular patches of translucent white or cream. There is also a small group of hyaline spots on the costa just below the apex. The dark-brown colouration is not uniform but has a marbled appearance and lightens towards the inner angle. The hindwing is similar with dark brown at the base extending irregularly down the inner margin, extensive hyaline patches in mid-wing, and marbled light brown and translucent cream areas near the outer margin. The hairs of the ciliate fringe become longer towards the anal angle of the hindwing.

　　　　　　　Where they are not hyaline, the undersides are cream-brown, although the forewing apex shades to chestnut-brown. There is a prominent black spot on the hindwing near the anal angle.

　　　　　　　The brown-tipped skipper is on the wing in all months of the year, but more so in the period from September to April when conditions are more favourable. It is never found in large numbers and usually flies singly. It occurs in bush habitats from the bushveld of the northern and eastern Transvaal south to the coastal forests of Natal and to the King William's Town area of the eastern Cape.

　　　　　　　It has the habit of sitting on an isolated twig and branch, from which vantage-point it chases off all intruding butterflies. It is also, however, a regular visitor to hilltops in the middle of the day.

Larval host-plants: *Grewia occidentalis* (cross-berry); *Dombeya cymosa* (Natal wild pear); *Pavonia burchellii.*

Spialia spio (Linnaeus, 1767)　　　　　　　　　　HESPERIIDAE

mountain sandman/bergsandmannetjie　　　　　　　**no. 225: p. 140**
Wingspan: ♂ 22-25; ♀ 25-28 mm

　　　　　　　The mountain sandman is one of 14 very similar members of its genus in southern Africa, and the only one dealt with here. Some are localized in their distribution and others are very widespread. *Spialia spio* is one of the latter group and is found in all regions of South Africa.

　　　　　　　The sexes are similar, the males being dark brown with several cream spots of various sizes scattered over the forewing and somewhat fewer on the hindwing. On both wings the smaller spots are concentrated near the outer margin where they form a submarginal row; the hindwing otherwise has only a very large cream blotch in mid-wing and a small spot near the base. There is a chequered brown-and-white ciliate fringe to the outer margins of both wings. The undersides are light brown and are also heavily spotted with cream spots, corresponding to those on the upperside but now more numerous on the hindwing. The row of submarginal spots is repeated on the forewing but not on the hindwing. There is a cream bar along the basal edge of the forewing costa. The ciliate fringe is chequered in light brown and white.

The mountain sandman is a fast flier but returns frequently to settle at its chosen station. The flight period extends throughout the year but in the colder months it is rarely encountered. Although it is called the 'mountain' sandman, it prefers the lower slopes of hills and valleys.

Larval host-plants: Many and varied, but include *Hermannia* spp., *Pavonia* spp., *Hibiscus* spp. and *Triumfetta* spp.

Metisella metis (Linnaeus, 1764)   HESPERIIDAE

gold-spotted sylph/reënboswalsertjie   **no. 226: p. 140**
Wingspan: ♂ 25-30; ♀ 25-30 mm

Two subspecies of the gold-spotted sylph are currently recognized in South Africa. The nominate race, *Metisella metis metis*, occurs from the Cape Peninsula eastwards to near Swellendam, being replaced from Swellendam by subspecies *paris*, which is the race found in the southern and eastern Cape, Natal and Transvaal parts of the species' range.

The sexes are similar. The species is dark brown – sometimes almost black – above, with gold-orange angular spots on both wings, concentrated on the outer halves of the wings. There is a dense dusting of gold scales at the basal end of the forewing costa and less prominent diffuse rays of gold radiating out a short distance from the bases of both wings. The male can usually be distinguished from the female by its more prominent and complete row of submarginal spots parallel to the outer margin of the hindwing (photograph **226b**, page 140).

The undersides of the male are dark brown, the hindwing unspotted and the forewing carrying large gold-orange spots similar to those of the upperside (photographs **226a** and **c**). The female has, however, lighter brown undersides and, while she has gold-orange spots on the forewing like the male, her hindwing has several 'faded' light-brown spots on a slightly darker-brown background.

The gold-spotted sylph is a woodland species and occurs from Cape Town along the southern Cape coastal areas to Transkei and thence to inland Natal and north to the forests of the Transvaal escarpment and the Soutpansberg. Large numbers can be found playing together and feeding on flowers. It does not fly high but appears to prefer to zigzag close to the ground where it often settles with wings upright but not fully open. It can be found on the wing at all times of the year.

Larval host-plants: *Stenotaphrum dimidiatum* (coarse couch-grass); *Stipa dregeana* (Bushman-grass); *Ehrharta erecta*.

Kedestes macomo (Trimen, 1862)   HESPERIIDAE

Macomo ranger/Makomo-swerwer   **no. 227: p. 141**
Wingspan: ♂ 22-25; ♀ 25-30 mm

The sexes are similar in this attractive little skipper, although the female is larger than the male and the outer margins of her wings are more rounded. It is dark brown above with a lighter ciliate fringe to the outer margins of both wings. There are several yellow-orange spots on both wings, distributed from the base outwards (not solely on the outer parts of the wings as in the next species, *K. callicles*). These spots tend to be squarish or rectangular towards the outer margins. The basal area of the forewing in particular has a covering of long orange hairs. The undersides are yellow-orange except for the third of the forewing nearest the inner margin which is a darker brown. The hindwing is spotted with black and, although the forewing bears one or two spots, it tends to be streaked with brown-black especially on the outer half of the wing. There is a narrow brown-black border to the outer margins of the undersides of both wings.

The Macomo ranger is a bushveld species which occurs from the low-lying coastal districts of the eastern Cape and Transkei through the bushveld of Natal and Zululand to the eastern, northern and western Transvaal.

It is a low and fast flier and is not easily netted. It does, however, rest frequently on grass-stems with wings erect and may be captured by stealth. Although it may be seen on the wing throughout the year, it can be scarce or absent in the colder periods.

Larval host-plant: *Imperata cylindrica* (cotton-wool grass).

Kedestes callicles (Hewitson, 1868)   HESPERIIDAE

pale ranger/bosveldswerwer   **no. 228: p. 141**
Wingspan: ♂ 24-27; ♀ 27-30 mm

Males and females of the pale ranger are similar in appearance although the female is slightly larger than the male and often slightly lighter in colour. The butterfly is dark brown above with several squarish or rectangular yellow spots on both fore- and hindwings, in each case mostly in the outer half of the wing. The basal area of both wings is covered with long yellow-brown hairs and there is a golden-brown ciliate fringe to the outer margin of both wings.

The undersides have a yellow-gold ground colour except for the half of the forewing nearest to the inner margin which is dark brown. The yellow spots of the upperside are repeated in the same situations on the undersides of both wings but are distinctly dark-edged. The wing veins are outlined in black as they approach the outer margins, which themselves have a narrow black border.

This little skipper is usually found flying in the shade, under trees or through low-lying bush. Although it is common, it is never found in large numbers. It is a bushveld species, occurring from around Durban northwards through Zululand and Swaziland to the bushveld of the eastern, northern and western Transvaal. Its flight period is from November to April.

Larval host-plants: Unknown, but probably one or more grass species.

Leucochitonea levubu Wallengren, 1857   HESPERIIDAE

white-cloaked skipper/witjasdartelaartjie   **no. 229: p. 141**
Wingspan: ♂ 30-35; ♀ 35-40 mm

The male and female of this exquisite butterfly are similar in appearance above and below. The uppersides are snow-white with a black border to the forewing costa and outer margin, and to the hindwing outer margin. The forewing has a second narrow black band parallel to the one on the outer margin and a third band crosses the apical tip from costa to outer margin. As the wing veins are blackened near the margins on both wings, a chequered appearance is created as they cross the black bands, reinforced by the black-and-white ciliate fringe to the outer margins. The undersides are very similar to the uppersides but have a black border to the basal half of the hindwing costal margin and heavier black markings towards the anal angle of the hindwing.

Conspicuous on the wing, the white-cloaked skipper is easily identified by the white of its wings. The males engage in 'hilltopping' (see page 18) during the heat of the day, but although the females appear more scarce they can be seen feeding from flowers in suitable localities. The species is on the wing from November to April.

It is only found in the northern parts of South Africa, from the extreme north-east Cape through most of the northern half of the Transvaal and thence south-east through Swaziland to the eastern side of the Ubombo Mountains in Zululand.

Larval host-plant: _Grewia flava_ (wild raisin).

Moltena fiara (Butler, 1870)   HESPERIIDAE

banana nightfighter/piesangskemervegter   **no. 230: p. 141**
Wingspan: ♂ 40-45; ♀ 45-55 mm

The banana nightfighter is one of the 'skippers' with crepuscular habits, that is, it tends to be active at twilight. It is in fact a frequent visitor to the ultraviolet lamps used by moth-collectors to attract moths at night. Its somewhat strange colloquial name derives firstly from its larval host-plant, the Natal wild banana (_Strelitzia nicolai_), and secondly from its fast, dashing – and audible – nocturnal flights.

This robust insect with its seemingly disproportionately large head, thorax and abdomen, is moth-like in appearance. The sexes are similar. The uppersides of the wings are deep chestnut-brown basally, progressing to darker brown at the margins. There is a narrow chestnut-coloured ciliate fringe to the outer margins of both wings. The undersides of both sexes are similar and are a fairly uniform brown, but lighter than the uppersides. The male can be distinguished from the female by his conspicuous white antennae (photograph **230b**, page 141), the female's being brown. These white antennae can be seen flashing like small spotlights when the male is flying. The female is larger than the male and her angular forewings have a rounded, not straight, outer margin.

The larvae of the banana nightfighter are easily found on the host-plant. The larvae nibble out sections of the leaf on which they feed and, with thread from a silk-gland, weave the leaf margins together forming a tube enclosing their bodies. The tell-tale tubes will yield larvae and pupae. The pupae are covered with a white powdery substance.

The banana nightfighter's distribution range matches that of the Natal wild banana, its host-plant. It occurs from the East London area of the eastern Cape north-eastwards through Transkei and the coastal districts of Natal to Zululand.

Larval host-plant: *Strelitzia nicolai* (Natal wild banana).

Artitropa erinnys erinnys (Trimen, 1862)   HESPERIIDAE

bush nightfighter/bosskemervegter   **no. 231: p. 142**
Wingspan: ♂ 40-45; ♀ 45-50 mm

The bush nightfighter is another crepuscular hesperiid with a moth-like appearance. It is usually observed on the wing in the late evening and at dusk although in warm rainy weather it flies during the day. The males and females are similar, with dark-brown forewings and darker-brown hindwings. The outer margins to the wings have a brown ciliate fringe, and there may be a very narrow orange border to the margin at the base of the fringe. There is a subapical cluster of three to five tiny hyaline spots on the forewing near the costa, another at the end of the cell and two or three fused or separate hyaline patches in mid-wing; the patch nearest the inner margin is often yellowish. The hindwing has an elongated orange patch in mid-wing, and the edge of the outer margin and its ciliate fringe are orange. There are numerous long brown or orange hairs on the wings, concentrated basally.

The undersides of the wings are mottled in various shades of brown on a dark-brown background with, of course, a replication of the hyaline patches of the upperside; however there is also a more- or less-developed cream-white patch in the middle of the hindwing.

The bush nightfighter is found in the eastern parts of South Africa, from Grahamstown in the eastern Cape east through Transkei to the coastal districts of Natal and thence to the eastern Transvaal rain-forests. It prefers the wetter forests where its larval host-plants may be found.

Its larvae and pupae have similar habits to those of *Moltena fiara* (page 243), wrapping themselves in sections of the leaves of their host-plant.

The peak flight period of this butterfly is from August until May, but when conditions permit it may be found in all months of the year.

Larval host-plants: *Dracaena hookerana*; *D. steudneri* (from tropical Africa).

Gegenes hottentota (Latreille, 1823)   HESPERIIDAE

Latreille's skipper/Latreille-springertjie   **no. 232: p. 143**
Wingspan: ♂ 24-27; ♀ 25-28 mm

Latreille's skipper is a common little brown butterfly with a wide distribution in South Africa. Two subspecies are currently recognized: subspecies *hottentota* extends southwards into the Transvaal and Natal from Zimbabwe while subspecies *ocra* occupies the Cape portion of the species' range, extending east to Natal. The exact geographical limits of the two species are still uncertain, owing in part to the history of confusion with the closely related species *Gegenes niso*.

The male is yellowish-brown above, darkening towards the outer margins. Subspecies *hottentota* (photograph **232b**, page 143) is easily distinguished from subspecies *ocra* by the male's possession of a large blackish patch on mid-forewing near the inner angle. The female is darker brown above with several yellow spots in the outer half of the forewing and a small group of yellowish streaks in the middle of the hindwing. The undersides of both sexes are yellow-brown, speckled with several darker spots and, in the case of the female, with lighter yellow barring on the apical half of the forewing.

Latreille's skipper occurs in grassland and open bush habitats, often on hill or mountain slopes, and it avoids the arid western parts of the Karoo, Namaqualand and the western half of the northern Cape. Its flight period extends all year round in the warmer areas. Like other skippers it is a very active insect, flying for long periods round and round in large circles, returning to its station on a twig or blade of grass to rest for a few seconds before taking off again to expel intruders from its domain.

Larval host-plants: *Ehrharta erecta*; *Pennisetum clandestinum* (kikuyu); other species of soft grass.

BUTTERFLY SURVIVAL STRATEGIES

For a butterfly population to remain healthy, the recruitment of new butterflies must match the mortality rate. No population of any animal, of course, ever achieves perfect stability. Numbers fluctuate from season to season, depending on several factors. In the case of butterflies the most important of these is probably climate, but veld-fires, surges in parasite or predator numbers, or the destruction of vegetation by a locust plague can play a part in upsetting the balance of a butterfly population in a particular year. In time, however, the balance is restored and for any given locality a butterfly population will fluctuate around a long-term average.

That butterflies are adapted to cope with adverse influences may be inferred from the large clutches of eggs they lay. Of these only two need to develop to adulthood, and to reproduce, for the butterfly population to maintain its numbers. The rest succumb at various stages to fungal and viral infections, parasite and predator attack, and accidental death.

In modern times, man has proved to be by far the most important enemy of the butterfly. Not man the butterfly-collector, but man the destroyer of the environment. Over the next few decades it is likely that many hundreds of species of butterfly will become extinct in different parts of the world, virtually all of them victims of man's uncontrolled population growth with the consequent demands for more land for agriculture, housing, industry and recreation. These inroads on natural habitats may be legitimate, if regrettable, but they always encroach even further than necessary on the remaining natural habitats through the seemingly inevitable consequences of 'progress' – pollution, the careless use of agricultural insecticides, erosion and the spread of invasive alien plants.

It would certainly be unjust to blame the butterfly-collector for the decline in butterfly numbers. A healthy habitat with an abundance of suitable larval host-plants is the key to butterfly survival. Even the most ruthless and selfish collector would have difficulty in eradicating a flourishing butterfly colony by catching all the adults before they had laid their eggs. The danger arises when a butterfly is brought to the brink of extinction by habitat destruction – then, it is true, it could be pushed over the edge by over-collecting. This topic, however, is dealt with more fully on pages 247 to 249.

What of the butterfly's traditional enemies? Butterflies and their immediate ancestors have had to contend with predation for at least 150 million years and it is therefore not surprising that with the passage of this enormous period of time they have developed a number of defensive adaptations. What is surprising is the variety of these adaptations and their astonishing degree of sophistication.

THE EGG

Eggs escape attention because of their small size, and to some degree because their colours blend into their surroundings. As discussed on page 11, they may be laid under leaves, in the axils of small new shoots, on seed-pods, or hidden in cracks in the rocks in the case of those species that feed on lichen. The eggs of some moth species are known to contain toxins which protect them from predation; at this stage, however, it is not known whether this phenomenon also occurs in butterflies although certain groups are toxic in the larval, pupal and adult stages (see below). Specialist insect predators and parasites are remarkably successful at finding butterfly eggs and it is certainly a vulnerable stage in the butterfly's life-cycle.

THE LARVA

The early stages of all larvae are very small, some only about one millimetre in length, and this inconspicuous size affords some protection. As they get larger, some species achieve protection by burrowing into the fruits, berries and seeds of different types of plant (for example, the playboys of the genus *Virachola*, pages 180 and 181), others will live and eat **between** the upper and lower surfaces of a leaf (*Gonatomyrina gorgias*, page 193), while still others 'plough' into a leaf leaving only a small part of their backs showing (*Stugeta bowkeri*, page 184). Certain lycaenid caterpillars (see page 18) spend most of their lives in ants' nests underground, where they develop on a diet of ant larvae and pupae; in this situation they are safe from predation and the ravages of veld-fires. Skipper larvae normally cut out a section of leaf and with threads of silk weave it around their body; they are hidden from sight in this cocoon by day, and emerge to feed only at night. One of our papilionid caterpillars, that of the emperor swallowtail (*Princeps ophidicephalus*), sits openly on the surface of a leaf in its early instars. Being black and white, however, it looks exactly like a bird dropping, curled up into a small U-shape. This form of cryptic – but conspicuous – disguise is particularly prevalent in moths and butterflies, where the larva mimics an object so familiar to a predator that it ignores it. Straightforward cryptic colouration is employed by many caterpillars where their colours exactly match the background they live upon; some extraordinarily elaborate spines and processes enhance the camouflage effect as in the nymphaline *Pseudacraea boisdu-*

valii trimenii (Trimen's false acraea) portrayed in photograph **53a** on page 55. Papilionid caterpillars also typically have a pair of 'horns', the osmeterium (pages 135 and 251), which can be erected at will when threatened; not only does this structure give off an unpleasant odour to discourage predators but it is waved around in a menacing manner as if to 'sting' its attacker. Danaine larvae are boldly coloured and very conspicuous but, as predators soon learn, they are distasteful and poisonous. Acraeine larvae are also unpalatable or poisonous and are additionally protected by rigid, branched spines (photographs **20a**, page 38; **26a**, page 40); for at least one species, *Acraea horta* (page 152), it is known that the hollow spines are filled with haemolymph containing cyanide. Certain caterpillars also obtain a measure of protection from noxious fluids which are exuded from their mouths.

THE PUPA
Pupae are immobile and if found, are vulnerable to predation. Consequently, they are normally positioned as inconspicuously as possible, some being rolled in leaves, others being hidden in cracks in the bark of trees and some being buried just under the surface of the soil. They rely mostly on their camouflage of colouration and shape to escape detection. Some pupae, however, are brightly coloured and are situated in exposed positions; in such cases, for example in the subfamily Danainae, the pupae are advertising their poisonous or distasteful properties.

THE ADULT BUTTERFLY
Adult butterflies are at all times prone to attack by insectivorous predators but, as with the larvae and pupae, they have developed a variety of strategies to avoid capture.

One method is to escape by rapid and erratic flight. The combination of speed and unpredictable direction can confuse the would-be predator as, for example, in the case of the lemon traveller, *Colotis subfasciatus* (page 226) and the Patricia blue, *Lepidochrysops patricia* (page 213). Other butterflies, particularly the browns (subfamily Satyrinae), have a weak, wavering flight and look like dead leaves being blown along by the wind; the common bush brown, *Bicyclus safitza* (page 147) is a good example of this type. Certain browns also have a habit of 'going to ground' when threatened.

Some butterflies of course are masters of cryptic colouration, which is used in combination with an ability to remain quite still when settled. Typical of this group is the twilight brown, *Melanitis leda helena*, whose underside bears a very close resemblance to a dead leaf; when settled among dead leaves and debris under trees it is almost invisible (photograph **5a**, page 34). Many butterflies of the subfamilies Charaxinae and Nymphalinae share the dead-leaf disguise, some having astonishingly realistic false 'midribs' on the underwings in addition to the mottled browns typical of a fallen leaf; examples of this are to be seen in the pearl charaxes, *Stonehamia varanes* (photograph **38b**, page 45) and the leaf commodore, *Junonia tugela* (photograph **71c**, page 64). The Amakoza rocksitter, *Durbania amakosa*, has undersides which closely match the mottled lichen-encrusted rocks on which it rests (photograph **85d**, page 71).

Another defence mechanism used by butterflies is the eye-spot. Large eye-spots have a pupil-like centre usually surrounded by concentric markings of different colours to enhance their effect. The citrus swallowtail or Christmas butterfly, *Princeps demodocus*, for example, has two eye-spots on each hindwing upperside, each with a blue and black 'pupil' surrounded by yellow and red (photograph **213e**, page 135). When at rest with its wings half-outspread, only the two eye-spots at the anal angles of the hindwings are visible; a potential predator presumably feels it is being stared at and threatened by a large vertebrate animal and may perhaps retire in confusion.

The lycaenids also have eye-spots but they are used in a completely different way. Instead of trying to discourage attack, the lycaenid appears actually to invite it. Its eye-spots are situated at the anal angle of the hindwing and are often associated with one or more hair-tails which look like antennae (photograph **95e**, page 75). Together, the eye-spots and hair-tails strongly resemble the eyes and antennae of the insect, an impression reinforced by certain behavioural tricks. The butterfly may sit with its true head pointing downwards and partly hidden by the wings (photograph **112b**, page 85); it may also rub its hindwings slowly together to give a 'live' appearance to the false 'antennae'; or it may execute an immediate 180-degree turn on landing so that the true head points back towards the direction it came from. The undersides may also be patterned in such a way as to direct a predator's eye to the false 'head', as for example with the stripes on the Natal barred blue, *Spindasis natalensis* (photograph **114b**, page 86). A predator which seizes the butterfly by the false 'head' will procure a mouthful of wing while the butterfly will escape with no damage to its vital organs. That this strategy is successful is proved by the numbers of lycaenids which fly about with damaged hindwings. In one study of a South American lycaenid with a well-developed false 'head', 22 per cent of the butterflies showed signs of having been unsuccessfully attacked by predators in this way.

Another defensive strategy developed by butterflies involves the use of toxins or repellent substances. Such substances may be acquired by the butterfly during its larval stage from its food-plant, as appears to be the case with danaine butterflies such as the southern milkweed butterfly or African monarch *Danaus chrysippus aegyptius* (page 145) and acraeines such as the garden acraea, *Acraea horta* (page 152). Some species, however, including certain acraeas, manufacture their own toxins and do not acquire them from a plant.

The toxicity of butterflies has been studied in considerable detail. In one experiment, caterpillars of a danaine butterfly were separated into two groups, one to be raised on their normal toxic host-plant, and the other to be raised on cabbage. The first batch of caterpillars acquired toxins and were unpalatable, the second batch acquired no toxins and were palatable to predators. Insectivorous birds were raised from nestlings to act as inexperienced test predators. From birth they were fed the palatable butterflies. When they were eventually offered the unpalatable butterflies, they readily ate them and promptly vomited and became distressed. Thereafter they refused to eat even the palatable butterflies, except when the coloured scales had been wiped off the wings, proving that they had learned to associate the colour pattern with an extremely unpleasant experience.

The colour patterns developed by unpalatable butterflies are usually striking and conspicuous, red and orange being particularly favoured as 'warning colours' as for example in the southern milkweed butterfly *Danaus chrysippus aegyptius* and most acraeas. Such butterflies tend to flaunt or 'advertise' their warning colours by flying slowly about without any attempt at concealment.

The unpalatability of certain butterflies has led to the evolution of mimicry. This phenomenon takes two forms. In **Batesian mimicry** a palatable butterfly, the 'mimic', takes on the colour pattern and often the behavioural characteristics of an unpalatable butterfly, the 'model', in order to exploit its immunity from predation. A good example is provided by the southern milkweed butterfly, *Danaus chrysippus aegyptius* (photograph **1a**, page 33) which is the model for the palatable nymphaline butterfly which bears the appropriate if confusing common name, the 'mimic', *Hypolimnas misippus* (photograph **61h**, page 61). Only the female *H. misippus* does the mimicking and it is a remarkable fact that it occurs in four colour pattern forms, each one corresponding to one of the four female forms of the model. Other examples of Batesian mimicry are as follows:

- The scarce diadem, *Hypolimnas deceptor* (**62a**, page 61), mimics the novice, *Amauris ochlea* (**3a**, page 33).
- The mocker swallowtail, *Princeps dardanus cenea* form *trophonius* (**209g**, page 133), mimics *Danaus chrysippus aegyptius* form *liboria* (**1a**, page 33).
- The mocker swallowtail, *Princeps dardanus cenea* form *cenea* (**209h**, page 133), mimics the layman, *Amauris albimaculata* (**4a**, page 34), as does the female of the white-banded swallowtail *Princeps echerioides* (**210b**, page 134) and the false chief, *Pseudacraea lucretia tarquinia* (**55a**, page 56).
- The variable mimic, *Hypolimnas anthedon wahlbergi* form *wahlbergi* (**63a**, page 62), mimics the friar *Amauris niavius dominicanus* (**2**, page 33).
- The false wanderer, *Pseudacraea eurytus imitator* (upper **54c**, page 56), mimics the wanderer, *Bematistes aganice* (**19b**, page 38).
- Trimen's false acraea, *Pseudacraea boisduvalii trimenii*, mimics the large-spotted acraea, *Acraea zetes acara*. Photographs **53c** (page 55) and **34a** (page 43) do not, however, illustrate this particularly well, as **53c** portrays form *colvillei* which mimics acraeas with partly transparent forewings such as *Acraea admatha* (**23**, page 39) and *A. satis* (**24**, page 39).

A refinement of the phenomenon occurs in **Müllerian mimicry** where two or more unrelated and unpalatable species share the same warning colouration. Where Batesian mimicry benefits only the mimic, Müllerian mimicry benefits all of the species involved – the 'co-mimic' butterflies benefit in that they share the toll taken by predators during the learning process, and the predator benefits in that it only has to learn to recognize one set of warning colours, not several. An example of Müllerian mimicry is provided by the two acraeines, *Bematistes aganice* and *Acraea esebria*. The male of the former is black and yellow-orange (photograph **19b** on page 38 shows the black and white female) and almost exactly matches the colouration of the latter's form *protea* (photograph **29c**, page 41).

BUTTERFLY CONSERVATION

As the twentieth century draws to a close it is becoming clear that mankind's swelling numbers pose an ever-increasing threat to the myriad of forms of life with which we share the Planet Earth. Habitat destruction and pollution have already eliminated many species world-wide, and predictions of mass extinctions by the end of the century involving between 750 000 and 2,5 million species have been made by responsible and respected biologists. Some of the species destined for extinction are butterflies and it is surely true to say that if we value these fascinating creatures highly enough to collect them, we can value them highly enough to conserve them. But can collecting and conservation be reconciled?

Over the past 300 years the physical collection of biological specimens for storage in museums has been essential for the cataloguing and understanding of the natural orders of plants and animals. Although the more visible and spectacular groups such as mammals and birds are now relatively well represented in collections, it has been estimated that six out of every seven of the world's creatures still await discovery and description; most of these are insects and other invertebrates and most, it seems, are doomed to disappear before they are found. The process of collecting and cataloguing must clearly continue – not least in South Africa where a massive amount of basic research still requires to be carried out on our huge invertebrate fauna.

Ethical attitudes are changing, however, and the emphasis among scientists has been modified from a simple 'collect, kill and catalogue' philosophy, to 'collect (within reason), kill (only if you have to), catalogue and conserve'. Many museum taxonomists are now in the forefront of the conservation movement, actively helping to preserve vestiges of the once flourishing, diverse and rich natural ecosystems of the world. Butterfly specialists in particular are only too aware of the fragility of butterfly habitats and of the dangers of over-zealous collecting by the many thousands of amateur lepidopterists throughout the world. It is quite clear that all of us, professional and amateur alike, have a moral duty to contribute to the salvation of our vanishing natural heritage – *now*. Tomorrow will be too late.

Collecting butterflies has always been a popular and instructive hobby. It is a particularly exciting and enlightening means of encouraging and educating young people who might be contemplating a career in one of the biological disciplines. It has considerable aesthetic appeal – the thrill of the chase and the recognition of the beauty of the netted insect – and what starts out as merely an interesting pastime soon evolves into a more serious hobby or even career. This is where individual responsibility has to take over. It entails the adoption of a more conservative and restrained approach to collection and a moving away from the practice of simply amassing large series of beautiful but very dead butterflies in endless ranks of insect cabinets. Lepidoptera, incidentally, are considered nowadays to be sensitive barometers of the state of the environment and it is therefore of paramount importance that we develop a more serious attitude to the study of the many fascinating aspects of their life-histories. There is, for example, still great scope for recording the life-cycles of butterflies, for determining the details of their relationships with other insects (parasitism and symbiosis) and for unravelling other aspects of their ecological adaptations. The challenge of recording photographically various aspects of a butterfly's metamorphosis without destruction of the insect can become a rewarding hobby in its own right.

As their contribution towards conservation, lepidopterists' societies throughout the world have drawn up a strict code of ethics. This has been endorsed locally by the fledgeling Lepidopterists' Society of Southern Africa and all butterfly-collectors in this country are urged to adopt its guiding principles. While it is acknowledged that the mere collection of a few butterflies is unlikely ever to be the main reason for the extinction of any species, the regular inroads made by many collectors into small localized colonies of butterflies will certainly in the long run adversely affect the species' prospects of survival – particularly in those cases where the butterfly larva has a symbiotic relationship with an ant species or feeds exclusively on one rare host-plant.

British lepidopterists incline to the following main principles and recommendations:

☐ take and kill no more specimens than are strictly required; a pair of each species should suffice for normal purposes.
☐ do not collect the same species at the same locality year after year.
☐ local forms and species known to be rare should not be collected at all.
☐ leave the environment as you find it (this recommendation is expanded on below).
☐ rearing larvae from a fertilized female is better than taking specimens from the wild; unwanted specimens of successfully reared material should be released *in the same locality* from which the mother was taken.
☐ when embarking on breeding experiments, never attempt to rear more larvae than you are able to support.

Self-restraint and caution should be the guiding criteria for all lepidopterists. Tampering with such sensitive microhabitats as ants' nests in the hope of procuring a few butterfly pupae can only be condemned outright if the life-history of the particular species being sought has already been conclusively established. Another practice which should be strongly discouraged – or subjected to penalties – is the stripping of large masses of parasitic mistletoe (family Loranthaceae) from trees to feed butterfly larvae. Pause to consider that a rotting log is a microcosm in its own right, whose faunal and floral inhabitants are dependent on its shelter; the ecological consequences of bark-stripping such a log, or even a living tree, may be little understood but will certainly be far-reaching, a fact which many of us unfortunately fail to appreciate sufficiently. It is also worth remembering that there are legal as well as ethical considerations to take into account. Each province of South Africa has its own nature conservation ordinance and the carefree gathering of plant material could bring a collector into conflict with the law.

Legislation to protect butterflies in South Africa has been introduced in recent years, especially in the Cape Province where 15 species are now included in the Nature and Environmental Conservation Ordinance, 1974 (Ordinance 19 of 1974) (Cape) along with one spectacular moth species; all *Charaxes* butterflies and a rare lycaenid are protected in the Transvaal. This list at present is as follows:

Cape Province
1. *Poecilmitis nigricans*
2. *Poecilmitis endymion*
3. *Poecilmitis lyncurium*
4. *Poecilmitis rileyi*
5. *Aloeides egerides*
6. *Aloeides lutescens*
7. *Trimenia wallengrenii*
8. *Oxychaeta dicksoni*
9. *Lepidochrysops bacchus*
10. *Thestor dicksoni*
11. *Thestor kaplani*
12. *Charaxes xiphares occidentalis*
13. *Stygionympha dicksoni*
14. *Metisella syrinx*
15. *Tsitana dicksoni*
16. *Leto venus* (moth)

Transvaal Province
17. *Charaxes* (all species)
18. *Poecilmitis aureus*

Although such laws certainly restrict and hinder the activities of casual collectors, they are well intentioned and are a welcome sign of belated official interest in invertebrate conservation. The Cape and Transvaal authorities are, generally speaking, not unsympathetic to well-motivated applications for permits to study these species. Having said all that, however, it is necessary to emphasize once again that ultimately butterfly conservation depends upon the maintenance of a healthy ecosystem – no amount of ordinances can save a butterfly species if its habitat is destroyed.

Fortunately in the last few years several conservation-minded individuals have succeeded in establishing the first of what we hope will be a national network of butterfly sanctuaries or reserves. In 1985 the South African Natural Heritage Programme was launched under the auspices of the Department of Environment Affairs, the four provincial nature conservation departments and the private sector through the Southern African Nature Foundation. One of the first sites to be registered under the Programme was the Heidelberg Training Area Natural Heritage Site (by courtesy of the S.A. Defence Force), one of only two known localities for the Heidelberg copper butterfly *Poecilmitis aureus*. In 1986 another milestone was reached with the establishment of a small reserve at Ruimsig near Roodepoort, also in the Transvaal, for the endangered lycaenid butterfly *Aloeides dentatis*. In addition, the Council for Scientific and Industrial Research (C.S.I.R.) has recently embarked on the formidable task of compiling a Red Data Book for our rare and endangered butterflies. Once this has been published, several other very localized, endangered or vulnerable species are likely to enjoy protected status.

Conservation principles must also be extended to private butterfly collections. All too often, valuable and sometimes irreplaceable material is collected by amateur lepidopterists and incorporated into their collections, only to be lost in the course of time through neglect. While private collections are all very well if they are carefully preserved and catalogued, it is unfortunately a regular occurrence for such owners to lose interest after a few years and simply forget their collections – with catastrophic results when the specimens are inevitably destroyed by beetles or other pests. Proper planning for the ultimate disposal of his collection must be the duty of every responsible lepidopterist. Ideally the destination of a private South African collection should be one of the two major national insect collections where professional long-term management is assured. When such an arrangement is made, the collector will not only have a sense of pride, feeling that in some small way he has contributed to an archive of material which will be available for future generations of scientists to study, but he will also feel obliged to maintain high standards during his stewardship of the collection. In all such cases, and especially in the case of very large collections, adequate provision *must* be made in the owner's will. In the past, delays and arguments following the death of a collector have resulted in serious deterioration of important collections.

In view of their great importance, type-specimens of new species *must* be placed in a museum where they will be cared for and made available for study. This should preferably be a national museum with adequate staff and funds for the proper management of such material, and in the case of new South African species it should be a South African museum. Holotypes should certainly remain in a South African institution, but when a good series of paratypes exists it is permissible to send material to overseas museums.

GLOSSARY

Aberration. A specimen with a strikingly different appearance from the average members of the same species. Sometimes loosely called a 'variety' or 'sport'. It is often incorrectly equated with a **form**, but it arises from a mutation and is not a regularly occurring, genetically fixed and recognized 'form'.

Abdomen. The hindmost of the three divisions of the insect body, housing most of the digestive tract and reproductive organs.

Anal angle. In this book refers to the angle on the hindwing between the **inner margin** and the **outer margin** (see diagram, page 9). The similar angle on the forewing is the **inner angle**.

Androconia. Specialized scent-scales usually situated on the wings of male butterflies and from which sexual attractants are dispersed. They may be clustered together in **scent-patches**, or elongated with hair-like endings and grouped into **hair-pencils**.

Antennae. The pair of stalked (and often long) sensory appendages on the head. In butterflies these are usually club-shaped towards the tip, although in the skippers they may be more tapered and end in a little hook.

Apex. The point on the forewing where the **costa** and **outer margin** meet. Used loosely for the area surrounding this point.

Apical angle. The **apex**. The angle at the outer upper apex of the forewing (see diagram, page 9).

Base of wings. The portion of the wings adjoining the thorax.

Batesian mimicry. An acquired superficial resemblance of one species (the mimic) to a different species (the model) to gain some protective advantage from predators. The model is always unpalatable to predators and the mimic is always palatable. See **Müllerian mimicry.**

Binominal nomenclature. A system of naming species of plants and animals in which the name is composed of two latinized words. The first represents the genus and the second is the specific name of the plant or animal (see page 14). Often also called 'binomial nomenclature'.

Caterpillar. See **larva.**

Cell (of wings). The open compartment in the vein system of each wing, situated at and near the base of the wing and extending into the middle of the wing. It is bounded by, but not crossed by veins (see diagram, page 9).

Chitin. A tough, amorphous, structurally supportive material which is the major component of the **exoskeleton** of an insect.

Cilia. In butterflies, the fine fringe of small hairs (modified scales) along the edge of the outer margins of both wings. (Singular: 'cilium').

Costa. Or 'costal margin'. The leading edge of each wing (see diagram, page 9).

Chrysalis. The pupal or third developmental stage of an insect; the term **pupa** is preferred in this book.

Compound eye. A compact organ of hundreds or thousands of individual visual units, each with its own sensory cells, but functioning as a single entity.

Cremaster. An arrangement of tough hooks by which the pupal stage anchors itself either to a silken pad or other supportive material.

Crepuscular. Active in twilight (dusk and dawn).

Cryptic. Descriptive of colour or behaviour patterns adopted by insects to conceal or camouflage themselves.

Cuticle. The hard chitinous integument of an insect.

Diapause. Temporary cessation of development of immature insect, usually in the larval or pupal phase, to cope with unfavourable conditions such as cold winter weather or periods of unusual drought or heat.

Diaphanous. Translucent or semitransparent, usually with a connotation of delicacy and flimsiness.

Dimorphism. The occurrence of two different colour forms of a species, sometimes genetically determined as in **sexual dimorphism** (see below), sometimes environmentally induced as in **seasonal dimorphism** (see below).

Discal cell. See **cell.**

Diurnal. Happening during the day-time; active by day.

d.s.f. The abbreviation for 'dry-season form'. See **seasonal dimorphism.**

Ecdysis. The process of moulting or shedding the exoskeleton or cuticle.

Entomology. The study of insects.

Exoskeleton. The rigid or tough exterior protective covering which supports the body of an insect. See **chitin.**

Eye-spot. The false 'eye' on the wing of a butterfly or on the thorax of a caterpillar, usually round and often with a dark pupil-like centre surrounded by concentric rings of paler colours (see pages 18 and

246). Sometimes, however, it is small and unicoloured, or black with a white centre. Often called an **ocellus** (see below).

Food-plant. The host-plant on which larvae of butterflies and moths feed. Although the larvae of some butterfly species will eat a wide range of plant species, many will only eat one species or a group of closely related species.

Form. A term used to describe a distinct and frequently occurring colour variant of a butterfly (*cf.* **aberration**). A form may be under genetic control and appear in accordance with the principles of heredity (Mendel's laws) in a species exhibiting **polymorphism** (see below), or in polymorphic mimics (see photographs **209g** and **h**, page 133). A form may also, however, be produced by environmental influences (see **seasonal dimorphism**).

Frass. Faecal droppings or pellets excreted by larvae.

Genitalia. Organs of reproduction.

Genus. A group of closely related species bearing a common 'generic' name. (Plural: 'genera').

Girdle. The silken thread woven by the caterpillar around the thorax and which supports the attachment of the pupa to a twig or other surface in certain butterfly groups.

Gynandromorph. An individual in which one part of the body is male, the other female. Sometimes the individual will have a mosaic of male and female characters, but more usually it will be a 'bilateral gynandromorph' where one half of the butterfly is male and the other half female (photograph **139c**, page 97).

Haemolymph. The circulating body fluid of insects, equivalent in function to the blood of vertebrates. It lacks haemoglobin.

Hair-pencil. A close grouping of specialized scale-hairs on the wing which assists in the dispersal of the pheromones or chemical 'messengers' used to attract or excite the opposite sex as a prelude to mating.

Head. The first of the three major divisions of the insect's body, bearing eyes, antennae, spinnerets and the mouthparts.

Hyaline. Clear and translucent. Used to describe the clear or semitransparent scale-free patches on the wings of certain butterflies, for example, *Acraea admatha* (photograph **23**, page 39).

Imago. Adult stage of butterfly or moth.

Inner angle. In this book refers to the angle on the forewing between the **inner margin** and the **outer margin** (see diagram, page 9). The similar angle on the hindwing is the **anal angle**.

Inner margin. The lower or rear margin of either fore- or hindwing (see diagram, page 9).

Inselberg. An isolated (usually) rocky hill rising abruptly from a flat plain.

Instar. Any one of usually four or five **larval** stages between moults prior to pupation.

Larva. The second stage of the butterfly life-cycle, between egg and **pupa**. Also known as a caterpillar or grub. See **instar**.

Lepidoptera. The order embracing all the scaly-winged insects such as moths and butterflies.

Melanism. An increase over normal in the amount of dark pigment ('melanin') present in an organism. This may occur as an individual **aberration** (see definition above and also photograph **185j**, page 117), or in **seasonal dimorphism** (see below), or in one subspecies as compared with another one.

Micropyle. The tiny pore on the eggshell through which the fertilizing sperm penetrates. After the egg has been laid, it respires through the micropyle, which is visible as a small depression.

Mimic. See **Batesian mimicry** and **Müllerian mimicry**.

Müllerian mimicry. An acquired superficial resemblance of several distasteful species, all of which are avoided by predators because their common colour pattern (**warning colouration**) is recognized as being distasteful or poisonous.

Nocturnal. Happening at night; active by night.

Ocellus. (Plural: 'ocelli'). Literally 'small eye'. The simple eye of insects consisting of a single, thickened, cuticular lens below which are transparent epithelial cells and then a cluster of light-sensitive nerve cells. The large compound eye of insects is made up of hundreds (or thousands) of similarly structured elements. Butterfly caterpillars have three pairs of ocelli on the head. Note that the term 'ocellus' is also used for the **eye-spot** (see above).

Osmeterium. A fleshy extensible organ situated on the back of the thorax of caterpillars of the family Papilionidae (swallowtails). This Y-shaped, brightly coloured defence mechanism is normally hidden in the thorax but is suddenly everted when the caterpillar is threatened. It emits a strong-smelling fluid abhorrent to predators.

Outer margin. The outermost margin of either the fore- or hindwing, furthest from the wing's point of attachment (see diagram, page 9).

Pheromone. A chemical substance secreted by an animal into its environment and which causes other members of the same species to react behaviourally or physiologically. The sex attractants produced by male butterflies are 'pheromones'.

Polymorphism. The occurrence of two or more genetically distinct variants within one population of a species. In butterflies one expression of this phenomenon is in colour pattern forms as in, for example, the mocker swallowtail *Princeps dardanus cenea* (page 233).

Proboscis. The coiled, tube-like 'tongue' through which a butterfly siphons its liquid nutrients.

Prolegs. False 'legs' on the abdomen of most caterpillars, used to support the long body. The third, fourth, fifth, sixth and tenth abdominal segments each carry one pair, those on the tenth and last abdominal segment being known as 'claspers'.

Pupa. The chrysalis, or third stage of the butterfly's life-cycle, in which the larva undergoes transformation into the adult butterfly.

Scent-patch. A cluster of scent-scales or **androconia** on the wings of males of some butterfly species, *e.g. Danaus chrysippus aegyptius* (page 145).

Seasonal dimorphism. The occurrence of two different colour (and/or size) forms in a species according to season. The winter form is the 'dry-season form' (**d.s.f.**) and the summer form is the 'wet-season form' (**w.s.f.**). All colour gradations between the two extreme seasonal forms may be found. This form of dimorphism is not genetically but environmentally controlled, by factors such as humidity and temperature.

Sexual dimorphism. The term used to describe the phenomenon where males and females of the same species have a strikingly different appearance. It is genetically controlled.

Silk-gland. Glandular structure situated in the head which produces silk strands via the **spinneret** (see below).

Spinneret. A more or less elongated process on the lower 'lip' of a caterpillar's mouth, at the tip of which the ducts of the silk-glands open.

Subapical. Below, or close to the **apex** of the forewing.

Submarginal. Below or near the margin.

Sympatric. Of two or more species, occurring in the same geographical location with the same or overlapping habitats, but breeding separately and maintaining their separate identities.

Thorax. The middle of the three divisions of the insect body, bearing the legs and wings.

Variety. See **aberration**.

Warning colouration. Conspicuous colouration patterns adopted by some insects to advertise their unpalatability to predators.

Wingspan. In this book, wingspan is defined as the measurement from forewing apex to forewing apex when the butterfly is set in the usual manner with the **inner margins** of both forewings forming one straight line. Ciliate fringes are included in the measurement where they occur.

w.s.f. The abbreviation for 'wet-season form'. See **seasonal dimorphism.**

♂ Symbol denoting 'male'.

♀ Symbol denoting 'female'.

SUGGESTED FURTHER READING
(**P** – popular; **S** – scientific)

ANON. 1959. *Butterfly list*. Government Printer, Pretoria. (**P**)

CARCASSON, R.H. 1981. *Butterflies of Africa*. Collins, London. (**P**)

CLARK, G.C. & DICKSON, C.G.C. 1952. *Some South African butterflies*. Longmans Green, Cape Town. (**P**)

CLARK, G.C. & DICKSON, C.G.C. 1971. *Life histories of the South African lycaenid butterflies*. Purnell, Cape Town. (**S**)

CLAASSENS, A.J.M. & DICKSON, C.G.C. 1980. *The butterflies of the Table Mountain Range*. C. Struik, Cape Town. (**P/S**)

COOPER, R. 1973. *Butterflies of Rhodesia*. Longman Rhodesia, Salisbury, Rhodesia. (**P**)

COTTRELL, C.B. 1978. Aspects of the biogeography of southern African butterflies. Supplement to *Zambezia* (the journal of the University of Rhodesia, Salisbury). (**S**)

COTTRELL, C.B. 1985. The absence of coevolutionary associations with Capensis floral element plants in the larval/plant relationships of southwestern Cape butterflies. pp 115-124. In: *Species and speciation*. (Ed.) VRBA E.S. *Transvaal Museum Monograph* 4. (**S**)

DICKSON, C.G.C. 1972. *What butterfly is that?* Purnell, Cape Town. (**P**)

DICKSON, C.G.C. & KROON, D.M. (eds.) 1978. *Pennington's butterflies of southern Africa*. Ad. Donker, Johannesburg. (**S**)

GERMISHUYS, H. 1982. *Butterflies of southern Africa*. Chris van Rensburg Publications, Johannesburg. (**P**)

GIFFORD, D. 1965. *A list of the butterflies of Malawi*. The Society of Malawi, Blantyre, Malaŵi. (**S**)

HANCOCK, D.L. 1983. Classification of the Papilionidae (Lepidoptera): a phylogenetic approach. *Smithersia* 2:1-48. (**S**)

HENNING, S.F. 1984. *Southern African butterflies*. Macmillan South Africa, Johannesburg. (**P**)

HENNING, S.F. (in press). *The Charaxinae of Africa*. (**S**)

KLOPPERS, J. & VAN SON, G. 1978. *The butterflies of the Kruger National Park*. National Parks Board of Trustees, Pretoria. (**P**)

PENNINGTON, K.M. 1963. A check list of the butterflies of Natal and Zululand. *Durban Museum Novitates* 7(2):27-70. (**S**)

PINHEY, E.C.G. 1949. *Butterflies of Rhodesia*. Rhodesia Scientific Association, Salisbury, Rhodesia. (**P**)

PINHEY, E. 1965 *Butterflies of southern Africa*. Thomas Nelson and Sons (Africa), Johannesburg. (**P**)

PINHEY, E. & LOE, I.D. 1977. *A guide to the butterflies of central and southern Africa*. Sir Joseph Causton & Sons, London and Eastleigh. (**P**)

QUICKELBERGE, C. 1986. *Familiar South African butterflies*. Natal Branch of The Wildlife Society of Southern Africa, Durban. (**P**)

SBORDONI, V. & FORESTIERO, S. 1985. *The world of butterflies*. Blandford Press, Poole, Dorset. (**P/S**)

SCHOLTZ, C.H. & HOLM, E. (eds.) 1985. *Insects of southern Africa*. Butterworths, Durban. (**S**)

SMITHERS, C. 1982. *Handbook of insect collecting: collection, preparation, preservation and storage*. Delta Books, Johannesburg. (**P/S**)

SWANEPOEL, D.A., 1953. *Butterflies of South Africa, where, when and how they fly*. Maskew Miller, Cape Town. (**P**)

VÁRI, L. & KROON, D.M. 1986. *Southern African Lepidoptera: a series of cross-referenced indices*. The Lepidopterists' Society of Southern Africa & The Transvaal Museum, Pretoria. (**S**)

WILLIAMS, J.G. 1969. A field guide to the butterflies of Africa. Collins, London. (**P**)

INDEX TO SCIENTIFIC NAMES

The numbers in bold refer to the pages on which the photographs appear. Certain scientific names have been changed in recent years; for the convenience of readers who may not be familiar with the 'new' names, the superseded names are given below in roman type.

INDEX TO COMMON NAMES
The numbers in **bold** refer to the pages on which the photographs appear.